VIRUS HUNTERS

GREER WILLIAMS

VIRUS HUNTERS

ALFRED A. KNOPF

NEW YORK

1959

L. C. Catalog card number: 59–9256
© Greer Williams, 1959

THIS IS A BORZOI BOOK,

PUBLISHED BY ALFRED A. KNOPF, INC.

FIRST EDITION

A small portion of this work has appeared in
different form in the *Saturday Evening Post.*

DEDICATION

Scientists are the bricklayers of knowledge. Each brick in the wall rests on the ones laid underneath it and gains support from the ones laid on each side of it. Hence, all scientific investigators who contribute so much as a brick or the mortar between bricks share credit for the entire wall.

This book is in itself an acknowledgment of help from the men, dead as well as living, who appear in it. But it is specifically dedicated to the many bricklayers of microbiology who are represented but not mentioned in its chapters.

CONTENTS

*

LIST OF ILLUSTRATIONS

VIRUS HUNTERS

INTRODUCTION:
VIROLOGY—
A NEW SCIENCE

THIS is the story, we might say, of possibly the biggest "double take" in the history of medical science. We could apply the superlative to the current virus hunt with greater confidence if it were not that science so often advances in this way, by new looks at old, familiar things.

Nothing in scientific research is more familiar to us, or has loomed more importantly in the prevention of disease and death, of course, than the image of a Louis Pasteur, in his skullcap, or a Robert Koch, in gold-rimmed spectacles, stooped over his microscope, peering at some microbe he has isolated from a drop of guinea-pig blood or has induced to colonize and grow in a dish of warm jelly.

We Americans know the old-fashioned microbe hunter's legend well—as well as that of Casey Jones or Wyatt Earp. First, the hero of bacteriology finds the "bug" that has killed many persons and that now is taking the life of his test animal. Then, perhaps after many attempts, or even by chance, he discovers the drug that will kill the bug—but not the guinea pig. Or maybe he will have made a vaccine of the germs, or a serum containing antibodies against them, which will make the animal immune to a million times a lethal dose. Hence, after much opposition, he proves that his new medicine miraculously saves the lives of many human beings.

Variations of this theme, like heroic ballads strummed out on a guitar by the firelight, tell us of man's hope for long, healthy life, of his fear of dangers that he himself cannot see or measure.

The microbe hunters in the last eighty or ninety years have taught us how to live with dangerous bacteria—or without them —by applying many different germicidal techniques. This epic poem reached its grand climax after its first classic telling.[1] We refer to chemotherapy—first the sulfa drugs in the 1930's and then the antibiotics in the 1940's. With the coming of the "wonder drugs," the day of microbes appeared almost, if not quite, a thing of the past. Here are some examples: bacterial pneumonia, the number-one killer in 1900, dropped to sixth place; tuberculosis, from second to thirteenth; and inflammation of the stomach and bowels, from third to nineteenth. Other bacterial diseases likewise appeared to be on their way out. Bacteriology, the mother of modern laboratory medicine, has become a trifle old-hat.

But now take another look. Suddenly it dawns on us, after ten years of continuous excitement regarding discoveries in virus diseases, with new vaccines hardly keeping pace with the finding of new virus diseases, that the old bacteriologist is not dead. He has merely shaved his beard, put on horn-rimmed glasses, changed hats, and reappeared in a new branch of microbiology as a virologist. He is still at the microscope, but he is more apt to know chemistry, physics, and genetics as well. And the microscope, about six feet tall, is of a kind that magnifies with a beam of electrons rather than light rays; it "sees" twenty times as much. The microbe age is past, at least romantically speaking, but today we live in the virus age.

The hunt for wild viruses, as virologists call those which have not been tamed through laboratory manipulations, is quite a dif-

---

[1] Paul de Kruif: *Microbe Hunters* (New York: Harcourt, Brace; 1926).

ferent story from that of the fat, easy-to-grow, one-celled form of plant life known as bacteria. For one thing, viruses, traveling mainly by person-to-person contact or possibly for some distance through the air, resist treatment with the miracle drugs; there are only one or two exceptions, such as parrot fever. Certain recent experiments suggest that this may not remain the case for too long, but vaccines, not drugs, still are the best bet in protecting ourselves against viruses.

Secondly, viruses are both a smaller and lower form of life. The normal human eye under optimum conditions can see a dot as small as eight thousandths of an inch in diameter. This is about 667 times larger than the largest and 13,333 times the smallest known virus; the single virus particle ranges from somewhat less than one millionth to about twelve millionths of an inch across.

A virus, in other words, lies in most instances just beyond the range of a good optical microscope. It is bigger than chemical molecules but smaller than most living cells, being more closely akin to the cell nucleus than to the cell itself. It appears to pursue its parasitic, infectious ends in a borderland between living matter and dead, existing in itself only as an invisible organic dust and yet coming alive and reproducing when it makes its way into the living cells of a susceptible host.

While this midget microbe lacks the ordinary microbe's capacity for independent life, most types of virus are fantastically choosy about what living creatures they will infect—in fact, about what cells in these creatures they will pursue their "borrowed life" in. Rabies, for instance, is very nearly the only virus that will produce the same fatal disease in man, dog, and a wide variety of animals. Even so, once inside the body, it will attack nerve cells only.

It is difficult to imagine something smaller than a living cell giving creatures billions and trillions of times larger any trouble. Were it not for the trouble viruses cause us, however, microbiologists never would have been able to detect them. Men, animals, insects, green plants, and bacteria all become infected with viruses at some stage during life, and often remain so throughout life, even though they may not appear to be sick.

As one illustration, the virus hunter can produce adenovirus from the tonsils or adenoids of nine of ten healthy children at some time during the year. The herpes virus that produces cold sores is an especially tenacious tenant. It remains hidden in the body, breaking out only during periods of stress or fatigue.

The harmless bacteria that universally infest our colons are themselves inhabited by a tadpole-shaped virus called a bacteriophage. This fascinating, much-studied midget microbe can invade the larger colon bacterium and produce from one hundred to two hundred full-grown replicas of itself within a half-hour. The offspring explode the cell to free themselves. But, for some mysterious reason, the same bacteriophage may enter the colon bacterium, mingle chemically with its nucleus, and then lie low during two or three generations of bacteria. Then, at some later time in one particular granddaughter cell, the virus reproduces and explodes the cell.

As a third possibility, the virus may stay on within the cell, stimulating it to grow and divide rapidly, the virus dividing at the same time the cell does. This is one theory of how viruses may cause malignant growth: cancer.

Here we see a second great characteristic of virus behavior. The first was infectivity. The second is variability. Virologists have come to realize that anything they hold to be true of one virus is almost certain not to be true of some other.

Viruses, we can well imagine, have affected the course of human history many times and in curious, sometimes frightful, ways. In the direction of man's cruelty to man, the Spanish conquistadors practiced viral warfare long before anybody had heard of bacteriological warfare. Finding the Indians of Mexico highly susceptible to smallpox, the Spanish colonizers deliberately infected the native population with the disease, virtually exterminating the Indian communities in many instances.

A virus infection was behind the tulipomania that occurred in Holland during the seventeenth century. There was wild speculation, and fantastic prices were paid for tulip bulbs that produced blossoms with colorful streaks, known technically as "breaks." Wealthy men were known to offer a daughter in marriage, and throw in a house and farm, for a single bulb—

containing, as botanists now know, a virus responsible for the color variations.

Many of the Irish potatoes we eat contain a latent virus x that almost universally infects certain species; for some reason, the potato plants are completely immune to it and the virus does not reveal itself or do any damage until put into another variety of plant.

Many of the cigarettes we smoke contain a virus. A test of ten brands of cigarettes at the University of California showed that, though the tobacco was flue-cured, the heat did not kill the tobacco-mosaic virus that all contained. This virus causes a mottling disease in the tobacco plant's green leaves. If you smoke a cigarette while setting out tomato plants and moisture from its tip gets on the leaves, the tomato plants may develop mosaic disease, too.

Fortunately, the plant viruses—there are hundreds of them—do us no apparent harm. Otherwise, we would all be mottled or dead.

We have more than enough viruses of our own. "Virus infection" is the most common diagnosis family doctors and pediatricians make today. When we stop to count all possible virus infections—all the common colds, influenza, common measles, German measles, chickenpox (shingles in adults), mumps, poliomyelitis, virus meningitis, virus encephalitis, virus pneumonia, common warts, and (some would say, theoretically) certain cancers—then it suddenly becomes obvious that viruses cause us more sickness than any other class of parasites on earth.

Few, if any, parts of our bodies appear to be safe from viruses, from our brains (virus meningitis and encephalitis) to the soles of our feet (plantar warts). They produce not only inflammation, fever, and general weakness, most commonly, but also congenital malformations, mental deficiency, blindness, deafness, sterility, muscle weakness, nerve paralysis, heart defects, and—it could be—cancer.

A half-century ago medical science knew of only about ten viruses infecting humans. Ten years ago the number was still less than seventy. Now our virologists have counted approximately one hundred and fifty that infect man, and are reasonably sure that there must be as many more as yet undiscovered. They also believe, some of them, that certain chronic physical and mental infirmities of old age will be explained in terms of earlier virus damage to the cells, or "human erosion."

Does this recent acceleration in knowledge of what ails us mean that, as bacterial diseases have receded, we have suffered an actual increase in virus diseases? This hardly seems possible when we recall that the 1918–19 influenza pandemic (caused, virus hunters deduce, by an unusually virulent virus mutant working in combination with bacteria) constituted the worst pestilence civilization ever has experienced.

Still, there are indications that some virus diseases which used to strike only sporadically, such as polio, have become truly epidemic in recent years. Measures of personal hygiene and sanitation greatly reducing bacterial infections—abundant soap and hot water for baths, flush toilets, sewers—have an opposite effect with these viruses. Such measures reduce opportunities to build up a natural resistance through mild virus infections that pass unnoticed in many instances.

Furthermore, the automobile and the amount of traveling and moving about that we now do expedites a continual mixing, mutation, and revitalization of some of the less stable viruses. At least we are exposed to viruses that are strange to us. This is seen in every military training-camp, where green recruits from all over the country take in one another's microbiological wash, so to speak; respiratory infections are especially prevalent there. It is also evident that in any fixed, isolated population the cold-like infections die out and do not reappear until there is fresh contact with people from elsewhere.

Whether we do have more virus infections than our grandparents or merely recognize more when they hit us, America reached the crest of a virus infection cycle in the 1950's. Polio was at an all-time peak in 1952 with 58,000 reported cases. Hepatitis, a virus infection of the liver, reached a high of 50,000 cases in 1954. The trend for both diseases since has been for the most part downward. Polio showed a small increase in 1958 despite previous vaccination of more than half the population under forty. But about nine out of ten cases were among the unvaccinated, which speaks very well for the Salk vaccine. In 1959 hepatitis again showed an upswing. The previous year, measles set something of a record with about 750,000 reported cases.

Then there was the Asian-influenza pandemic. Asian flu, spreading world-wide from southwestern China, accounted for something like 20,000,000 of the more than 100,000,000 respiratory infections that put Americans to bed in the fall and winter of 1957–8. The situation could have been worse without the concurrent crash program of flu vaccination.

While we are inclined to take most virus infections without alarm—polio excepted—we can get some inkling of their possible impact by noting that in the United States the longtime downward trend in the annual death rate ended in 1954. Each year since then it has shown a slight upward trend. In 1957 the infant mortality rate—babies born alive but dying with the first year—rose slightly after a dramatically continuous decline during the previous twenty-one years. The steady increase in average life expectancy meanwhile reversed itself for the first time since 1943, dropping from 70.2 years to 70, according to life-insurance statistics. It is difficult to assign a primary cause for these small breaks in a healthful over-all trend, but some authorities name Asian flu as the main villain.

Viruses are parasites in the animal kingdom and, like poor relations, they seem to have come to stay. There is little reason to doubt that they have been on earth as long as or longer than mankind—some scientists regard them as the earliest form of life; others regard them as a degenerate or backward step in the evolution of life. In either case, we are inhabited by an incredible number of these perfect parasites.

As the result of discoveries in the last thirty years, particularly of new knowledge developed in the last ten years, and, most of all, of findings in the last five years, we, their victims, are getting to know viruses better. As the virologists themselves say, the virus hunt only has begun.

PART ONE: DAWN AGE OF VACCINATION

THE
POCK-MARKED WORLD
OF DR. JENNER

IT IS a little hard to conceive of what smallpox was like in the time of Dr. Edward Jenner (1749–1823). For us it is a thing of the past, though there were 110,000 cases in the United States as late as 1921. Today the mere appearance of one or two cases is cause for great excitement and mass vaccination of everybody in sight. No one has died of smallpox in this country for several years now. Yet great epidemics of this disease still rise in India and the Far East, often with a large death toll. If we imported smallpox and allowed it to run unchecked, two thirds of Americans could get it. While half of us have been vaccinated at some time, our immunity doesn't necessarily last.

In Europe in the eighteenth century, perhaps as many as one person in ten died of smallpox, more than half of them children. Different strains of smallpox virus moved through the big cities. The death toll among those infected ranged from as low as one or two per cent to as high as thirty-three per cent. About ninety-five per cent of the Europeans who survived into adulthood had had smallpox.

The disease is a flesh-eater. Commonly, smallpox forms ulcers— not just one, as in a vaccination mark, but hundreds. In the worst cases they all run together and leave one agonizing mass of rotting flesh. "Those who survived," commented one early observer, "were frequently wrecks—consumptive, scrofulous, asthmatic, dropsical, lame, deaf, blind."

People lived in terror of the consequences. Thomas Macauley pictured smallpox as "turning the babe into a changeling at which the mother shuddered, and making the eyes and cheeks of a betrothed maiden objects of horror to the lover." The beautiful lady of two hundred years ago confronted other facial hazards than sun, wind, and age. When an epidemic was sweeping London, her friends at court were sure to twit her about what the disease might do to her pretty face.

About half of the survivors were pock-marked. Facial disfigurement was so common in the lower classes that its absence was considered identifying in this 1688 advertisement for the arrest of a counterfeiter: "Thomas Bayley, a short, burly man . . . without pock holes, flat-nosed, under 40 years old, commonly wears a fair Periwig. . . ."

Smallpox was an asset if you had survived it in good shape, for all who had had it in a natural way were believed to be absolutely safe from another attack.

A typical want ad for a servant would read thus: "Wanted, a man between 20 and 30 years, to be a footman and under butler in a great family; he must be of the Church of England and have had the small-pox in a natural way."

The disease, technically termed *variola,* has been known since the beginning of history. So, it appears, has the fact that its victims are usually immune to a second attack. Consequently, intentional infection of children became popular among the ancient Chinese and Arabians. With typical Oriental face-saving, the Chinese called this smallpox inoculation "heavenly flowers," and "sowed the pox" by using powdered scabs as snuff. This had to be done on a lucky day, of course, because there was no control over the dosage.

The Arabians were much neater about it. They developed a system of "ingrafting." The idea was to use matter from a mild epidemic. Old women went about, after the hot summer was over, and gathered groups of fifteen or sixteen to have smallpox inoculations in isolation. They carried the virus, taken from smallpox pustules, in nutshells and injected it on the point of a needle, in four or five places about the body. The Greeks, it is related, preferred the middle of the forehead, each arm, and the breast, in the sign of the cross.

About a week later the beneficiaries of this strange practice took to bed with a fever of two or three days' duration. They then broke out with numerous pocks, but these healed in another week or so without scarring, as a rule. Seldom did anyone die.

The practice was introduced in Great Britain in the early 1800's and became popular by mid-century, especially among the nobility. Inasmuch as they called the disease "variola," doctors called this form of immunization "variolation." But to the common folk it was simply inoculation against smallpox. In 1746 a Hospital for the Inoculation against Smallpox was established for the benefit of the poor in London. Smallpox inoculation—it should not be confused with vaccination—became a stock in trade for surgeons, as popular as leeching or bloodletting.

In good hands the smallpox-inoculation death rate was insignificant. As generally practiced, with every midwife, butcher, and grandmother acting as an inoculator, it was reported to be about one in three hundred. The inoculations also proved to be an excellent way of spreading the disease and producing fresh epidemics, despite attempts at isolation of patients.

Smallpox is one of the most contagious of diseases, spreading by personal contact and possibly through the air. Lister, Pasteur, and the principles of antiseptic surgery and sterilization were another century away. The best surgeons were sometimes smallpox carriers, and so were the nurses. Eventually, too, it was noted that a few persons who were inoculated later caught smallpox naturally. The net result was a variable period of protection for a relatively few at the expense of many. The tidy-minded Germans would have none of it.

This was the state of the scarred and pock-marked world to which vaccination, in the hands of an imaginative country physician and surgeon from Gloucestershire, offered a new hope.

THE
MAN WHO LISTENED
TO A MILKMAID

EDWARD JENNER was born on May 17, 1749, in the rural village of Berkeley, in Gloucestershire, not far from the southwestern coast of England.

Wars were as popular then as now, and during his seventy-four years he scarcely knew a time when Great Britain and the western European nations were not at war. The Seven Years' War, the American Revolution, the French Revolution, the Napoleonic Wars, and the War of 1812 all occurred during his lifetime.

The weapons of war weren't so efficient then, but life was cheap. People who did not die of malnutrition or some infectious disease might well be killed in battle or die of infectious wounds. There were no wonder drugs, vaccines, or sanitary engineering, and no germ theory of disease. *Virus* was even then a common word, but a vague one meaning a disease-associated poison of some sort.[1]

[1] In the Middle Ages, *virus* was almost synonymous with *venom*, and meant a slimy, liquid poison, particularly the corrupt matter discharged by a

Only a minority reached the prime of life, and fewer survived it. The annual death rate was about twenty-five per thousand (it is now about nine per thousand in the United States). Looking at it another way, in the eighteenth century a family of eight could expect a death in the house once every five years. People grew up in the presence of the graveyard next to the church.

Son of the Vicar of Berkeley, Jenner was several times blessed. By being born in the country without having to labor in it, he developed that deep love of homeland which characterizes a landed gentry; by being born a preacher's son, he grew up in an atmosphere of books, rhetoric, and love of his fellow man; also, he inherited just enough to give him independence. He did have the misfortune to lose his father and mother; he was raised by an older brother, a preacher, whom he liked.

As a lad, Jenner was sensitive to noises, both real and imaginary ones, and could not sleep well. The Reverend Thomas Fosbroke, Jenner's local biographer, blamed this "hypochondriacal habit," persisting throughout life, upon Jenner's own experience with smallpox inoculation at the age of eight. His ordeal began with six weeks' preparation. He was bled, purged, and made to fast, except for a vegetable drink to sweeten his blood. According to Fosbroke, "he was removed to one of the then usual inoculation stables, and haltered up with others in a terrible state of disease, although none died." [2] Recovery took another three weeks.

Sickly for some time after, Jenner studied Latin, Greek, and the classics under clergyman tutors. At thirteen he was sent to Sodbury, near Bristol, as the apprentice to a surgeon, Mr. Ludlow. While in Ludlow's service, Jenner first heard that cowpox protected against smallpox. To the suggestion that she might be coming down with smallpox, a milkmaid said: "I cannot take that disease, for I have had the cowpox."

Following his seven-year apprenticeship, Jenner was further

---

wound or ulcer. By Jenner's time, physicians recognized that such a poison could transmit disease to others—was an agent of contagion, in other words. As time has gone on and viruses have been identified as specific agents of infection, the original meaning of the word has been reversed: what was thought to be an effect of disease has proved to be a cause.

[2] The Berkeley Manuscripts (1821).

trained in anatomy, surgery, and materia medica, plus experimental daring, by one of the all-time great men of British surgery, John Hunter (1728–1793). Beginning at twenty-one, Jenner worked for two years under Hunter, who had trained Ludlow's son. When Jenner told Hunter he thought there was something to this cowpox business, Hunter—his bear-trap mind always springing on unanswered questions—listened, shrugged, and said: "Don't *think*, but *try;* be patient, be accurate."

Jenner lived with his preceptor, as was the custom then. What a man to live with! A rude, crude Scot with a high temper and equally soaring ideas, Hunter maintained a house in Earl's Court, on London's outskirts; it was a combination of museum and zoo. Hunter practiced surgery to make money to buy, observe, and dissect God's creatures. In his two-acre garden were zebras, panthers, a buffalo, rams, Turkish sheep, jackals, hedgehogs, and a variety of birds, living together more or less in harmony. Hunter could often be found lying on his stomach beside the fishpond, trying to determine whether fish could hear, or up to his armpits in the dissection of a whale from Greenland. Under Hunter, Jenner became an elegant dissector and pickler of specimens.

Hunter's tireless, often amoral curiosity must have made a tremendous impression on his student. In 1767, three years before Jenner came to train with him, the great surgeon performed an experiment on himself which resulted in the primary lesion, or sore, of syphilis being named the Hunterian chancre. Fielding H. Garrison, in his outstanding history of medicine, tried to put the best possible face on the matter, calling it an accident. It was no accident, as Hunter revealed in his report: "Two punctures were made on the penis with a lancet dipped in venereal matter from a gonorrhea. . . ." Subsequently, Hunter gave a good description of the progress of syphilis through his system. The only fault with the experiment, outside of the shocking fact that it was performed at all, was that Hunter confused gonorrhea and syphilis!

Hunter apparently suffered no recognizable damage from the infection (many don't), but died of angina pectoris, a spasmodic chest pain often associated with a hardening of the coronary artery of the heart. That Hunter's student was no country apoth-

ecary, as some have called him, but an able clinician was proved
by the fact that Jenner was probably the first to link angina pectoris with heart disease. He diagnosed the disease in Hunter before
the latter died and predicted that a hardening of the coronary
artery would be found at autopsy. It was.

Jenner and Hunter continued to collaborate by mail when
Jenner decided to return to Berkeley in 1773 and become a country doctor, at twenty-four. Together they investigated the breeding habits of toads, the sex of eels, and whether breeding a dog to
a fox would produce offspring. Jenner found it didn't. Hunter sent
Jenner paintings, candlesticks, and a jackal bitch for a pet.
Jenner sent Hunter a live porpoise after sampling a cow porpoise's milk and finding it creamy rich.

There was a long correspondence about Jenner's study of the
cuckoo's strange nesting habits—it lays its eggs one at a time in
smaller birds' nests. Jenner was the first naturalist to observe that
the baby cuckoo always wound up as the lone occupant of its
step-parents' nest. Being larger and heavier, it shouldered the
rightful occupants to the top and dumped them overboard.
Hunter aided Jenner in having the paper published in the *Transactions* of the Royal Society of London for the Advancement of
Science; the Society elected Jenner a member in 1789.

In 1778 Jenner had been "crossed in love." All we know about
it is found in a typical Hunter letter:

> I own I was at a loss to account for your silence. . . .
> You have two passions to cope with, viz. that of being
> disappointed in love, and that of being defeated; but
> both will wear out, the first soonest. I own I was glad,
> when I heard that you was married to a woman of for-
> tune; but let her go, never mind her. I shall employ you
> with hedge-hogs. . . . I want you to get a hedge-hog in
> the beginning of winter and weigh him . . . then
> weigh him in the spring. . . . About the month of Jan-
> uary, I could wish you would make a hole in one of their
> bellies, and put the thermometer down into the pelvis
> . . . then turn it up towards the diaphragm. . . .[3]

[3] John Baron: *Life of Edward Jenner*, Vol. II (1838).

The hibernation habit of this animal fascinated Hunter more than a woman's fickleness; Jenner was able to establish that during a cold-winter sleep the hedgehog's stomach temperature might fall to thirty degrees Fahrenheit, or below freezing, without hurting him.

His success as a surgeon was established soon after his return to Berkeley when he performed an operation for a strangulated hernia which a Gloucester surgeon would not attempt. Jenner had made a nice dissection, it is reported, when the patient, a man, had a vomiting impulse, causing his intestines to spill out on the infirmary table. Jenner replaced them and finished the operation; the patient lived for another twenty years. Considering that an unrepaired strangulated hernia is a speedy killer, that there were complications, and that nothing was then known of anesthetics or aseptic technique, the young surgeon showed himself to be both skillful and lucky.

Jenner made his house calls on horseback. The life was a rugged one, but, though of nervous temperament, he was physically robust. One night he almost froze to death in the saddle; he was removed bodily from his horse and carried in to thaw out with brandy by a warm fire.

Doctors had amazing notions then. Witness Jenner himself: "It has long been my creed that *stomach* is the governor of the whole machine, the mind as well as the body. . . . The seat of action is certainly in the brain; but the stomach gives the word of command. . . ."

At any rate, physicians then believed in giving the stomach a helping hand. If a patient vomited, they gave him something to make him vomit, reasoning that "nature was wishing to throw something off the stomach." Though he attracted some attention by purifying emetic tartar and making it more dependable in inducing vomiting, even Jenner had some misgivings. When he fell deathly ill in 1794 with typhus (possibly typhoid) fever, he took his own medicine and "increased by this means the malady; for I did not cease vomiting ten minutes for several days." The next time he was nauseated he took a glass of wine and said it made him feel better.

There were many strange and—as we would see them—inhuman treatments in Jenner's times. The weirdest was dipping. The practice was presumed to provide a cure for hydrophobia, a term referring to one of the terrible symptoms of rabies. When the rabid person attempts to drink, he suffers a throat spasm and feels as if he were strangling. He may have a convulsion. After a few efforts to quench his intense thirst, the mere sight of water will bring on this attack.

A doctor Jenner knew took such a patient to the Severn River and there "dipped" him, on the theory that the shock of it might somehow affect his vital principle and deaden the action of the virus. There is no record that Jenner did this, but in a letter he once asked the dipping doctor how long he kept his patients under water. The doctor replied that he pushed them down three times and each time held them until "they have done kicking." It is not clear whether the patients survived.

In his prime Jenner was a broad-faced, blond, and blue-eyed man, solidly built and of slightly less than medium height. He wore his hair in a sort of wind-swept bob, tied in a club at the back. He was neat in dress. Commonly, when he called on patients, he wore a broad-brimmed hat, blue coat with yellow buttons, buckskin pants, well-polished jockey boots, and silver spurs. In lieu of the gold-headed cane that was the mark of the city doctor, he carried a good whip with a silver handle.

He lived comfortably, as a country squire should. His table was well set, the food well served and often accompanied by five or six wines. He was fond of good company, at home or at a tavern, and often met with six or eight doctors of the county in what Jenner called the Medico Convivio Society. He played the violin and flute, sang, and found time to dash off verses.

In 1788, when he was thirty-nine years old, Jenner married Catherine Kingscote. A well-bred woman from an old family, Catherine had been an invalid and continued in delicate health, often confined to her apartment, until her death from pulmonary consumption in 1815. For all this, she was a deeply religious woman, did much good for the poor of Berkeley, and was a great source of strength to Jenner. With Dr. John Baron, his friend and worshipful biographer, Jenner liked to philosophize about life, "and when dwelling on . . . our blindness, our ignorance, the

evils connected with our physical structure . . . and our un-
fathomable capacity both for suffering and enjoyment; he observed, Mrs. Jenner can explain all these things; they cause no
difficulties for her."

  She bore him two sons and a daughter. For the next ten years,
or until he published his observations on cowpox, Jenner accounted himself a happy man.

JENNER'S SECRET
SWINEPOX EXPERIMENT

In his Berkeley practice Edward Jenner had many occasions to reflect on what the milkmaid had told him when he was an apprentice. The story that cowpox protects against smallpox was a common one in Gloucestershire. It was just as commonly dismissed by Jenner's doctor friends.

When he persisted in taking this "vulgar cowpox legend" seriously, they threatened, in good spirit, to throw him out of the Medico Convivio Society. There was nothing to it, said his colleagues; they had known smallpox to occur in persons who had had cowpox. When he attempted to discuss the question with London doctors, he ran into something else: really, what could this country doctor possibly know of science, except maybe about cuckoos and hedgehogs?

All this only made Jenner more determined to prove himself right. In 1780, when he was thirty-one, he revealed how he felt about cowpox to a friend. Commented Jenner, as they rode together: "Gardner, I have entrusted a most important matter to you, which I firmly believe will prove of essential benefit to the human race." He cautioned his friend not to discuss it with others, for fear of ridicule.

A few years later Jenner embroidered his observations with one twist he lived to regret. One day he took his nephew George, a clergyman and physician, to the stable to look at a horse with an infection known as "the grease," or "greasy heels." "There," said Jenner, pointing to the horse's sore hoof, "is the source of smallpox. I have much to say on that subject, which I hope in due time to give to the world."

Jenner regretted something else much more deeply, we can surmise. This incident he did his best to forget, but it must have tormented him nonetheless. John Baron gave only the barest facts, and no other historian of Jennerian vaccination comments upon it at all. The fact is that little James Phipps, who was to make history in 1796 as the first person vaccinated, was not the subject of Jenner's first experiment. The first was Jenner's older son, Edward, Jr., born in 1789, the year the American colonies constituted themselves a nation. Later that year, when his son was about ten months old, Dr. Jenner inoculated him with swinepox.

We do not know how Mrs. Jenner felt about this rash experiment on her first-born. Inasmuch as Jenner did not record why he did it, we can only conjecture what was in his mind at the moment. In science, as elsewhere in human behavior, there is such a thing as an irresistible impulse to satisfy one's curiosity. We know, of course, that Jenner was schooled in daring experiment by John Hunter.

We also can appreciate that Jenner may have felt compelled to make the most of his opportunities. Cowpox made only sporadic appearances on the teats of cows in Gloucestershire, limiting Jenner's chances to observe it. It was natural for him to take an interest in the fact that not only cows but also horses and pigs had a pox disease that bore some resemblance to smallpox. Furthermore, Jenner was only a spare-time researcher; until his nephew Henry joined him, he had no assistance in his practice, and he was obliged to collaborate by mail with Hunter as well as look after his wife and at various times serve as mayor and justice of the peace in his village.

In any event, Jenner injected his baby son with the virus of pox found on a pig. This happened a good one hundred years before anyone had any evidence that there was an ultra-microbe entitled to be identified as a "virus." In Jenner's day, when one took matter from an animal or another human, there was no way of telling what was in it. On the eighth day the baby became sick and not one but several small pustules appeared. It is not known how long Jenner waited, but later he inoculated smallpox matter in little Edward's arms five or six times—without producing the slightest inflammation, we are told. In other words, he apparently got an immune reaction.

In 1791, when the boy was a bit past two, the father tried to infect him with smallpox again. Now Jenner was to see something that at a later date threatened to undermine vaccination's use—contamination. Within two or three days his son had an inflammation in his arm, spreading to his armpit; it was presumably erysipelas, a fever-producing disease now known to be due to several strains of bacteria (hemolytic streptococcus). But the boy is said to have recovered quickly.

A year later the persistent Jenner tried this smallpox experiment on his son again. This time there was an ulcer about the size of a sixpence, but only a small amount of inflammation around it, as one might expect in a vaccination or inoculation that "took."

About the best we can say for this experiment is that it muddied the water. Jenner may also have had inner misgivings about the possibility that he could have injured his son's health; we do not know. But Jenner himself, as a boy, was in poor health for some time after his variolation experience. Of the son, John Baron wrote: "He had been always delicate in health, and had, moreover, rather a defective understanding." Whether the experimental infections had anything to do with this mental retardation it is impossible to say. Obviously, it was a rigorous experience for an infant, and there is such a thing as post-vaccination inflammation of the brain.

Young Edward died at the age of twenty-one, of pulmonary hemorrhages apparently due to consumption, as did his mother five years later. Long afterwards Jenner would talk of his son to close friends and burst into tears.

Some time following the swinepox episode Jenner returned to his notion that cowpox began as horsepox, or "the grease," and was transmitted to cows by men who had dressed the heels of horses and had not washed their hands before milking. In fact, he came to believe that horsepox was "a morbid matter of a peculiar kind" that would not infect man, or protect him from smallpox, until passed through the cow. He wanted to make the experiment of applying the matter to a cow's teats, and so produce a pox that he could then pass on to a child. But he was unable to find an infected horse. "I even procured a young horse," Jenner wrote, "kept him constantly in the stable and fed him with beans in order to make his heels swell, but to no purpose."

Meanwhile, Jenner collected a good bit of circumstantial evidence. This made up the bulk of his famous seventy-page monograph, published in June 1798: *An Inquiry into the Causes and Effects of the Variolae Vaccinae, a Disease Discovered in Some of the Western Counties of England, Particularly Glouchestershire, and Known by the Name of Cow-Pox.*[1]

Case I in this curious work—little Edward Jenner is not mentioned at all—was that of Joseph Merret, undergardener of the Earl of Berkeley. The man recollected milking some of his master's cows after attending horses with sore heels. The cows developed a pox, and soon he had sores on his hands. Twenty-five years after this incident Jenner tried to inoculate the gardener with smallpox, but got an immune reaction. Jenner described a dozen cases of this sort.

Next he reported on Sarah Nelmes, who got cowpox in a general epidemic of the disease during the spring of 1796. Then came James Phipps, vaccinated on May 14, 1796, with matter from the ulcer on Sarah's wrist.

---

[1] Jenner did not explain his use of *variolae vaccinae*, meaning smallpox of the cow, anywhere in his report. *Vacca* is Latin for "cow"—hence "vaccinia," the proper name for "cowpox." The word "vaccine" as applied to the immunizing agent against smallpox came into use following publication of his paper. Jenner's friend Richard Dunning in 1800 introduced "vaccination" as an apt description of the act of inserting the vaccine.

We may as well note here that modern virologists make a false distinction between "cowpox virus" and "vaccinia virus." This is done in an effort to differentiate natural cowpox from the laboratory-cultivated virus used in smallpox vaccine, and to eliminate arguments about the origin of the vaccine virus. This definition of convenience confuses the outsider, who notes that Dorland's *Medical Dictionary*, 23rd edition, treats "cowpox" and "vaccinia" as synonymous. We shall do the same in *Virus Hunters.*

This was the classic experiment that stands at the threshold of vaccination. Jenner performed it three days before his forty-seventh birthday—a few months before George Washington gave his farewell address as the first president of the United States.

The actual place—and this we can only guess—was probably a garden house behind his English-style cottage in Berkeley. Near by on the lawn was the luxuriant green willow tree that had grown so well after he watered it with a spot of his son Edward's blood, let during an illness as was the medical habit at that time. Just beyond the hedge was the church where the doctor's father had preached, its tower entwined with the ivy that had raced upward from a root Jenner had planted there.

The garden house itself was rather odd—circular, with a thatched conical roof, like an African hut, but with walls of gnarled oak-tree trunks implanted stockade-fashion. Here Dr. Jenner liked to see his patients when the weather was warm.

History, including Jenner's own letters and reports, tells us little about James, the eight-year-old boy he chose for his experiment. We don't know who James's father and mother were, or whether they consented.

We are told that the milkmaid Sarah was young, but not whether she was pretty. Selecting a pustule on Sarah's wrist—later he poetically described the typical cowpox vesicle as "like the section of a pearl on a rose-leaf"—Jenner pierced it with a clean lancet. Then, with the lancet now laden with the clear lymph, or matter, he made two scratches an inch long on the arm of little James.

Such person-to-person passage was customary in smallpox inoculation, of course. Later it became known that Jenner was not the first to transmit cowpox to a person to protect him against smallpox, though Jenner *thought* he was first. He was first to eliminate the cow from the picture by employing the technique used in smallpox inoculation.

On the seventh day James complained to the doctor of an "uneasiness" in his armpit. On the ninth day he became "a little chilly," lost his appetite, and had a headache. Meanwhile he developed a single pustule on his arm. It resembled the smallpox-inoculation ulcer, and took its place in history as a primary reaction, or a vaccination that "took." On the tenth day James was quite well again, except for a scab surrounded by a rosy efflorescence. In the subsequent weeks the scab fell off, leaving the well-known pockmark, a tiny crater indented in the skin, with a flat round bed of scar tissue.

Six weeks later Jenner inoculated the boy with smallpox from a pustule on the body of a patient. As Jenner said, this was "in order to ascertain whether the boy, after feeling so slight an affection of the system from the cow-pox virus, was secure from the contagion of small pox."

Nothing happened. All that this inoculation produced was a slight inflammation of the skin—an immune reaction. Jenner tried it again several months later. In the next quarter-century the doctor tested "poor Phipps," as he invariably spoke of him, some twenty times. There was never another pustule, much less any general eruption on the body.

Eventually Jenner built Phipps a cottage, planted the roses in front of it himself, and generally looked out for him until the doctor's death twenty-seven years later. What finally became of Phipps or of Sarah Nelmes is not known. For years the hide of the cow that gave Sarah the pox hung in Jenner's coach house, after which someone gave it to St. George's Hospital, operating-base of a vaccinating doctor whom Jenner came to detest so much he once said: "I will not daub my paper with his name."

Having demonstrated that Phipps was immune to smallpox, Jenner was unable to go further in 1796; both horsepox and cowpox disappeared from the neighborhood. The following year he offered a report of his observations to the Royal Society for publication in its *Transactions*. Sir Everard Home, Hunter's brother-in-law, received the paper, showed it to the Society's Council, and returned it to Jenner, rejected.

He consulted some of his medical friends. Some said: "Publish it yourself;" others advised him to be sure of his evidence first. The pox, horse and cow, reappeared early in 1798. Now he was able to show that cowpox could be passed indefinitely from arm to arm, without dependence on an infected cow. It was this technique of serial passage, using the last person vaccinated as the source of virus matter for the next, which made Jenner a pioneer.

But again his experiments got off to a bad start. A servant, Thomas Virgoe, developed a pustule on his hand from an infected mare's heels. Jenner inoculated five-year-old John Baker with matter from Virgoe's hand. At the same time he took another boy of the same age, William Summers, and vaccinated him with matter from the teat of an infected cow.

The Baker boy became ill on the sixth day with symptoms like those of cowpox; he appeared well on the eighth day. Jenner said he could not make the variolation test in this horsepox case, however. "The boy," he said, "was rendered unfit for inoculation from having felt the effects of a contagious fever in a workhouse soon after this experiment was made." He might have said, as an unkind critic later remarked: "The child, it appears, was rendered unfit for inoculation by unhappily becoming a corpse." John Baker's ulcer spread and he soon died of a subsequent fever (possibly another streptococcus infection).

We can be thankful that, in contrast, the Summers lad did fine. Vaccine from his pustule was passed from him to a boy of eight and from the latter to several children and adults. From one of these last children Jenner passed the Summers line of virus to four others. One was his second son, Robert, eleven months old. Robert's vaccination did not take. Three of these proved to be immune to smallpox inoculation.

"I presume," Jenner said, "it may be unnecessary to produce further testimony in support of my assertion that the cow-pox protects the human constitution from the infection of the small pox."

This was an unwarranted assumption, in view of all the questions that were raised. Nowhere in *An Inquiry* can one find solid ground for his statement that "what renders the cow-pox virus so extremely singular is that the person who has been thus affected is for ever after secure from the infection of small pox." *For ever after* is a long time.

When he had finished his experiments in April 1798, Jenner placed his two sons in safe hands and, with Mrs. Jenner and his small daughter Catherine, took a carriage to London. He also took his manuscript and a quill dipped in vaccine from the Summers line of virus.

Jenner arranged to have his work published privately and meantime sought to demonstrate cowpoxing to some of the doctors in London. He sought in vain. Nearly three months later he returned home in disappointment. He gave his quill of virus to a London friend, Dr. John Cline, who said he might try it sometime.

VACCINE CLERK TO
THE WORLD

WHAT Jenner failed to do in person, his pamphlet did quickly when it appeared in the bookshops. Its promise of freedom from smallpox "for ever" won it immediate attention. Within two years *An Inquiry* had been translated and reprinted in several foreign languages and circulated around the world.

The first vacination in London was performed with the Summers virus about two weeks after Jenner returned home in the summer of 1798. It was done by Dr. John Cline, but not for protection against smallpox. Cline had operated on a boy for a hip infection. He inserted the virus in the wound in the hope that counter-irritation would produce "an issue," or drainage. It did not have that effect, but the doctor subsequently determined that the boy was immune to smallpox.

Cline attempted to transmit the virus from the ulcer in the hip to three other children, but without result. Thus, the line of arm-to-arm passages of the virus from William Summers became lost. This in itself was a minor setback, for the successful use of this so-called humanized lymph (the cow having been left behind) is analogous to a chain letter. The object is to keep passing it on, without a break.

Cline tried to persuade Jenner to move his practice to London, assuring him it would prove lucrative for him to vaccinate in a center of smallpox epidemics. It was the place to be if a man hoped to show he could rid the world of this disease. Jenner declined. He regarded London as a dirty, smoky place.

Jenner had no more love for the first two London doctors to promote vaccination.

The first was Dr. George Pearson of St. George's Hospital. Within six months after Jenner's pamphlet came out, Dr. Pearson obtained some cowpox matter from the Marylebone Field Dairy, tried it, and published an inquiry of his own. Pearson had good intentions, but eventually Jenner would not even speak Pearson's name. The trouble with Pearson's report was that it questioned Jenner's notion that cowpox came from horsepox.

Pearson sought to flatter Jenner: "I know you are too good a philosopher to be offended at the investigation of truth, although the conclusions may be different from your own. I think, too, your principal facts will be the better established than if it had happened that I had uniformly acceded to all your doctrine." This was sensible, but he went on to appoint himself chief promoter of Jenner's immortality: "Your name will live in the memory of mankind . . . and if I can but get *matter* I am much mistaken if I do not make you live forever."

Jenner was furious, the more so when Pearson publicly criticized as inconsistent the term *variolae vaccinae,* or cow smallpox. As mentioned, Jenner had used the term in the title, but had not discussed it in the text of *An Inquiry.*[1] This lack of literary tidiness annoyed various scholars as much as their scrutiny offended Jenner. They were further irritated by his loose data and sloppy reasoning. Here he was calling it *cow* smallpox while holding,

---

[1] Even so, it appears that Jenner had good intuition in his use of *variolae vaccinae.* Many later scientific experiments with animals indicated that cowpox virus is an attenuated smallpox virus—permanently changed and gentled down by life in the cow. Some modern virologists discount these experiments. Whether the cowpox is an offspring of the smallpox virus is unproved. In any event, they are so closely related that they produce like antibodies in human beings.

without experimental evidence, that the disease really began as *horse* smallpox!

Though Pearson wrote: "I would not pluck a sprig of laurel from the wreath that decorates his brow," Jenner heard from his nephew George that he had better get to London and defend his laurels or Pearson would be wearing them.

Seeing the need for a centralized, organized effort to promote vaccination, Pearson went about establishing a charity institution for inoculating the vaccine pock, as he called it. He wrote Jenner that he had obtained the patronage of the Duke of York for his institution, and offered Jenner the position of "an extra corresponding physician." Jenner expressed astonishment that Pearson had organized such an institution without consulting him. He declined the honor, and went to London and saw the Duke of York. The Duke and other members of royalty then withdrew their patronage, and Pearson's institute folded up. Jenner explained his jealousy thus: if vaccination should fall into disrepute, "I alone must bear the odium."

A second man whom Jenner was to denounce as an enemy of vaccination was Dr. William Woodville, superintendent of the Hospital for the Inoculation against Smallpox. To this place, essentially a pesthouse, the poor came for free smallpox inoculations. Woodville, also well-meaning, recently had published the first of a two-volume history of variolation. The second never appeared. He said he felt it his public duty to try cowpoxing. He asked Jenner for some vaccine, but Jenner had none.

Woodville then tried to inoculate cows' teats with horse grease, and also to pass the horsepox directly to humans. He didn't succeed. This led him to agree with Pearson and say Jenner was mistaken about the horsy origin of cowpox.

Woodville heard of a cowpox epidemic in the dairy at Gray's Lane Inn, near London, and found, to his delight, that some of the milkmaids were infected. With a group of distinguished doctors looking on, he examined a pustule on the hand of Sarah Rice; they pronounced it a true cowpox, identical with that pictured in Jenner's pamphlet. Woodville saturated several pieces of thread with the matter.

Thus armed, he ran up a series of two hundred, three hundred, and finally six hundred cases, all cowpoxed in his smallpox hospital. Among them was one death, of a nursing baby, and several severe reactions. Woodville immediately had run into a problem as modern as it is ancient—contamination of his vaccine supply through lack of control over its content.

Not bothering to ask Jenner about proper technique, Woodville went ahead in his own way. He collected the matter from the milkmaids' sores at various stages. He vaccinated patients in one arm and only five days later inoculated them with smallpox in the other arm, before their vaccination had taken. Thus some of his cases had both cow and smallpox viruses at work in them simultaneously.

One way or another, Woodville got his vaccine so fouled up that in a patient named Ann Bumpus he produced not one but 310 pustules by the fifteenth day! Many other cases broke out as if they had smallpox, some with from five hundred to one thousand pustules. Woodville published a paper contending that cowpox was an eruptive disease of great severity. Old-fashioned smallpox inoculation was still the best.

Jenner was mortified. He went to London and saw Woodville, coming away with the opinion that the doctor was a bungler, a walking source of smallpox himself. Truly, a pesthouse was no place to be trying to vaccinate people *against* smallpox.

Jenner asked for some of the vaccine from Ann Bumpus, and got a thread soaked with it. He tried it on twenty cases, including his nephew Stephen. The physical manifestations were somewhat different from those he had got with his own cowpox vaccine, but the protective element was still there. Jenner, true to Gloucestershire, was inclined to blame the difference on "the mode of action of the virus upon the skin of those who breathe the air of London."

Two months after Jenner published *An Inquiry,* the seeds of an anti-vaccination movement were planted. Dr. Benjamin Moseley seems to have been the first of the "Anti-Vacks," as the anti-vaccinists were presently called. Moseley began his public protest reasonably enough; he asked that "public credulity" await "calm and dispassionate scrutiny." However, he then introduced a line of snide attack and irrational comment. He imagined that the human body might gradually assimilate the features of the cow if vaccination became universal. He suggested that cowpox was "lues bovilla"—syphilis of the bull. Soon the Anti-Vacks were displaying posters picturing bull-faced boys who had been cowpoxed.

To Moseley's charges of "cow mania," a Jenner supporter, Dr. John Ring, replied "cow phobia." The charge that the human frame was being poisoned with bestial humors Ring parried with the question of why consumption of milk, cheese, and "beefstake" hadn't poisoned people.

More repugnant was the idea that cowpox originated in the filthy heels of horses. One anonymous physician, explained that he had no enemies and wanted none, wrote an unsigned pamphlet just as wildly attributing cowpox to simple irritation resulting when rough-handed men were permitted to milk "the meek, unoffending ruminant." No one had seen cowpox in Cambridgeshire, he said. "And why? Because there the dairy-maid maintains her right of tenderness and cleanliness against the rude rustics' invasions, with their dirty fist and savage impatience, during the double act of corrupting the maiden's morals and the cow's teats."

Jenner quietly dropped the horsepox theory.

On the whole, in other hands and other lands, cowpoxing behaved the way Jenner said it should. Vaccination circled the world as fast as an epidemic of smallpox itself. By 1800 at least one hundred thousand persons had been vaccinated throughout the world, and in another two years this number was doubled or tripled.

Dr. Luigi Sacco of Milan became Jenner's champion in Italy. Starting with himself, Sacco and his assistants vaccinated 1,300,-000 persons in eight years. Without benefit of a law, vaccination became a family custom in Italy as the result of this favorable experience.

Germany and Sweden quickly adopted the practice and within a few years had compulsory-vaccination laws. Germany, more than any other country, was to furnish the solid body of mass statistics supporting vaccination's effectiveness in reducing smallpox. Ironically, Jenner himself hated arithmetic.

Dr. Benjamin Waterhouse became "the American Jenner." He

put a notice of Jenner's discovery in a Boston newspaper in 1799, under the title "Something Curious in the Medical Line." Waterhouse obtained a thread of vaccine from Pearson and successfully vaccinated his own son, aged five. Waterhouse called Thomas Jefferson's attention to vaccination in 1800; the President, observing that "one evil more is withdrawn from the condition of man," soon was busy with vaccination in his own family. Six years later Jefferson wrote Jenner that his discovery exceeded Harvey's discovery of the circulation of the blood, for he could not see that any great benefit in lifesaving had come from the latter (nor was there any, until after physicians stopped contributing to circulatory collapse by bloodletting).

Thus, Jenner became "vaccine clerk to the world," as he called himself.

Doctors from all over the world wrote to praise him, beg a piece of thread or a quill dipped in vaccine, seek instructions, and raise questions. Waterhouse, for instance, found that in very hot weather the strength of the vaccine seemed to vanish. It is now known that the virus is quite stable under most conditions, but it weakens if exposed to ninety-nine-degree heat for a half-hour.

Then, much instruction was needed in the Golden Rule of Vaccination, as Jenner called it. To be effective, the vaccine had to be taken from the pustule when it was clear and limpid, never after the eighth day.

At home in Berkeley, Jenner might have as many as three hundred poor people waiting for free vaccinations around his "Temple of Vaccina," the garden house in his back yard. When Jenner was otherwise preoccupied with his "clerkship," either his nephew, Henry Jenner, now a doctor, or a servant, Richard, vaccinated all comers. Henry, an enthusiast, even vaccinated babies nursing at their mother's breast. This was done in a spirit of triumph over smallpox inoculation, now fast becoming discredited. Variolation of infants was not generally acceptable to mothers because of the eruptions on the nursing child's face. "In a little time it may occur that the christening and vaccination of children may always be performed on the same day," one enthusiastic doctor wrote Jenner.

Jenner noticed that first he had but few patients from one

neighboring parish, then suddenly many. Inquiring, he found
that a churchwarden had begun urging vaccination to save the
cost of coffins to bury those dying of smallpox!

From the first, Jenner had been determined to deliver his discovery to the world and so, as he revealed, to establish himself as
a benefactor of mankind. He had not reckoned, however, on the
large sums he had to pay out of pocket for postage and the printing of his pamphlets (soon a series of pamphlets), or all the trips
he had to make to London.

But his chief occupation was answering his mail. He wrote his
letters with a sharpened quill from a pet eagle, and laboriously
copied many of them into his records. Sometimes he was as many
as two hundred letters behind.

All this, of course, forced Jenner to neglect his practice, and in
consequence he felt the financial burden even more. Vaccination
was not bringing him the security he had hoped for when he
penned in his notebook: "The joy I felt at the prospect before me
of being the instrument destined to take away from the world one
of its greatest calamities, blended with the fond hope of enjoying
independence and domestic peace and happiness, was often so
excessive, that in pursuing my favourite subject among the mead-
ows I have sometimes found myself in a kind of reverie."

In 1802 he petitioned the House of Commons for a grant. In a
one-month period a committee headed by Jenner's onetime
neighbor Admiral Berkeley heard forty-five witnesses. The majority of opinion was favorable to Jenner, though Pearson did tes-
tify that he had learned that a farmer named Benjamin Jesty was
the first to cowpox a person. In 1774, Jesty had inoculated his wife
and two children. Jesty could not come up to London for the hearings from his home on the Isle of Purbeck because he feared an
attack of gout. He did petition for a share of Jenner's grant, but
received no serious consideration. He had done nothing to advance the art and science of vaccination, as had Jenner.

The committee recommended to the House of Commons that
it give Jenner its unanimous endorsement, plus a grant. Berkeley
suggested £10,000—a small amount to pay a man for saving a
reported forty thousand lives a year, he conceded. £20,000 was
proposed, but the Chancellor of the Exchequer pleaded for econ-

omy. Quite frankly, he said, Jenner was mistaken in making his discovery public; he could have remunerated himself by promoting vaccination as a secret remedy and perhaps saved trouble by seeing that it was done right. In any event, Jenner already had received the greatest award any individual could have—"the unanimous appoval of the House of Commons." The vote for £10,000 as against £20,000 was close, 59 to 56.

A grant worth $50,000 in those times was certainly a singular display of public gratitude for a humanitarian deed. It did not satisfy Jenner, however. The vote for the lesser sum struck him as ignoble. As an anticlimax, the Treasury delayed payment for two years and then deducted nearly £1,000 for taxes and fees.

All that remains to be said of the money question is that in 1807 the British Government had a new Chancellor of the Exchequer and that he raised the question of further remuneration for Jenner. He proposed £10,000, but this time the House upped it to £20,000 and that carried, 60 to 47. The Act specified that there should be no deductions. It was paid promptly. So, all told, Jenner was granted £30,000, or about $150,000

In view of this, he himself seemed to show a lack of gratitude when he was presented to the Emperor of Russia by the Grand Duchess of Oldenburg, the Emperor's sister. For the occasion Jenner wore a diamond ring given him by the Emperor's mother, the Empress Maria. The Emperor said: "You have received, sir, the thanks, the applause, the gratitude of the world." Jenner answered: "Your Majesty, I have received *the thanks* and *the applause* of the world." Thus corrected, the Emperor flushed, we are told.

THE
VIRUS CALLED VANITY

EDWARD JENNER became Father of Vaccination at the age of forty-nine. The remaining twenty-five years of his life were quite different from anything he had known. He had yearned for glory. Now he had it. He still had to pay for it.

No longer could he play the role of the charming, humble country surgeon and squire who had time to listen to a bird's song, hold his invalid wife's hand, compose a verse, write philosophic letters to his friends, or report on his nature studies to John Hunter (who died too soon to witness his pupil's triumph).

Jenner received a tremendous number of honors—medals, portraits, busts, degrees, scrolls, money. He had many loyal friends at home and admirers abroad. One of them was Napoleon. That Jenner didn't completely lose his old sense of humor was shown when someone proposed to present him with a gold cup and asked him about an appropriate inscription. He suggested a cow jumping over the moon.

But the bittersweet contents of the cup baffled him.

Part of the difficulty rose from the conflict of his desire to keep his family, with its continual health problems, in Berkeley, whereas it was obvious that he was needed in London to head a vaccine movement. Several efforts were made to revive Pearson's idea of a vaccine institute.

One was that of the Royal Jennerian Society for the Extermination of Smallpox, patronized by the King and Queen. Jenner hoped his presence would not be required, but the Society elected him president. Jenner recommended Dr. John Walker as secretary and resident inoculator. For a year or two the Society's institute enjoyed a moderate success, vaccinating people who came to its thirteen London stations and distributing vaccine throughout the world. But its two top officers fell out when Jenner found that Walker was publishing opinions on vaccination procedure contrary to the Society's regulations. It took Jenner three years to oust Walker; meanwhile, of course, the program collapsed.

The Prime Minister, following the first grant, told Jenner it was his duty to come to London and establish a vaccination practice there. The idea was painful to Jenner, but he did so, taking a ten-year lease on a house in Mayfair. Unfortunately, the world did not beat a path to his London door. People who wanted a vaccination apologized for bothering the great Jenner with such a small thing. After three months he gave up and "again commenced the village-doctor," as he put it. His summation of the way he felt did him no great credit:

"I found my purse not equal to the sinking of a thousand pounds annually . . . nor the gratitude of the public deserving such a sacrifice. How hard, after what I have done, the toils I have gone through, and the anxieties I have endured in obtaining for the world a greater gift than man ever bestowed on them before (excuse the burst of egotism), to be thrown by with a bare remuneration of my expenses!"

According to one account, Jenner averaged only about £350 a year from his vaccination practice in Berkeley. Following his London fiasco, he was said to have spent £6,000 in four years. A friend told him: "You are sadly deficient in worldly wisdom."

There was agitation, at the time of the second grant, for a new British vaccine establishment with a government-appointed board. Jenner was asked to draw up the plans; once again when he ventured into the world of affairs, bad luck dogged him. Both his sons, Edward and Robert, became ill with typhus and he was called home to Berkeley, missing the first board meeting. Jenner was appointed director, but soon felt, he said, like "a director directed." He had nominated eight persons for staff offices, and the board accepted only two of them. The board's position was that if Jenner received all the patronage, the public would suspect that he had bought staff support of his opinions. Only now did Jenner learn that the board conceived its real purpose was to evaluate vaccination's benefits and drawbacks. Jenner resigned, crying: "Alas, poor Vaccina, how art thou degraded! . . . The whole world bears testimony to the safety and efficacy of the vaccine practice. . . ." This was the greatest source of his difficulty: the vaccine was neither entirely safe nor entirely effective.

First, there was the maddening fact that, just as his medical neighbors had insisted, smallpox did appear in some cases that had been cowpoxed. Within five years after the James Phipps experiment, some physicians correctly observed that the protection diminishes with a lapse of time in many instances. Jenner treated the suggestion as an attempt to discredit the vaccine.

He had to admit that there were vaccination failures, but he sought the explanation in other directions. There were a "true" and a "spurious" cowpox, he said, and they were being confused; only the true cowpox afforded protection. But some doctors insisted they saw smallpox in persons who had been successfully vaccinated with true cowpox. Jenner countered that the specific protective qualities of the true cowpox might somehow be lost in sucessive milkings of an infected cow. Or maybe the doctors were taking the vaccine lymph from pustules later than the eighth day. Or maybe their vaccine had putrefied. Any statement that a correct vaccination did not confer absolute protection was intolerable to him.

In a way, it is unfair to sit in the twentieth century and second-guess Jenner. It is like beginning a mystery story after reading the last chapter. Smallpox and cowpox have been studied longer than any other virus disease. We now know why the smallpox death rate tobogganed in the first few years after vaccination began and then later shot up, even among the vaccinated.

The one thing that eventually enabled science to triumph over the Anti-Vacks was the one thing Jenner fought as long as he lived—periodic revaccination. A year after Jenner's death in 1823 it was authoritatively stated that a vaccination in infancy was impaired by the time of puberty. All that remained to conquer smallpox was establishment of the practice of revaccination, and this meant interminable discussions of how often a person should be vaccinated. Every ten, seven, or three years? In infancy and again at puberty? At birth and again in the first grade? The United States Public Health Service now requires a person entering this country to show evidence of vaccination within three years of his arrival time, and recommends that anyone living in a smallpox-epidemic area, such as India, be revaccinated once a year.

Then there was the problem of contamination. Jenner would not accept the fact, later established, that a variety of infectious diseases, including syphilis, could be—and sometimes were—transmitted by passing an impure vaccine from one human arm to another ad infinitum, even when vaccination was performed in the manner he prescribed. As we have seen, the Father of Vaccination himself infected his son with erysipelas and exposed John Baker to a fatal infection.

The smallpox vaccine reached reasonably certain freedom from contamination only when, in the latter part of the nineteenth century, Adelchi Negri of Italy introduced calf lymph, the vaccine being supplied by passing the cowpox virus from calf to calf rather than from human to human. Calfpox is the kind used today. It is as safe as it can possibly be in human hands. In every million vaccinations one can expect four or five cases of brain inflammation and one death. This is perhaps the irreducible error.

Jenner's greatest embarrassment was still to come. In 1811, Robert Grosvenor, son of a London nobleman, developed a severe case of smallpox. Jenner himself had vaccinated the boy ten years before. For a few days Master Robert was at death's door.

The case created considerable comment, criticism, and confusion in London. Jenner's nervous constitution ached under this fresh insult, so much so that he needed sedatives to sleep. It was as he once warned a friend: "My nerves are in such an odd state, so exquisitely tuned, that unless they are touched by the most delicate finger, one who knows the instrument perfectly, in an instant all is discord." Publicly he suffered in silence, but privately he denounced the people of London as fools and idiots for making so much over this "mere microscopic speck on the page . . . of vaccine discovery." Like a martyred prophet, he lamented: "All my past labors are forgotten, and I am held up . . . as an object of derision and contempt."

Jenner was over-reacting, of course. "I cannot bear to see my darling child whipped with so much as a feather," he said at one time, with good insight.

In the end, Jenner died with merciful swiftness and little suffering, from a cerebral stroke. His death came in January 1823 when he was nearly seventy-five. Only twelve days before, he had jotted on the back of a letter: "My opinion of vaccination is precisely as it was when I first promulgated the discovery. It is not in the least strengthened . . . for it could gain no strength; it is not in the least weakened. . . ."

To the last, then, Edward Jenner showed himself unable to entertain any viewpoint but his own; thus, he constantly renewed the opportunities for attacking him. None were more aware of his blind side than his closest friends. He tried their loyalty greatly. Richard Dunning had protested that Jenner was placing himself in a bad light, and pleaded: "Let vaccination, for God's sake, rest on its own foundation." Jenner heatedly insisted he *was* doing that! "I placed it on a rock, where I knew it would be immovable, before I invited the public to look at it."

The placed-it-on-a-rock statement is one of the most quoted in the history of vaccination, and always has been used to extol a cardinal virtue of the scientific investigator—precise experiment and suspension of judgment until the evidence is irrefutable!

It does not detract from Jenner's demonstration of the truth of the milkmaid's belief that cowpox protected against smallpox to point out that the rock was polished by the gritty abrasives of skepticism, disagreement, and modification over a hundred-year period. Ironically, during the 1896 centennial celebration of Jenner's discovery there was a smallpox epidemic in Gloucester and members of the Anti-Vaccination League were on the steps of the

London hall of celebration, passing out their scurrilous literature.

In his last few years, with his wife, his older son, and many other close relatives dying around him, Edward Jenner lived mainly in retirement. Now he found an opportunity to return again to his first love and end his life on a sweet note. He produced a nature study that the Royal Society was happy to publish, shortly after his death. In it Jenner observed that robins, larks, and other birds migrate with the seasons. Until then the disappearance of these birds in the fall was attributed to hibernation —in the mud at the bottom of ponds! Such was the state of ignorance against which Jenner struck his blows.

LET'S IMMUNIZE
EVERYBODY AGAINST
EVERYTHING

In Paris the scientists came to the meetings of the Academy of Medicine to hear and be heard. In the reports presented and the lively discussions of them, a man could keep in almost daily touch with the thinking and doing of his colleagues. Much of the world-wide talk about smallpox vaccination—it went on for years—took place before the Paris Academy of Medicine. Some of the talk was tall indeed. For example, a physician named Joseph-Alexandre Auzias-Turenne led Academy discussions a half-century after Jenner's death on a proposal to inoculate all French youths with syphilis!

Auzias-Turenne was an early champion of the germ theory of disease. He spoke and wrote so eloquently that friends collected his works and, after his death, published them in 1878 in a large book, *La Syphilisation,* a punning title that rather outdid itself in capturing his aspiration to "syphilize" civilization.

Auzias-Turenne had sound ideas about the variation of virulence in "viruses," as he called infectious poisons in general, but his notion about syphilis was baseless. He thought that the genital lesion known as soft chancre was an "attenuated," or weakened, form of the hard chancre of syphilis—just as cowpox was thought to be an attenuation of smallpox. There was nothing to show that chancroid, as soft chancre is known today, protected against syphilis, or that the two were related. It was the same sort of mistake Hunter had in confusing syphilis with gonorrhea. The cause of syphilis eventually was established as a microscopic corkscrew-shaped protozoon in 1905; the cause of chancroid, as a rod-shaped bacterium in 1938.

Precisely what brought the chemist Louis Pasteur (1822–1895) into the field of immunization is a matter of conjecture. Probably Auzias-Turenne deserves some credit, for Pasteur heard him speak and later kept a copy of *La Syphilisation* in his desk drawer at his laboratory in the Paris Normal School, where he was director of scientific studies. Pasteur, we know, found the debates in the Academy of Medicine a challenge.

He reached the decision to investigate immunity to disease in 1877, when he was fifty-five. He was already a lively folk hero as the result of pasteurization and his proof of the germ theory of disease. A stubby, big-headed, black-haired, gray-eyed, near-sighted, sharp-tongued, softhearted Frenchman who believed in working hard and living dangerously "for the glory of France," as he never forgot to say, Pasteur now had to depend on the hands of others to carry out his ideas. At forty-six he had suffered a cerebral stroke that slowed his mind not at all, but left him with a stiff hand and dragging leg.

Pasteur and his two physician associates, Charles Chamberland, then twenty-six, and Emile Roux, twenty-four, now began studies of seven different diseases, including one caused by a virus—rabies. In the virus hunt it is only these last eighteen years of his life, his discovery of the basic methods of making a vaccine, and his work with this one virus disease which concern us. During this period, however, Pasteur and the half-dozen who carried out his ideas produced five vaccines—against chicken cholera, anthrax (in cattle), swine erysipelas, rabies (dogs and humans), and diphtheria (in children). In all but the diphtheria antitoxin, which was the work of Roux, the great Pasteur—extolled by one contemporary surgeon as "the most perfect man who has ever entered the kingdom of Science," and certainly the best-known medical scientist of all time [1]—was the mastermind. Thus, we can credit him not only for being among the first to put medical science on a sound experimental basis, for enabling surgery to introduce sterile techniques, for rendering the milk bottle on our doorstep non-infectious, and for making bacteriology—or, better, microbiology—a popular science. Pasteur also fathered the science of immunology and, though not a physician, became the prophet of modern preventive medicine.

It was characteristic of the famous "Pasteur luck" that he did not get caught in Auzias-Turenne's mistake. Pasteur was not above rhetorical statement, but on the few occasions when he went off on a false scent, he soon put himself back on the right track. Thus, unlike his great German rival Dr. Robert Koch, who stubbornly insisted that tuberculin, a toxin of tuberculosis, was its cure, Pasteur had the singular good fortune never to be knocked off his high horse in broad daylight or be bushwhacked on some dark scientific night.

When inspired to test his mettle on immunity, Pasteur wisely stayed away from venereal diseases. The means of immunizing humanity against syphilis—or, for that matter, chancroid—is still not available. These were not diseases for a good family man to identify himself with.

"We must immunize against the infectious diseases of which we can cultivate the causative micro-organism," Pasteur told Chamberland and Roux.

It was in chicken cholera that Pasteur first recognized the experimental possibilities of producing immunization. While he definitely hoped to find methods of producing vaccines, he hit upon his first vaccine quite by accident, as is so often the case in the great discoveries of medicine.[2]

---

[1] As René J. Dubos points out in his excellent biography, *Louis Pasteur: Free Lance of Science* (Boston: Little, Brown and Company; 1950), "Few lives have been more completely recorded."

[2] Science has a pretty name for these happy accidents—serendipity. This refers to Horace Walpole's three fictional princes of Serendip who in their travels were always discovering interesting things they weren't looking for, due to chance and their own keen observation. Pasteur often said: "Chance favors the prepared mind."

Cholera kills a chicken practically overnight; it can destroy an entire flock in a matter of two or three days. The chicken-cholera microbe had been discovered, and Pasteur found it could be easily grown in a glass flask containing chicken-gristle broth, using a germ-culture technique discovered by Koch. When a few drops of culture broth were injected under each chicken's skin, the birds died with remarkable regularity.

In 1879, returning from his summer vacation, Pasteur met with a surprise. When chickens were inoculated with an old broth that had been left to stand for several weeks, they got a little sick and then recovered, instead of dying.

Well, maybe the stuff wasn't any good any more. At this point the plodding laboratory worker often throws his material down the drain, washes his dishes, and starts over. Things can go wrong in technique; they often do. Pasteur made new cultures from a fresh epidemic and got a new batch of chickens. When inoculated with the new culture, the new chickens promptly died. *But* he also challenged the chickens surviving the old culture with injections of new, virulent broth. They kept right on pecking!

History is vague on just what Pasteur was thinking when he had his laboratory workers inject the new culture into the chickens who had survived the old broth. Certainly it was accidental that he had aged one batch of microbes before using them. Paul de Kruif reconstructed the scene to make it appear that it was also an accident that chickens receiving the aged microbes were later exposed to the new ones.

On the contrary, there is better reason to suppose that Pasteur was carrying out a controlled test. The theory of the small or weak dose of infection as a protection against the real thing was already an old story. Furthermore, he was already a great exponent of the controlled experiment.[3]

The only difference between Pasteur's treated and untreated chickens was inoculation with the old broth before they received the new. Or so he immediately concluded. It looked to him like the smallpox vaccine all over again. He quickly expanded the

[3] Scientific control of an experiment requires that one set up a parallel experiment in which all conditions are the same except the one being tested. Thus comparisons can be made and inferences drawn if one can eliminate the possibility that the result is due to chance or to some unaccounted-for factor.

meaning of the bovine-inspired "vaccination" to cover his new concept of immunization as something applying to chickens as well as cows. Soon, too, he was talking immunization at the dinner table. Pasteur was a good husband and father, except that he put work ahead of family and insisted on polishing the silverware with his napkin. He talked of a general law of immunity governing every microbe and making vaccination possible against most, if not all, infectious diseases of humans.

Meanwhile, he pursued his chickens. What was it that worked the change between new and aged chicken-cholera broth? It was not the death of the bacteria, for even after three months they could be transplanted and cultivated again. But they couldn't kill a chicken any more! Pasteur concluded that it was oxygen, or oxidation, that weakened the cultured organism. He also showed that this weakening, or attenuation, could be graded according to the age of the culture. Thus, with a fresh culture he could kill ten out of ten hens. With the passage of time, the same culture would kill eight of ten, five of ten, one of ten, and finally after three months all ten would survive.

It was typical that, following his first report on chicken-cholera vaccine to the Academy of Medicine, Pasteur sent a copy to a friend and said: "Do repeat to me every criticism you hear; I much prefer it to praise, barren unless encouragement is wanted, which is certainly not my case: I have a lasting provision of faith and fire."

It was Pasteur's chicken vaccine, plus his willingness to seek out and dispose of criticism, that brought him into the only challenge he is known to have ducked—a challenge to a duel. As a matter of fact, the occasion took a little more than chickens and criticism—it took his own delight in badgering the doctors of medicine, in those days often more impressed by their own elegant language than by facts.

In 1880, before the Academy of Medicine, Pasteur argued that his knowledge of chicken cholera was further advanced than the prevailing knowledge of smallpox. He pointed out that "the identity of the smallpox virus with the cowpox virus has never been demonstrated."

An eighty-year-old surgeon named Jules Guérin rose to state that "human vaccine is the product of animal variola (cowpox and horsepox) inoculated into man and humanized by its successive transmissions in man."

"So," retorted Pasteur, "vaccine is—vaccine." He accused Guérin of "mere equivocation."

Words flew back and forth, until Pasteur thought to ridicule Guérin's operating techniques. Guérin rose from his seat and started for him, stopped only by a friendly baron. The next day Guérin sent his seconds to Pasteur's laboratory to ask for a settlement on the field of honor.

We do not have Pasteur's thoughts on the matter, but we can imagine he may have smiled inwardly. Pistol or sword, what a duel that would have been—a semi-paralyzed chemist with a grizzled beard and a patriarchal, white-haired octogenarian! At any rate, it would have been quite different from dueling with words, and was not Pasteur's dish. He referred Guérin's men to the Permanent and Annual Secretaries of the Academy, who were in charge of publication of the proceedings. "I am ready," he said, "having no right to act otherwise, to modify whatever the editors may consider as going beyond the rights of criticism and legitimate defense."

Pasteur entertained the possibilities of achieving vaccination by two different methods worked out in his laboratory. The first was attenuation, or weakening, of the chicken-cholera bacterium by exposing it to oxygen. The second was used in making swine-erysipelas vaccine: passed from rabbit to rabbit, the bacteria, when reintroduced in swine, no longer had the power to make them sick.

In February 1881, Pasteur rose to report that he had a third technique—attenuation of anthrax germs by cultivating them at high temperature, so they would not form the spores by which the disease was transmitted in nature.

René Dubos said in 1950 of these three approaches to vaccine production: "This achievement will appear little short of miraculous to anyone familiar with the technical problems involved. It is difficult to comprehend how Pasteur and his collaborators found it possible, in the course of three years, to work out the practical techniques of vaccination while still struggling to formulate the very concept of immunization."

7

PASTEUR
AND THE VIRUS
THAT DRIVES YOU MAD

RABIES is not now, in 1959, a major health problem. It never has been. But for those in whom rabies takes hold, the prospect is today, as it was in Pasteur's time, almost certain death. Often the death is a terrible one, for the virus moves along the nerve pathways to the brain and inflames it, producing crawling sensations in the skin, wild excitement, terror, convulsions, paralysis, and, after two or three days of this, merciful death.

The French call the disease *la rage* or, commonly, hydrophobia. Rabies causes the salivary glands to work overtime and thus produces much drooling and a great thirst. Dogs, in contrast to humans, do not appear to develop a morbid fear of water, yet even their suffering is such that we would still conclude that rabies is the kind of disease one would expect a Count de Sade to invent.

The disease has evoked equally brutal methods of treatment. We already have read in the story of Jenner about the weird custom of dipping, or half drowning, the human victim of hydrophobia. While rabies rarely has been known to be transmitted from one person to another, panic reactions are such that in ancient times persons bitten by mad dogs were occasionally hunted down by a mob and killed like wild beasts, strangling or suffocation being favorite ways of relieving the situation.

But the most popular and most rational early method of treating the bite of a rabid animal was to cauterize it with a red-hot iron. When he was a boy of nine in Arbois, Pasteur saw this done to a man named Nicole. A mad wolf raged through the neighborhood, attacking people and animals. Eight persons who were bitten on their hands and faces eventually died, but Nicole was saved. The blacksmith near the Pasteur tannery burned Nicole's wounds with a red-hot iron, a sight that remained seared in Pasteur's memory.

Bouley, general inspector of veterinary schools, and Bourrel, an army veterinarian, had sought the cause of *la rage* in the 1870's without success. While human deaths from rabies in all Europe might number only a few score a year, the disease was a great veterinary problem because dogs bite people tens of thousands of times annually and, when rabies is suspected, the law requires that the dog be put to death. Bouley found, in a study of 320 persons bitten by rabid dogs, that 40 per cent acquired rabies and died. Still other findings ranged from 5 to 60 per cent. Rabies from wolf bites ran much higher, 30 to 95 per cent. The threat is obviously a variable one, depending on how much virus the dog has in its saliva, whether it bites through clothing that may absorb the saliva, how deep the bite goes, and how many times the person is bitten (wolves are more savage biters).

At the time his veterinarian friends interested Pasteur in rabies, they seemed to know only three things about its origin: (1) the cause, whatever it was, was to be found in the saliva; (2) the cause was transmitted only by a bite that penetrated the skin; (3) it was always from several days to a few months (rarely less than fifteen days or more than five months, we now know) before the disease appeared in the bitten victim. Those who believed in the germ theory of disease said the cause was a "virus," and they were right, of course, except that in those days the word described a general idea rather than a specific thing.

Pasteur's first object was to find the micro-organism. Once

found, he assumed it could be cultured and passed from one experimental animal to another. In 1880 he injected saliva from a five-year-old child who died of rabies into a rabbit and it died. Examining the blood of this rabbit, he found a microbe shaped something like a figure "8." Focusing his microscope more sharply, he saw an aureole around the germ which he recognized as a mucous capsule. Was this the cause of rabies?

For a time Pasteur thought it was. However, the microbe could also be isolated from the saliva of normal children. Refusing to be confused or sidetracked, he forgot about this organism and got on with his rabies search. Thus he passed by a famous killer and far greater menace than the rabies virus—the pneumococcus of pneumonia. Albert Frankel showed it to be the cause of lobar pneumonia three or four years later.

Pasteur never found the filterable virus that causes rabies, though he correctly deduced that the disease was caused by an ultra-microscopic organism beyond the range of the microscope. (Paul Remlinger identified the virus in 1903 at the Pasteur Institute in Constantinople.) On the other hand, he was able to carry isolation of the organism to the point that, although he could neither see nor cultivate the organism, he learned where to find it and thus could work with it.

Whenever Bourrel heard of a rabid dog, he would report it—often by telegram—to Pasteur. The latter would then send one of his laboratory staff by cab or train with a cageful of rabbits to be injected with saliva. This was hazardous stuff. One day two of Bourrel's assistants threw a noose around a mad bulldog's neck, hauled him foaming from his cage, and then held him down on a table while Pasteur took a glass tube between his lips and through it sucked up a few drops of the deadly saliva from the animal's mouth. One slip could have meant a fatal bite on his face.

Rabies could be sometimes transmitted by injection of this saliva into a rabbit, another dog, a monkey, or a guinea pig, but there were many exceptions and, in any event, the disease took a long time to appear. It was a most unsatisfactory method for laboratory work.

What Pasteur needed was a way of passing the infection from

one animal to another every time, and some way of cutting down the incubation period. He began to make progress when he read reports that rabies made its home in the nervous system. This made sense, for several reasons. Rabies could not be transmitted through an animal's blood. Its earliest symptoms were of a nervous nature—the spasms in swallowing and the skin sensations, among others. Then, as it progressed, rabies produced mental symptoms and finally a general paralysis, indicating that it had reached the central nervous system. The long incubation period would be due, quite logically, to the length of time it took the germs to migrate from the bite wound to the spinal cord and brain.

Pasteur and Roux found a somewhat better way of transmitting the disease to a rabbit than through saliva: they now injected a rabbit with a solution containing grindings from the tip of a dead dog's spinal cord. But they were still putting the rabies under the skin, and that meant a long incubation. And they still had complete misses.

It was probably Roux who suggested injecting the rabic spinal-cord mixture directly into the living brain. If rabies was a nerve-inhabiting disease, why not transmit it directly to a nerve center? This would require a trephining operation—removal of a small scallop of bone from the animal's skull.

Here Pasteur balked. Although anti-vivisectionists pictured him as a sort of laboratory executioner of helpless animals, and addlepated English ladies wrote him letters denouncing his crimes against chickens, Pasteur really was an old sentimentalist. Roux tells the story of Pasteur's horror about inflicting suffering upon animals:

"He could assist without too much effort at a simple operation such as a subcutaneous inoculation, and even then, if the animal screamed at all, Pasteur was immediately filled with compassion, and tried to comfort and encourage the victim, in a way which would have seemed ludicrous if it had not been touching.

"The thought of having a dog's cranium perforated was very disagreeable to him; he very much wished that the experiment should take place, and yet he feared to see it begun. I performed it one day when he was out. The next day, as I was telling him

that the intracranial inoculation had presented no difficulty, he
began pitying the dog.

"'Poor thing! His brain is no doubt injured, he must be paralyzed!' I did not answer, but went to fetch the dog. . . . Pasteur
was not fond of dogs, but when he saw this one, full of life, curiously investigating every part of the laboratory, he . . . spoke to
the dog in the most affectionate manner. Pasteur was infinitely
grateful to this dog for having borne trephining so well, thus
lessening his scruples for future trephining."

In any event, the operation—performed under chloroform and
followed by stitching of the scalp incision—was a success. Receiving the virus directly into his brain, the dog became rabid in fourteen days and died five days later.

Now Pasteur and Roux went ahead and passed rabies into one
rabbit brain after another. In this serial passage, repeated one
hundred times, the period of incubation became progressively
shorter, until it was down to six days. The virus thus became
more virulent for rabbits, until it became "fixed," Pasteur's word
for *stabilized*. Now, however, it showed but little capacity to infect dogs when injected under the skin. Yet it would kill a rabbit
almost as if working by timetable.

Pasteur now had a satisfactory source of supply of rabies virus,
simply by getting rabies from a dog's spinal cord started in a rabbit's brain and then taking it from the rabid rabbit's spinal cord
and passing it to another rabbit brain.

Now, how to make a safe vaccine?

The way he hit upon was that used against chicken cholera—
passage of time, or aging. Again the solution to the problem was
suggested by Roux, who was studying the survival time of rabies
in pieces of spinal cord hung from the stopper inside a glass flask
with a second opening in its side to ventilate it. Pasteur, seeing
Roux's flasks sitting in an incubator, fell into one of his famous
spells of impenetrable concentration. Finally he ran his hand over
his face in a familiar gesture, roused himself, and returned to his
office, where he ordered a batch of similar flasks from the glass-
blower.

Pasteur placed some caustic potash in the bottom of a flask to
aid in drying and sterilizing the air and added a cotton-wool plug

in the side opening to keep out atmospheric dust. A rabid rabbit's spinal cord was hung from the stopper by a thread, and the flask stored at a constant temperature of seventy-three degrees Fahrenheit—in other words, at "room temperature."

Now the experiments in the attenuation of the rabies virus began. The degree of attenuation would be determined on each successive day by crushing a bit of spinal cord, mixing it with pure water, and injecting a few drops into some rabbits, then watching to see if and when they got rabies. The power of this mixture to kill a rabbit gradually diminished, and after two weeks was almost completely lost.

Pasteur reversed the process to build immunity in a dog. On the first day the animal received rabbit cord aged fourteen days; on the second day, cord thirteen days old, and so on. On the fourteenth day he received a one-day-old cord.

So protected, it was found that a healthy dog could be put in a kennel with a rabid one and emerge a little battered and much bitten but with never a sign of rabies. Roux could put the rabies virus directly into the immunized dog's brain and he still would pant happily and wag his tail!

Progress had been slow, by Pasteur's standards, but this was the state of affairs in May 1884. Pasteur immediately called upon the Minister of Public Instruction to appoint a commission to verify his results, and it was done. Bouley would be chairman.

The commission wished to establish a kennel where vaccinated and unvaccinated dogs could be exposed to rabid ones. It first chose an isolated site in the Meudon woods, but the people of Meudon protested, and the state-owned park of Villeneuve-l'Etang was selected. Here, too, the neighboring people soon protested, fearing the dogs might get out and bite Sunday picnickers. By May 1885 there were sixty dogs in the old stable at Villeneuve. Forty more were housed in the old Rollin College building, next to the Normal School. Its courtyard was full of chicken, rabbit, and guinea-pig coops. About twenty-five dogs were quartered elsewhere.

At first Pasteur avoided the word "vaccination," and merely said his treated dogs were "refractory to hydrophobia." Within the first year, however, he was certain he had an effective vaccine against "canine hydrophobia."

The question of vaccinating people against rabies immediately arose. Pasteur refused many requests, from abroad as well as at home. At first he entertained the idea of vaccinating all the dogs in France—an estimated two and a half million. This seemed impractical, under his fourteen-day plan of treatment. Kennel clinics would have to be established, personnel trained, and dogs housed and fed for fifteen days. Also, where would one get enough rabbits to make the vaccine?

He thought about persuading some condemned criminal, awaiting execution, to volunteer for the first human experiment. If the man survived both vaccination and subsequent exposure to rabies, he could be pardoned. It did not appear, however, that Justice was in the mood to invent new punishments or make bargains with criminals.

Even if both safe and effective, a human vaccine was not too appealing. The course of treatment was rigorous, and the risk of later being bitten by a rabid animal was negligible even for those who had dogs. However, Pasteur saw that, because of rabies's usual long incubation and the fact that immunity could be established in two weeks, there was an excellent opportunity to employ the vaccine as a prophylactic treatment after a person was bitten.

"I have not yet dared to treat human beings after bites from rabid dogs, but the time is not far off," Pasteur wrote a friend. "I am much inclined to begin by myself—inoculating myself with rabies, and then arresting the consequences, for I am beginning to feel very sure of my results."

This was written in 1885 at the height of the rabies season—occurring everywhere in the late winter and spring despite the popular superstitution associating mad dogs with the sultry "dog days" of summer.

Roux was still of the mind that they had not done enough testing of the vaccine to justify human experimentation. As a physician, he was well aware that his medical colleagues regarded rabies as incurable from the time it entered the body.

8

THE SECOND
HUMAN VACCINE

ON JULY 4, 1885, a mad dog sprang upon nine-year-old Joseph Meister as the lad was walking to school at Meissengott, in Alsace. The dog knocked him to the ground and bit him repeatedly, while the boy hid his face in his hands. A bricklayer saw the attack, ran over and beat the dog off with an iron bar. The dog then ran home to his master, Theodore Vone, a grocer, whom he bit on the arm. Vone got his gun and shot the dog. Meanwhile, the bricklayer carried Joseph, covered with blood and saliva, to his parents. That night they took him to Dr. Weber of Ville. The physician cauterized the boy's fourteen wounds with carbolic acid, and advised Mme Meister to take her boy to Pasteur in Paris. Pasteur was not a physician, said the doctor, but he would be the best judge of what to do.

So it was the tribute of a country doctor to a city chemist which put Mme Meister, her son, and Grocer Vone on Pasteur's laboratory doorstep on Monday, July 6. Hearing the story and noting that Vone's shirt sleeve had remained intact, so the saliva probably had not reached the tooth marks in his skin, Pasteur reassured Vone and told him to go home.

He then pondered the fate of the boy, who was so stiff from

his many wounds that he could hardly walk. Pasteur arranged for mother and son to stay in a room in Rollin College and told them to return at five p.m. He sought the counsel of the physiologist Edme Vulpian, who was on the commission investigating the vaccine, and Dr. Jacques Grancher, one of the first French physicians to study bacteriology. The two decided that it was Pasteur's duty to try his vaccine on the boy. They examined Joseph Meister with Pasteur that evening, gave the first inoculation immediately, using fourteen-day-old spinal cord.

Little Joseph had cried a great deal before the injection, expecting more burning acids, but stopped when he discovered it was hardly more than a skin prick. The treatments were repeated every morning. Within five days the boy was sleeping and eating well, and playing with the animals in the courtyard. As the inoculations were increased in virulence, Pasteur became anxious. He dreaded the last shot of one-day-old vaccine. He couldn't work and slept fitfully. He had a nightmare in which he saw little Joseph suffocating in his own saliva, in the mad struggles Pasteur had witnessed in the child from whom he had first obtained the virus in 1880.

Joseph Meister received twelve shots in eleven days. The last one, on July 16, was one day old—strong enough to kill a rabbit by the seventh day. That night the boy insisted: "Dear Monsieur Pasteur, kiss me good-night." He slept peacefully. Pasteur continued to have insomnia.

Roux had no part in all this, and wanted none. He refused to sign the first report of treatment with Pasteur, withdrew from the rabies study, and did not return to the laboratory until the following year when the old master found himself in serious trouble. While René Vallery-Radot's "official biography" of Louis Pasteur skirts the break between Pasteur and Roux completely, and Roux handled it in a discreet manner, we can judge the effect for ourselves. In a sense, his walkout paid back the bad faith Pasteur had exhibited toward him during their field trial of anthrax vaccine at Pouilly-le-Fort in 1881. At the climactic moment Pasteur, under the strain of the great suspense, had made it plain that the triumph would be his but the mistakes Roux's. So now the mistake, if any, would be Pasteur's.

Except that there was no mistake—simply one more triumph for M. Pasteur!

Dr. Grancher kept little Joseph under observation for another ten days and then sent him home to Meissengott. The boy flourished. Eventually he grew up and became the gatekeeper of the Pasteur Institute. He was still minding the gate at the age of sixty-four when, in 1940, the Nazi army invaded Paris. The Nazis ordered Meister to open Pasteur's crypt. Rather than do so, Meister committed suicide.

One dramatic case after another now came to Pasteur for treatment. The commission endorsed his work, and he was asked to establish a rabies-prevention service. In the Meister case there had been a lapse of two and a half days between the bite and the first injection of vaccine. In the second case, that of a fourteen-year-old shepherd, the lapse of time was six days. Then, in November, came ten-year-old Louise Pelletier, who had been bitten on the head by a mountain dog thirty-seven days before. Her wound was still infected and discharging.

"This is a hopeless case," thought Pasteur. "It is much too late for the preventive treatment to have the least chance of success. Should I not, in the scientific interest of the method, refuse to treat the child? If the issue is fatal, all those who have already been treated will be frightened, and many bitten persons, discouraged from coming to the laboratory, may succumb to the disease!"

But the girl's mother and father pleaded, and Pasteur the scientist became Pasteur the humanitarian. Louise returned to school following her two weeks of treatment. Then, eleven days after her last injection, fits of breathlessness appeared, soon to be followed by spasms, convulsions, and the inability to swallow.

Pasteur went, on December 2, from Bouley's funeral to the child's bedside in her parents' rooms in the rue Dauphine. Louise seemed to have rallied, and she asked that the professor stay with her. He spent the rest of the day there, watching her writhing and gasping, and seeing her hand feel out for his each time the attack subsided. She died that day. As he departed, Pasteur said to the parents: "I did so wish I could have saved your little one." Descending the stairs to the street, he burst into tears.

Many of those who were now pouring into Pasteur's laboratory for anti-rabies treatment mistook him for a physician, so much so that assistants explained: "He does not cure individuals; he only tries to cure humanity." Though Dr. Grancher presided, the procession of patients—1,726 in the first year, with only ten deaths—made Pasteur a doctor of medicine, whether he or the physicians with degrees and licenses liked it or not.

In his anti-rabies treatments—which have gone on and on in all parts of the world and today number in the millions—he was unable to pursue the kind of experiment that would dispel doubts. As Pasteur himself well knew, not everybody who is bitten by a rabid dog will die. In untreated rabies, death following a bite may be regarded as proof of whether rabies was actually transmitted. The percentage of the unvaccinated who die varies, but it is ordinarily far higher than the death rate of the vaccinated. With Pasteur's treatment, the death rate was—and has remained—one half of one per cent or under. Such comparisons are impressive, but the cold-minded scientist would still have to be convinced that the biting dog had rabies in his saliva and had actually infected the patient in each case. Then he would require some control such as letting every other person bitten by a mad dog go completely untreated. Then one could compare treated and untreated. Pasteur, the great protagonist of the controlled experiment, had to lay down his strongest weapon when he turned to the business of helping humans. This, in his rabies research, put him in the same boat as Jenner in relation to smallpox—without the clinching evidence.

And Pasteur's enemies made the most of the situation. While the patients rolled in—nineteen wolf-bitten Russians, three of whom died; four New York City children, all of whom survived—Dr. Michel Peter hopped on Pasteur in the Academy of Medicine. First, he denounced the treatment as useless. Then, when he had Louise Pelletier's death (and later two or three others) to talk about, he called the treatment dangerous. He charged that Pasteur was giving people "laboratory rabies," the hydrophobia of rabbits.

With the advent of this second human vaccine, and with the Pasteurians and anti-Pasteurians arguing among themselves, the

Antivivisection League, a direct lineal descendant of the Anti-Vaccination League, found a fine opportunity for a campaign against reason in general and Pasteur in particular. In 1886 the father of one girl who had died following anti-rabies treatment (not Louise Pelletier) brought suit against Pasteur and Grancher. Nothing came of it, except that it brought Roux back. With the old master now under fire on medical grounds, the young physician returned to his side. After all, this *was* the Pasteur-*Roux* method.

Often the careless let the word "murderer" slip out in their heated discussions of the Pasteur treatment. There were scurrilous unsigned letters, insulting newspaper articles, and insinuations that the laboratory was keeping its failures secret. Ordering that the name of every patient who entered the door be published, Pasteur said: "I did not know I had so many enemies." Vulpian assured him that, with four or five vocal exceptions, almost the entire Academy of Medicine was on his side. Only rarely, however, did Pasteur flinch or sulk or show fear for his reputation. Unkind words rattled off his strong mental hide like pebbles off an armored tank, to the point where some defined his boldness and his success as matters of sheer willfulness and colossal good luck.

Within two years after Mme Meister brought Joseph into his laboratory, Pasteur's health began to crumble under the punishing pace that he set for himself. As he stood with Grancher and helped record the patients as they came in, or reached into his drawer to hand out copper coins or sweets to bitten children, or wandered among the animal cages in the basement, the courtyard, and the various buildings that had been annexed for his use, he appeared thin, tired, and sad-looking in his little black skullcap and cape. He now suffered from heart trouble, and his famous energy was fading fast. In 1887 his tongue became paralyzed and speech temporarily failed him, in the course of two cerebral strokes.

In his declining years fresh honors were heaped upon him, best of all perhaps in a letter written by the father of Louise Pelletier, Pasteur's first treatment casualty. Said M. Pelletier of the great Pasteur:

"Among great men whose life I am acquainted with . . . I do not see any other capable of sacrificing, as in the case of our dear little girl, long years of work, of endangering a great fame, and of accepting willingly a painful failure, simply for humanity's sake." From all over the world, emperors and charwomen, dukes, dog lovers, and peasants sent in contributions for the fulfillment of Pasteur's dream, a large research laboratory, the Pasteur Institute, in Paris—there were already a score of Pasteur Institutes throughout the world. The total of these gifts was 2,586,680 francs, quite enough for the 1888 conversion of the Normal School laboratory into a full-fledged scientific institution that continues today to produce both rabies vaccine made according to Pasteur's original formula and occasionally a scientist of Pasteurian spirit.

The present strains of rabbit rabies virus used in the Institute's vaccine have survived two thousand and more passages from one animal to another. They are still one-hundred-per-cent lethal for rabbits and dogs if injected into the brain, and kill rabbits if injected into muscles, but they appear unable to infect either man or dog if injected under the skin.

Elsewhere, desirable modifications of the Pasteur vaccine have followed in more recent times. Rabbit brains were substituted for spinal cords as a more productive source of the virus. An attenuated virus killed with carbolic acid was substituted for an attenuated one simply weakened by drying. The vaccine most commonly used in the United States has been a rabbit-brain, killed-virus suspension introduced by the British physician Sir David Semple in 1919. In 488,795 persons treated with this vaccine, there were 55 cases of vaccine paralysis, with 14 deaths. These were reportedly due to an allergic reaction of the brain to the rabbit brain tissue; sensitivation had been built through the fourteen daily doses.

In recent years, however, Dr. Hilary Koprowski, formerly of the Lederle Laboratories in Pearl River, New York, now of the Wistar Institute in Philadelphia, and others have induced the rabies virus to grow in hen and duck eggs. Thus they have been able to produce an attenuated, live-virus vaccine that eliminates the danger of a brain inflammation, makes it possible to give only one dose, and achieves a more solid and durable immunity. This vaccine is in general use in immunization of dogs and is also recommended for protection of persons running a high risk of exposure to rabies. It also is used, like the Pasteur treatment, after exposure, in combination with a blood serum containing antibodies against rabies.

The continuing need for rabies vaccine has been underscored by the discovery in recent years that the common insect-eating bats of North America have become rabies carriers, apparently having acquired the disease from the blood-sucking vampire bats of Latin America. In 1956 it was reported that the Carlsbad Caverns of New Mexico were infested with rabid bats. Foxes, skunks, and other carnivorous animals also carry the disease.

The annual number of rabies deaths in humans in America now ranges from five to ten. In 1955 an estimated five hundred thousand Americans were treated for animal bites of various kinds; sixty thousand were presumed to have been exposed to rabies and given the Pasteur treatment; three died.

In his last eight years, when he was no longer able to keep on working in his laboratory from eight a.m. to six p.m., or to spend his afternoons in animated discussion at the Academy, Pasteur could do little but collect his honors and ponder some unanswered questions.

What was it in the human body which produced immunity? This question he had to leave to others then coming on the scene. And what was the nature of attenuation that reduced a microbe from a killer to something that could hardly infect and yet conferred protection? He knew nothing of virus mutations—or hereditary chemical changes—as they are now understood. But microbiologists still know little about the nature of virulence or changes in virulence.

Early in his career Pasteur had refuted those who believed in the spontaneous generation of microscopic life. He and his assistant Jules Joubert at the time observed that water filtering through sandy soil into deep wells often was free of germs. This gave Chamberland the idea of making an unglazed porcelain filter, shaped like a candle, that would strain out bacteria. It was so good that it was often used, years ago, as an attachment to kitchen faucets in the name of pure drinking-water.

Pasteur and, indeed, every bacteriologist used the Chamberland filter as one means of proving that the bacteria that stuck in the filter pores and not the clear fluid that passed through were the cause of the disease. But Pasteur also knew that in some diseases, such as chicken cholera and diphtheria, the bacteria produced a toxin, or chemical poison, that dissolved in the fluid and went through the filter. This toxin produced the disease, but would not transmit it beyond its immediate victim. Those who didn't believe in the germ theory of disease might have had sport with Pasteur for finding a morbid quality in the "sterile" filtrate itself, but he had cowed them into relative silence. The all-time champion of specific germs for specific diseases had poured the morbid humors of Jenner's day down the drain of history.

Pasteur himself was anything but fixed in his ideas. Already he visualized that probably there were ultra-microscopic organisms too small to be seen through a microscope and too small to be caught in a Chamberland filter. This would explain rabies. Here he was only one step from the discovery of filterable viruses, as differentiated from toxins, the products of bacteria. Had he filtered his rabbit spinal cord, he could have isolated the rabies virus from the host's nerve cells and made this discovery, too.

But even a giant among geniuses must stop somewhere. His last words, as he lay dying of his paralysis at the age of seventy-three, were "I cannot." The Louis Pasteur who had once exclaimed over the beauty of the word *enthusiasm,* and pointed out that it meant "God within," was gone. There has been no one quite like him since.

PART TWO:
DISCOVERY
OF
THE
MILLIMICROBE

Approximate Sizes of Viruses and Reference Objects

Diameter or
width X length in mµ

Red blood cells	7500
B. prodigiosus (Serratia marcescens)	750
Rickettsia	475
Psittacosis	270
Myxoma	230 x 290
Vaccinia	210 x 260
Pleuro-pneumonia organism	150
Herpes simplex	130
Cytoplasmic virus (Tipula paludosa)	130
Rabies fixe	125
Newcastle disease	115
Avian leucosis	120
Vesicular stomatitis	65 x 165
Polyhedral virus (Bombyx mori)	40 x 280
Influenza	85
Adeno	75
Fowl plague	70
T2 E. coli bacteriophage	65 x 95
Chicken tumor I (Rous sarcoma)	65
Equine encephalomyelitis	50
T3 E. coli bacteriophage	45
Rabbit papilloma (Shope)	45
Tobacco mosaic and strains	15 x 300
Cymbidium (orchid) mosaic	12 x 480
Genetic unit (Muller's est. of max. size)	20 x 125
Southern bean mosaic	30
Tomato bushy stunt	30
Coxsackie	27
Poliomyelitis	27
Turnip yellow mosaic	26
Tobacco ringspot	26
Yellow fever	22
Squash mosaic	22
Hemocyanin molecule (Busycon)	22
Foot-and-mouth disease	21
Japanese B encephalitis	18
Tobacco necrosis	16
Hemoglobin molecule (Horse)	3 x 15
Egg albumin molecule	2.5 x 10

The chart, in relative scale, shows that viruses are so small that hundreds might be packed within a single red blood cell (7,500 millimicrons, or ten times the largest circle pictured above). The virus size-range falls generally between the micro-organisms, bacteria and rickettsia, and the molecules of organic substances—that is, between the largest circle at the top and the smallest speck at the bottom of the page. All sizes are stated in millimicrons; twenty-five millimicrons equal one millionth of an inch. Thus, viruses range generally from about 15 to 300 millimicrons, or well under one millionth, up to twelve millionths of an inch in diameter. Some of the viruses listed above are strangers to us, but others cause some of our most familiar diseases. (The chart, appearing as Figure 1 in *Viral and Rickettsial Infections of Man*, third edition, 1959, was revised in 1958 by R. C. Williams from W. M. Stanley: "Chemical Studies on Viruses," in *Chemical and Engineering News*, Vol. XXV [1947], pp. 3786–91.)

* 9 *

FIRST MAN TO SEE

A VIRUS—BUIST

DOCTORS and science writers often remark that no one has seen a virus under an ordinary microscope. This merely goes to show what nonsense we have to put up with, even from our friends. It is true, of course, that most viruses are too small to be seen with an optical microscope, depending for magnification on light waves. But the statement completely overlooks, among other things, the discovery of the cause of cowpox. Likewise, the statement overlooks Dr. John Brown Buist (1846–1915), who competes with George Sternberg, discoverer of the virus-neutralization test in 1892, as one of the most overlooked trackers of viruses.

Buist became the first man to see a virus, though he did not recognize it as such. It was in 1887, the year of Queen Victoria's Jubilee, when this proper lady had been on the British throne fifty years—two years after Pasteur and his physician friends gave the first anti-rabies treatment to little Joseph Meister. It would be a good ten years before medical science would be presented with the new concept of a filterable virus.

John Buist was born in the County of Fife, the son of a farmer. He became a surgeon and superintendent of a smallpox hospital in Edinburgh as well as a follower of Pasteur, a promoter of vaccination, and, at the time of his discovery, a bacteriologist at the University of Edinburgh, his alma mater.

Buist took clear fluid from a smallpox vaccination ulcer on the arm of a patient—or, as Jenner might say, lymph matter from a cowpox vesicle. He spread this fluid on a glass slide, dried it, and stained the barely noticeable residue with a gentian-violet dye. This was the orthodox method of bacteriology for bringing one-celled microbes into view under the microscope.

Now placing the slide under his microscope, Buist saw many reddish, round granules. This was about all he did do, except to make some—for his day—rather accurate measurements of these red dots. We now know, because it has been done hundreds of times since, that he was looking at single virus particles of cowpox. We also know that cowpox virus is identical in appearance with smallpox virus.

Buist estimated his granules to be 150 millimicrons in diameter. He was not too far off. The usual size of the virus is about 260 by 210 millimicrons, or about $\frac{1}{100,000}$ of an inch on one side and somewhat less on the other. It is not surprising that the virus looked round to Buist, but in recent years the electron microscope has revealed that the virus is a rectangle with rounded corners, containing a ring-shaped nucleus surrounded by a double membrane.

Buist held the granules to be the infectious agent of cowpox and smallpox. He was correct in regard to cowpox, at least. But he couldn't prove his claim, because he was unable to culture his granules and transmit the disease.

Inasmuch as the granules did not resemble any bacteria he knew of, but did remind him of the spores of various bacteria and fungi, Buist thought they must be spores—that is, primitive seeds produced by the micro-organism and in turn becoming new organisms. Here he followed a false scent.

Nobody paid much attention to Buist at the time, and for the next fifty years he received scarcely any recognition for his discovery. This neglect appeared to be owing to a combination of circumstances. In the first place, what he saw did not seem to fit into the existing body of microbial knowledge and practice.

Secondly, there was the law as laid down by Robert Koch, now universally known as Koch's Law or Koch's Postulates, though, as a matter of fact, these rules for proving a specific microbe as the cause of a specific disease were originated by Jacob Henle in 1840. Koch's Postulates are almost as sound today as they were then. They hold that the scientific investigator must meet the following conditions to prove the cause of an infectious disease:

(1) He must show that the micro-organism is present in every case of the disease.

(2) He must cultivate the disease agent in pure culture.

(3) He must be able to inoculate the culture into susceptible animals and reproduce the disease.

(4) He must be able to recapture the organism from the infected animal and culture it again.

Koch was the first one to do this with a bacterial disease. Pasteur was the first one to violate the law, in the case of the rabies virus, inasmuch as he could not culture it and could not see this virus, 150 millimicrons in diameter, under the microscope. However, he and Roux were able to pass the virus from one dog brain or one rabbit brain to another and hence accomplish isolation by using the animal as a culture medium. The disease could be identified from the unmistakable symptoms it produced.

Buist was unable to do this. But there was another reason why, for a long time, he got no credit for what he did do. It involved Professor Enrique Paschen of Hamburg.

In 1904 the ingenious French bacteriologist Amédée Borrel was able to spot a virus from chickens with his microscope. What he saw was the fowlpox virus, quite similar to cowpox. In 1906 Paschen rediscovered the virus of cowpox. Like Buist, he labeled it as also the cause of smallpox, following the theory that cowpox is simply a modified human smallpox.

After that, many persons stained and visualized "Borrel bodies," "Paschen bodies," "elementary bodies," and "inclusion bodies" of various pox diseases under regulation microscopes. There was a good deal of debate as to whether they were looking at single virus particles or a sort of convention of viruses—many stuck together in crystal-like masses within a single host cell.

Doubts that the microscope could pick up and visualize anything so small as the single particle persisted until 1929, when Drs. C. Eugene Woodruff and Ernest W. Goodpasture at Vanderbilt University made an important discovery clearing up the matter. They showed that a fowlpox inclusion body could be broken up into as many as twenty thousand elementary bodies, each of which was an infective unit. These, too, were seen without the help of an electron mircoscope, an invention still to come.

Buist was right about having seen the cowpox virus, but the Germans never heard of the Scot, apparently, and Paschen thought *he* was first. He was sick for some years before his death in 1936. Out of respect for Paschen, we are told, scientific authors who learned of Buist's priority did not stress it during Paschen's lifetime. Buist already being dead, it was not important to show respect for him. But the fact of his discovery now has been put in the record.

To be sure, the optical microscope did not take the virus search far. Yet it belongs at the beginning of the story of the virus isolationists. For some time to come, these isolationists would occupy the stage—as soon as it was established that there was such a thing as a virus.

* 10 *

LONELY BEIJERINCK:
FIRST VIROLOGIST

PASTEUR left the new science of microbiology, or bacteriology, in one great motile, multiplying mess of activity. Everybody, everywhere, tried to hunt microbes, see them, grow them, identify them, explain them, escape them. Their primary activity as the nineteenth century ended and the twentieth century began was finding and naming the causes of infectious diseases. It was the Day of Diagnosis. This was the function, especially, of bacteriologists and pathologists, specialists in disease organisms and diseased tissues. Their indispensable tools were the microscope, various dyes to stain the membranes of cells and microbes and thus bring out their outlines so they could be seen and photographed, food that bacteria would grow in, culture dishes, test tubes, and some laboratory animal that would accept and transmit the disease under scrutiny.

Doctors were not long in referring to this as the Golden Age of Medicine. Actually, it was the Childhood of Scientific Medicine, a period of great stimulus and rapid growth, filled with the excitement of learning new things—and also filled with childish certainties. Everything appeared so systematic and definite—and little was.

Bacteriology furnished the yeast for the great advances, if you will excuse playing with words. Classically, this branch of science concerns itself with bacteria, yeast, and molds, all forms of plant life. Protozoa, the one-celled microscopic animals such as cause syphilis and malaria, presented a classification problem, but protozoology found some sort of place under bacteriology.

Virology, still to be born, came as something of an orphan on bacteriology's doorstep. The chief instrument of this delivery was the porcelain filter developed by Charles Chamberland in Pasteur's laboratory.

The chief obstetrician was not trained as a bacteriologist or even a pathologist; he was a botanist named Martinus Willem Beijerinck (1851–1931). He was the first to discover and recognize a filterable virus as a cause of infectious disease.

This does not account for Dmitri Iwanowski, a bacteriologist, who sometimes gets the credit for being the first to discover a filterable virus. For example, if you pick up one textbook on virology, you may find that it mentions Iwanowski and not Beijerinck as the first to isolate a virus as the cause of tobacco-mosaic disease; in another you may find Beijerinck but not Iwanowski cited. Still others compromise by saying Iwanowski did it in 1892 and Beijerinck reported the discovery independently in 1898.

This makes Iwanowski appear to be the hero and Beijerinck very much the runner-up. Actually, both require mention, but the Russian was not in the same league with the Dutchman. Here is what happened:

In the early 1890's, shortly before Pasteur's death, nobody but the master himself seemed to have given much thought to the possibility that there might be something different from bacteria which could be distinguished as a virus or, at any rate, an ultramicroscopic agent too small to be seen with the microscope.

But Pasteur did not take the next logical step. This would be to see if such an agent could be passed through a porcelain filter with pores so tiny that clear fluid could be forced through, but not bacterial cells. This meant using the "bacteria-tight" filter for a purpose precisely the opposite of what bacteriologists ordinarily expected of it. They used it to prove that the cell-free filtrate passing through was "bacteriologically sterile"—that the specific cause of disease was in the one-celled organisms that stuck in the pores.

It would be a new twist to use the filter to prove that whatever passed through into the "sterile" filtrate was the transmissible agent of disease—and not a cell of any known size or structure!

Iwanowski performed the crucial experiment, but did not provide the fresh thought that would reveal its significance. Little is known about the man except that in 1892 he presented a four-page paper, "On the Mosaic Disease of the Tobacco Plant," before the Academy of Science in St. Petersburg. For the most part, he merely reported his observations on the disease as a source of crop losses to tobacco farmers in the Crimea, but near the end was this one sentence:

"Yet I have found that the sap of leaves attacked by the mosaic disease retains its infectious qualities even after filtration through Chamberland candles."

Since he had already assumed that the disease was caused by a bacterium, the only significance he saw in this discovery was that there must have been a defect in the filter—or perhaps the unknown bacterium produced a toxin that was dissolved in the clear filtrate.

Beijerinck, in contrast, was just obstinate enough that he would not think along old ruts—probably because it was a rut of somebody else's making and not his own. If Beijerinck—pronounced "buyer-ink"—were alive today, we doubtless would call him a "square-headed Dutchman." He craved knowledge as an alcoholic craves drink, and was one of the greatest faultfinders since Jeremiah.

One observer recalls the high tension Beijerinck maintained in his laboratory at the Delft Polytechnical School, where he was professor of bacteriology. He would begin his day by giving a hundred instructions to his male secretary, Kokee, who was never heard to make any complaint except "How exacting the Chief was again this morning."

Then the professor would dash into his laboratory, slam down the windows, sniff out any suddenly concealed and smoldering cigarettes, and approach the first student's experiment. He might talk for minutes or hours, pouring out a wonderful torrent of ideas and suggestions, all of which the student was expected to carry out before the professor's next visit. And so Beijerinck would move from student to student, his mind awhirl and theirs plain numb.

Beijerinck was ill at ease when giving a lecture. But if he chose an assistant to demonstrate an experiment, he was sure to drive the poor fellow to stage-fright and then sneer, before the class, at the least mistake. Likewise, Beijerinck would bawl out a student for untidy work and remain oblivious to the magnificent disorder of his own workbench, where he could scarcely find room for his elbow among the culture flasks, stacks of culture dishes, and dusty bottles of reagents surrounding his microscope.

He was the stereotype of the tyrannical professor, much feared and respected, but little loved, a breed of antisocial intellectual that is nearly extinct these days. Arrogantly handsome in the large mustaches he wore in his prime, positively patriarchal as he aged, he remained a bachelor.

It is said Beijerinck was disappointed in love. The biography [1] written by his colleagues in Delft is otherwise quite revealing, but it skirts the nature of this affair with a delicacy that we can barely forgive. If Beijerinck was badly treated by the opposite sex, he took ample revenge, his two spinster sisters hardly excepted. He would explode with anger if he saw a roving eye or hand move among his boy and girl students. When one assistant took a bride, Beijerinck banished him with a sentence: "A man of science does not marry." His favorite slight to women, however, was contained in his standard opening to all lectures: "Gentlemen and ladies!"

On the other hand, Beijerinck loved to read Byron's poems. He did so with sadness after learning that the poet had been unfaithful to his wife. He drew well, but music merely fatigued him. He thought that the teaching of history and all its wars should be barred from the schools. Also, he made it clear he did not think well of God for permitting all the misery and suffering in the world.

In his early years he felt little need for friendly relations with other professors or students, and repelled most of them. It made

[1] G. Van Iterson, Jr., L. E. Den Dooren de Jong, and A. J. Kluyver: *Martinus Willem Beijerinck: His Life and His Work* (The Hague: Martinus Nijhoff; 1940).

his life simpler—also lonelier. As he grew older, he felt this isolation bitterly. The diary of his sister Henriette pictures him, late
in life, as an old man shorn of his great egotism, worried that he
was not popular, longing for sympathy, "a fossilized scholar."

But, as those who knew him scientifically pointed out, Beijerinck was "like a mighty building," majestic when viewed from
afar, strange and complicated when viewed from inside. His colleagues liked to remember him as the working scientist, a glitter
in his brown eyes, a left forefinger uplifted as he revealed the
significance of a discovery to his listeners.

Beijerinck was born in Amsterdam in 1851, the last of four
children. His father, Derk, was a brave and cheerful soul who
never did well, despite titanic efforts. He was a freight clerk for
the Holland Railway Company, moving from city to city and
working all hours. Martinus's mother, Elisabeth, was a minister's
daughter and read to her children each morning from the Bible.
When he was fifteen, he entered a contest put on by the Netherlands Agricultural Society for boys and girls under sixteen. The
Society offered a prize for the best herbarium, or collection of
dried and pressed plants. Martinus collected one hundred and
fifty kinds of plant, labeling each with its Dutch and Latin names
and the date and place he found it. His collection was not well
dried; it became moldy, and he had to start over. A second try
also failed. His mother urged him on. On the third attempt he
mastered the technique. When he sent his collection in, he said:
"Whether I get a prize or not does not matter, but I'll stick to
botany." He won first prize, and did not stick to botany.

A generous uncle on his mother's side offered to put Martinus
through the three-year technology course at the Delft Polytechnical School, where he majored in chemistry. He found an inspiration in Jacobus H. Van't Hoff, a fellow student. Five years later,
when he was only twenty-two, Van't Hoff became world-famous
by discovering the asymmetrical spatial arrangement of the carbon atom in organic compounds. In 1901, Van't Hoff won the
Nobel Prize in chemistry for his further work in establishing the
laws of osmosis.

Beijerinck and Van't Hoff lived together as students, mainly on
rice and beefsteak because they didn't like anything else. They

also cooked up chemical experiments in their rooming-house. On one occasion they boiled dead moles in a solution of caustic soda to free the skeletons, and then treated the bones with hydrochloric acid, in the hope of producing glue; their landlady threatened them with eviction.

Beijerinck otherwise is pictured as a melancholy grind in his college days. Graduation only served to depress him. His first job was as a teacher in a small-town agricultural school, at Warffum. The following year, 1875, Beijerinck's mother died. The son himself was ailing. Finding nothing wrong, a professor of medicine told him he was nervous. The next year Van't Hoff nursed him through a serious illness, probably typhoid fever.

He then moved on to the Agricultural High School in Wageningen, where he had his first opportunity to teach his favorite subject—botany.

Beijerinck had to obtain his academic "union card," the degree of doctor of science, in poor-boy fashion. While teaching, he studied the structure of galls, a disease caused by gall wasps, and submitted his doctoral thesis to the University of Leiden in 1877. He received his "promotion" in a public ceremony, as was required for non-students of the University. Nervously, he put on black gown and white gloves and drove a "carriage and pair" to the great hall of the University to join the procession of beadle, or mace-bearer, professors, candidates, and "opponents"—colleagues who were chosen to attack the thesis the candidate defends. Such attacks were not too serious; one of Beijerinck's two opponents was his friend Van't Hoff. A professor accepted Beijerinck's thesis, and made a long speech in Latin.

The new doctor of science returned to his agricultural teaching post, somewhat less melancholy than usual, and began perhaps the happiest period of his life, teaching botany and studying plant diseases.

Following his father's death in 1879, Beijerinck's two sisters, Henriette and Johanna, came to live with him. Often he baffled them by remaining silent for hours. While at Wageningen, Beijerinck had his introduction to tobacco mosaic, the disease that was to make him a virologist.

At various times and in various parts of the world, including the

United States, the mosaic disease presents something of a problem to tobacco growers. It dwarfs the plants, mottles the leaves in a mosaic pattern, and sometimes blisters them. It reduces both the yield and the quality of tobacco and, like all virus diseases, resists chemical treatment. Another professor at the Agricultural School, Adolf Mayer, showed Beijerinck the contagious character of the disease. He asked the young man to see if he couldn't find the micro-organism causing the infection. Beijerinck, who then knew little about bacteriology, had no luck.

Friction with the School's director and also with students— Beijerinck much preferred insulting people to getting along with them—ended his happy days in Wageningen. His first-class studies of how the gall wasps lay their eggs in plants came to the attention of J. C. van Marken, director of the Netherlands Yeast and Spirit Works at Delft. Van Marken wanted a well-rounded young biologist in his yeast factory to handle production-control problems—yeast is sometimes attacked by micro-organisms that interfere with its growth.

He offered Beijerinck the position of bacteriologist at a salary more than twice his teacher's pay, plus a new laboratory of his own, and promised the young man considerable freedom in research.

Even with all this, Beijerinck wrestled with the decision for several months before agreeing, in 1885, to become an industrial scientist. He was not a bacteriologist, he pointed out. Van Marken assured him that he could visit outstanding bacteriological laboratories and learn what he needed to know while his laboratory was being built.

As a traveler, Beijerinck remained in character. He never sent a postcard home to his sisters or, on his return, said a word about what he had seen. He had put three well-known laboratories on his list. The first was that of De Bary, in Strasbourg, but he found so much fault with the way things were done there that De Bary felt compelled to ask him to shut up. Beijerinck complained that at Hansen's laboratory in Copenhagen he was shown nothing of importance. As for the laboratory of the great Robert Koch in Berlin, he simply crossed it off his list. He figured, he said, to learn even less there!

Coming from the pleasant rural village of Wangeningen to Delft, with its factory environment, did not brighten Beijerinck's outlook. Yet there were compensations. Delft was his alma mater. It was also the home town of a man whom he revered, Anthony Leeuwenhoek, the first investigator of micro-organisms. In the seventeenth century Leeuwenhoek was janitor of the city hall, ran a dry-goods store, and spent the greater part of his time making microscopes and gazing through them at "mites" and other strange creatures too small for the naked eye to see. Hence, by strange coincidence, as we shall see, microbes and millimicrobes were discovered in the same city in the Netherlands.

But Beijerinck was more of a solitary figure than ever, and much given to periods of depression and vain regrets. His first suggestion at the yeast factory cost it money. He thought the distillery wastes would make excellent slop for pigs. The company hired a veterinarian, purchased pigs, and fed them the wastes. For some unexplained reason, their teeth turned black, so no butcher would buy them.

In the next ten years Beijerinck became well known in agricultural science as the result of his discovery of one of several strains of bacteria that work in close harmony with certain leguminous plants, such as beans or peas, in forming root nodules. These nodules have the peculiar power to take free nitrogen from the atmosphere and to convert it into chemical compounds that the plant can use in producing proteins, a function of significance in food consumption as well as soil enrichment.

Encouraged by this discovery, Beijerinck returned in 1887 to his search for the cause of tobacco-mosaic disease. He was better prepared now, but still couldn't find it under the microscope or in his culture dishes.

What all this had to do with the manufacture of yeast was difficult for even an understanding man like Van Marken to see. Outside of routine production details and his dispelling of the rumor that pressed yeast was a carrier of cholera germs, Beijerinck made no contribution to the promotion of yeast production.

A conscientious man, Beijerinck counted himself a failure at his job, and talked of resigning. Van Marken persuaded him to stay on, but meanwhile got busy in government educational circles, touting Beijerinck as a brilliant scientist and suggesting he would make someone an excellent professor of bacteriology. Beijerinck received a series of offers extending over a five-year period, the last being from his alma mater, the Delft Polytechnical School, in 1892. As usual, he was apprehensive.

The next year Beijerinck got down to serious negotiations with the director of the Polytechnical School. He asked for a salary twenty per cent higher than he was getting in industry and, indeed, higher than that of the School's director. He also asked for a new laboratory. The matter had to go to the House of Commons, and dragged on. After much debate, the House voted Beijerinck his salary, a new house, and a new laboratory.

But no sooner had he returned to academic life in 1895 than he wished himself back in the factory! He feared he would not be popular with the students, bacteriology not being a compulsory subject. He was sure, because of his frequent mental fatigue, that he would have to resign within a year. Few people have faced good fortune more dolefully than Martinus Beijerinck.

The director of the School invited Beijerinck to discuss its reorganization at a college level. Said the director: "One thing must remain, and that is the directorship of the school." Replied Beijerinck: "Sir, if anything has to disappear, it *is* the directorship!" He also had trouble with the Minister of Home Affairs; he could get money for teaching but not for research—quite the opposite of the problem in the United States today.

During the subsequent twenty-six years Beijerinck performed a monumental amount of scientific work and demonstrated his virtues as well as his faults. Any great scientist attracts students who wish to learn from him, however reprehensible he may be personally. Furthermore, Beijerinck was fortunate in his selection of associates, who benefited from the importance he attached to money. He saw that they, too, got higher salaries than others on the faculty.

A. H. Van Delden was the professor's only assistant during his greatest microbiological discoveries, and quite possibly deserves more credit as a collaborator than Beijerinck allowed him. As his biographers pointed out, "Beijerinck did not always stop to consider the justice of giving credit where credit was due. . . ."

When a boy of fifteen, Beijerinck had to try three times to make a herbarium that won first prize in the botany contest. Likewise, he had to try three times before, as a man of forty-six, he made the discovery entitling him to be called the first virologist. It occurred in 1897, soon after he moved his two spinster sisters into his new house and opened his new Bacteriological Institute.

Now the situation was right for another go at the cause of tobacco-mosaic disease. We do not know why he was able to accomplish what he wanted this time without much difficulty, but it could be that his triumph over school and government authorities in getting all he wanted—salary, home, and laboratory—freed his mind for imaginative effort and, thus, further triumph.

It was really a rather simple maneuver, one that today would be dull routine. Certainly there was little about it which was dramatic. After all, this was only a diseased tobacco plant that Beijerinck squeezed in a press for its essential juices—not a human patient.

As a matter of course, he put a drop of this juice on a slide and looked at it under his microscope. As in Wageningen and at the yeast works, Beijerinck could see no microbe in his specimen.

Again he went through the culture routine. He put a drop of the infectious juice on a plate of agar, a gelatin medium in which ordinary bacteria thrive when incubated at body heat or thereabouts. But, as usual, nothing grew there. He covered the same old ground. He could not see the cause. He could not cultivate the cause.

About the only thing he had not done was force the juice through a porcelain candle, so he did that. This was simply a check test to see if there was any difference in infectivity between what went into the filter and what came out.

In the absence of a culture medium, the only way Beijerinck could prove that the agent of disease was not in the filtrate was to rub the filtered juice on the leaves of a healthy tobacco plant. But now, within two or three days, he proved the opposite. The characteristic mottling of the mosaic disease appearing on the tobacco leaves, and it spread! The spreading took place, he saw, at the time the leaf cells themselves divided and reproduced.

Could this be a toxin that had passed through the filter? If so, where were the bacteria that produced the toxin? Furthermore, he also found that this new kind of disease-inducing poison could be transmitted from each infected plant to a healthy plant ad infinitum. Life went on. So this was not a toxin. It was not a one-time thing, not a by-product of a disease agent, but the agent itself.

Beijerinck made other observations. Pasteurize this filtered juice from an infected plant at a temperature of 162 degrees and it loses its power to infect. This would also be true of a bacterium or its toxin; the one dies and the other decomposes at high temperatures. On the other hand, the infectivity of the juice survived drying at low temperature without hurting it. This again was in line with bacteriological experience, and again made his disease agent sound like a microbe.

But this was a microbe-free fluid, as clear as clear can be. Or so it seemed to Beijerinck.

Now this man who liked to read Byron became a little poetic. Perhaps he thought of the ancient Greeks and their four elements of life—fire, air, water, and earth. What Beijerinck seemed to have here, he thought, was a living, infectious kind of *water*.

Something else convinced him. Though he could not get the disease to grow in an agar medium, he did notice something else. The juice soaked into the agar to the depth of nearly one tenth of an inch in the course of a week or so; agar mined from that depth produced infection in his plants. Surely if the infectious juice would pass through that much solid jelly, it contained no solid particles, corpuscles, or cells.

Having exhausted his conception of the finite, or measurable, Beijerinck concluded that he had discovered an infectious principle of a completely fluid nature. He called it *contagium vivum fluidum*, or living contagious fluid.

This was in the title of the short report that he published in Amsterdam in 1898. While he might have taken his cue from Pasteur, who believed that ultra-microscopic organisms—millimicrobes—existed below the range of the microscope, Beijerinck parted company with the chemist. He passed over the possibility that there might be something with definite structure, but so small that it could not be distinguished from clear fluid and would readily pass through the filter.

This something, as we can now second-guess, is a rod-shaped virus 300 millimicrons long by 15 millimicrons wide. The reason Beijerinck could not see the tobacco-mosaic virus with his microscope was not its lack of length—that is within microscope range —but its lack of breadth. Naturally, its narrowness enabled it to slide through the finest filter pores with ease.

Throughout his paper Beijerinck used the term *virus* and thus gave the word its first currency in connection with a cell-free filtrate as a cause of disease—in other words, a *filterable* virus, as others promptly called it.

Beijerinck's report attracted considerable attention. Among those who read it was Iwanowski. In 1899, Iwanowski, who had thought there was something wrong with his filter when it passed the cause of tobacco-mosaic disease into the filtrate, published a note in a scientific journal claiming priority in the discovery.

With unexpected modesty and kindness, Beijerinck readily acknowledged Iwanowski's claim in a reply published in the same issue. He repeated this acknowledgment when he reviewed his discovery in 1900. Others might put the Russian down as something of a credit-grabber.

Even then, eight years after his 1892 observation, Iwanowski continued to maintain that the cause of tobacco-mosaic disease was a bacterium of some sort. Therefore, this bacteriologist stands out primarily for his lack of imagination when his great moment came. He still lacked it after reading Beijerinck's findings and interpretations.

And what an eloquent man Beijerinck could be! In 1913 he wrote: "The existence of these contagia proves that the concept of life—if one considers metabolism and proliferation as its essential characters—is not inseparably linked up with that of structure; the criteria of life . . . are also compatible with the fluid state. . . .

"In its most primitive form, life is, therefore, no longer bound to the cell, the cell which possesses structure and which can be

Upper left: Edward Jenner, whose curiosity about a "vulgar cowpox legend" among milk-maids brought us the first vaccine. *Upper right:* Louis Pasteur. Described as "the most perfect man who has ever entered the kingdom of Science," Pasteur fathered the science of immunology and became the prophet of modern preventive medicine. He discovered the second human vaccine. *Lower left:* Martinus W. Beijerinck, the fierce, lonely Dutch botanist who discovered a filterable virus in tobacco-mosaic disease and became the first virologist. *Lower right:* George M. Sternberg. This much-overlooked American medical officer and bacteriologist showed virus hunters how to track viruses by the antibodies they produce.

PLATE 1

Upper left: Gilbert Dalldorf. He discovered the first of the two dozen new Coxsackie viruses cause of a variety of polio-like, influenza-like, and cold-like infections. *Upper right:* Albe H. Coons. His development of fluorescent antibodies added an ultra-modern touch to th discovery of Sternberg—a virus-neutralization test equipped with neon lights. (*By Fabia Bachrach, Boston*) *Lower left:* Alice M. Woodruff, who grew a virus in a hatching egg Goodpasture's laboratory at Vanderbilt University. *Lower right:* Ernest W. Goodpastur His genius produced the chick-embryo technique of virus cultivation and the first vacci break-through.

PLATE 2

compared to a complex wheel-works, such as a watch which ceases to exist if it is stamped down in a mortar.

"No; in its primitive form life is like fire, like a flame borne by the living substance—like a flame which appears in endless diversity and yet has specificity within it . . . which does not originate by spontaneous generation, but is propagated by another flame."

In 1925, Félix d'Hérelle—who gave bacteriophages, the viruses that live in bacteria, their name—summed up Beijerinck's contribution rather well:

"People have discussed the concept of Beijerinck a great deal, but I do not think that they have grasped all its profundity. All biology rested, still rests, upon the fandamental hypothesis that the unit of living matter is the cell. Beijerinck, the first, freed himself from this dogma, and proclaimed the fact that life is not the result of a cellular organization, but derives from another phenomenon, which cannot reside elsewhere than in the physicochemical constitution of a protein particle."

Of course, Beijerinck himself had said nothing about protein particles in his fluid of life.

After Beijerinck showed the way, two German scientists, Friederich Loeffler and Paul Frosch, in 1898 discovered one of the smallest of all viruses—the twenty-one-millimicron speck that causes foot-and-mouth disease in cattle.

The yellow-fever virus was the first to be filtered in human disease. Walter Reed and his associate, James Carroll, did it in 1901. After that, in the years to come, the microbiologists turned up dozens of plant, animal, and human diseases that could be transmitted by inoculation with the clear fluid that passed through a bacteria-proof filter.

By far the greatest of the filtrationists was Dr. William J. Elford of the National Institute for Medical Research in Hampstead, England. Elford disposed of Beijerinck's idea of living fluid. In 1931 he introduced a system of ultra-filtration so technically refined that it left no doubt that viruses were solid particles of some kind.

For the porcelain or other types of earthenware filters, he substituted a permeable membrane of collodion, a film made from cellulose nitrate. Elford noticed, in making collodion membranes with various alcohol solvents, that the membranes contained pores of different sizes, some that could be seen with a microscope and others that could be detected only in microphotographs made under ultra-violet light. In some fantastically precise experiments, he now set out to make membranes from his nitro-cellulose jellies with pores all of one size or another. He next graded the porous membranes from coarse to fine, like a set of sieves for separating gravel, coarse sand, and fine sand—except that the mesh in his sieves had openings ranging from around 10 to 3,000 millimicrons, or roughly from $\frac{1}{2,500,000}$ to $\frac{300}{2,500,000}$ of an inch.

Elford saw that a virus particle must require a certain amount of elbow room to float through one of the incredibly small holes in his filters. For example, when he came to experiment with the influenza virus, he found that a membrane with a pore size of 140 millimicrons would hold the virus back every time, whereas one of 180 would allow a few particles to pass. The uninitiated might naturally assume that the size of some particles was between 140 and 180, but, with due allowance for the factor of elbow room, Elford deduced the size of the virus as between 80 and 120. Eventually, electron-microscope studies showed it to be a bit over 100. He was equally accurate in estimating the sizes of the cowpox and cold-sore viruses, among others.

We do not know how Beijerinck would have received these measurements of the solid content of his *contagium vivum fluidum*. Elford reported his discovery the year Beijerinck died, and required four or five more years to demonstrate the full import of his findings. Even if Beijerinck had been willing to abandon the idea of a life in fluid form—few bacteriologists apparently took this part of his discovery seriously—he might still have been impatient with Elford's work. Beijerinck particularly disliked the measurement of small things. The idea that his fluid contained millimicrobes measurable in millionths of inches might not have suited his artistic nature.

He continued his researches in Delft until the day of his involuntary retirement in 1921, and then left that day in indignation that he should be put out of the laboratory that had been his private property for a quarter-century. When someone proposed to raise the Netherlands flag in celebration of his seventieth birth-day, the professor vetoed the idea: "One does not hoist the flag on the day of one's funeral."

Beijerinck never went back to bacteriological research or to Delft. He took his two sisters to an idyllic spot in Gorssel, where he studied botany and for ten more years lived gracefully and energetically, though he suffered mightily during his last two years from cancer of the rectum.

When death must end a man's life in such an ignoble fashion, as if he were without feeling or self-respect, we admire the one who manages to go peacefully, without cracking, whatever his pain. Beijerinck, according to his surviving sister, Henriette, did so, apparently realizing that, however acidly he reacted to life, he was expected to leave it without complaint.

11

STANLEY:
FIRST MAN TO
CRYSTALLIZE VIRUSES

THE VIRUS remained largely a sub-microscopic pig in a poke for the first quarter of the twentieth century. Microbiologists—few had the nerve to call themselves virologists as yet—confirmed the existence of transmissible viruses that would pass through bacteria-tight filters many times over, in one member of the vegetable or animal kingdom or another. They could isolate them to this extent, and they could identify them with diseases. Otherwise, not a great deal more progress was made, either in immunization against viruses or in understanding their nature.

In fact, the experiments of Beijerinck and even those of Elford produced as much frustration as they did satisfaction. Normally, the laboratory worker uses a filter to separate fluid from any matter suspended in it—as is the case in water purification. Yet hardly anybody took seriously Beijerinck's poetic theory that the fluid itself was alive. There *had* to be organic matter to sustain life.

It was a rather strange sensation for the scientist, trained in precise description and measurement, to have to depend on proving the physical invisibility of a living thing in order to prove its physical presence.

Or *was* it a living thing?

Here and there was someone so rash as to hint that the virus lay somewhere below the threshold of life, since it was too small to take the form of a living cell. Physicians, trained in the germ theory of disease, would have none of such speculations. After all, the germ theory required acceptance of the fact that agents of infection are alive, and not spontaneously generated from mud or dust.

The doctors of medicine had other questions. The pathologist wanted to know how the virus organism differed from one of the cells in his tissue specimens, other than its being much smaller. What was life like without a cell? The bacteriologist wanted to know what the virus ate, as it would not grow in his tempting culture dishes. And both, of course, wanted to know the answer to the next question: how did it reproduce?

The one thing they were now sure of, thanks to repeated observations of virus bodies within infected cells, was that the virus is compelled to live and reproduce within a living host cell. This vital need of viruses for a host is why they are called "obligate parasites." Borrel, Paschen, and Goodpasture—yes, and Buist —had glimpsed pox viruses under the microscope. As for a live fluid, Elford couldn't see viruses, but could prove they came in different sizes. They must be midget microbes simply too small to be seen, not a live fluid.

When medical science gets into such an intellectual stew, it sometimes requires a chemist or possibly a physicist to fish it out —or perhaps stir the stew a little faster. Perhaps, as D'Hérelle had suggested in regard to Beijerinck's discovery, the answer lay in regarding the virus not as a cellular structure but as a protein particle, a "physico-chemical structure"—not as life but the makings of life.

This is where Dr. Wendell M. Stanley, the boy chemist, came upon the scene, a fact immediately reminding us that Pasteur himself was a chemist, that he began his career with observations of the way chemical molecules form themselves into crystals, and that, to the end of his life, he seemed to feel as a matter of inner conviction that here, somewhere, lay the secret of life.

We are also reminded that Pasteur said chance favored the prepared mind. Stanley's preparation was in organic chemistry; what he seemed prepared to do, specifically, was to play the heretic and cast doubts on the idea of a virus as a midget microbe.

When Stanley went to college, in the 1920's, proteins had recently captured the minds of chemists interested in the nature of living matter. For a hundred years organic chemistry had been busy breaking down and building up molecules of sugar, fat, fruit, acids, soap, and alcohol. These are largely made up of carbon, hydrogen, and oxygen atoms. Protein molecules always include those three atoms plus nitrogen—the distinctive badge of a protein. They belong to a class of substances known as macromolecules or high-polymer molecules—simply giant molecules made up of many parts.

It hadn't seemed possible to do much with proteins because they were so complicated, tough, and difficult to dissolve, melt, or crystallize. They remained for a long time just a nuisance—the waxy, gluey, sticky residues that interfered with the washing of laboratory glassware.

But protein molecules are keystones of bodily life, a fact recognized in their name. *Protein* means "holding first place." These molecules were named, of course, before the era of nuclear chemistry. Actually, proteins share first place with nucleic acids; both are always found in the nuclei of living cells and, in fact, in the genes of heredity. The importance of these amazing acids of the cell nucleus will emerge later, when we come to discoveries made in the last five years. It is enough to know here that the proteins are part of the nucleus, and help the nucleic acids hold body and soul together.

Seventy per cent of the human body is water. Half of the rest of it, in dry weight, is one protein or another. It has been estimated that there are one hundred thousand different kinds of proteins in the human body, meaning that thousands of kinds will be found in any single cell. Nerves, muscles, tendons, skin, hair, and bones are made up, in large part, of protein molecules.

It is important to realize not only how essential proteins are but also how complicated they are.

The German chemist and 1902 Nobel Prize winner, Emil Fischer, pioneered in protein chemistry through analysis of the amino-acid building-blocks making up the protein molecule—anywhere from a few hundred thousand to many millions of atoms. These are strung together in long chains of amino acids called peptides and polypeptides, depending on the length of the fragment.

It since has been determined that there are about twenty-five amino acids. This means that the possible combinations are about as numerous as those in the English language, with its twenty-six letters. With these few letters we have been able to put together upwards of four hundred thousand words. The possible number is much greater. Few men of learning are so pretentious as to assume that they could use all of these words in a lifetime. Chemists are generally humble about their knowledge of the protein language, too.

Following Fischer, chemists were able to score some major break-throughs with high polymers; these resemble proteins, but are a great deal simpler. The Du Pont chemist Dr. Wallace H. Carrothers, for example, was able to synthesize hundreds of carbon compounds, including nylon and neoprene rubber, and the English developed the popular plastic called polyethylene.

Nobody, at the time Stanley began work, had completely analyzed a protein molecule of any kind. This now has been done. Two events were of immediate interest at the time he joined the virus hunt. In 1926, Dr. James B. Sumner of Cornell University became the first man to isolate an enzyme in pure, crystalline form. Sumner crystallized urease, from jack beans.

An enzyme is a protein that speeds up reactions between other chemical compounds without undergoing change itself. By means of enzymes, the ordinary living cell can take a miscellaneous number of proteins of the wrong type for its own use, split them, and rebuild them to suit its own purpose, either for new building-material or for energy. This system is known as metabolism, literally meaning "change," or the process of building up and breaking down the various materials in the living cell.

Secondly, in 1930, Dr. John H. Northrop of the Rockefeller Institute for Medical Research pushed enzyme chemistry still further by first crystallizing the enzyme pepsin and then, shortly thereafter, another enzyme, trypsin.

The significance of these discoveries lay not so much in the isolations themselves, of course, but in the availability of these active ingredients of body chemistry in pure form. The chemist has a great passion for purity in his chemical compounds, for purity is essential in establishing precise cause and effect in his experiments.

When a chemical compound can be separated in solid form from a mixture of other compounds, or precipitated as a solid out of a solution in which it is dissolved, its molecules may form into a connected mass, or crystal, as in the case of grains of sugar or salt. True crystals are made up of like chemical molecules attaching themselves to each other's flat surfaces and extending ad infinitum in many-angled patterns determined by the internal structure of the molecule itself. The result is an infinite variety of geometric shapes—for example, snowflakes or ice crystals, the crystalline form of water. Crystallization, you might say, is an elementary form of social gregariousness—birds of a feather flock together.

But nobody had been able to purify viruses in such a chemical manner, or to crystallize any living thing without destroying its quality of life.

Nor would anyone have been so foolish as to predict that Wendell Stanley would do this, or anything like it.

Today, at the age of fifty-four, Stanley is a distinguished scientist-citizen, the first virologist to win a Nobel Prize, and founding director of the Virus Laboratory at the University of California in Berkeley.

In his physical appearance there are many traces of his growth and development. He remarks that his early loss of hair lent him "greater personal authority" at a time when he needed it. In all, his moon face, healthy skin, appraising blue eyes behind gold-rimmed glasses, civil smile, well-cut, conservative suits, and energetic stride leave you with the impression that this man knows where he is going and will not be easily thrown off balance. The impression is enhanced by the fact that, though he is of no more than medium height, he is solidly built and his neck is bowed.

Above Stanley's gray fringe of hair, the close observer notes a marked indentation over one temple. This is a scar from his childhood in Ridgeville, Indiana, where his parents published a weekly newspaper. Stanley was born there in 1904. As a small boy, he fell from a wall and struck his head on the corner of a concrete step. The blow produced a severe skull fracture, requiring an operation to decompress the brain.

Scientifically, we can draw no conclusion whatsoever from the report of one case. We cannot, for example, conclude that every mother and father who would like to produce a Nobel Prize winner should drop their infant candidate on his head. On the other hand, Stanley is living, flourishing evidence that babies who have this misfortune don't necessarily turn out as badly as folklore might lead us to believe.

In his Hoosier grade-school, high-school, and college years in Union City, Ridgeville, and Richmond, where he attended Earlham College, Stanley showed greater aptitude in blocking and tackling than mathematics and chemistry. As a matter of fact, he became captain of the Earlham football team and made all-state end in 1925, despite the competition of Notre Dame and Purdue players. He did graduate, with a B average, but it was his full intention to become a football coach.

Instead, chemistry stole him away. One Saturday morning in the spring of 1926 his chemistry professor, Ernest A. Wildman, was driving over to the University of Illinois, at Urbana, to arrange a graduate assistantship for another Earlham senior. Stanley went along for the ride, in the hope of meeting Bob Zuppke or maybe Red Grange; they had been making football history at Illinois, one as a winning coach and the other as the player most often assigned to carry the ball.

Instead, Stanley met Dr. Roger Adams, professor of chemistry, and saw the chemistry building. Adams said some interesting things about a future in chemistry. Stanley enrolled in summer school and applied for an assistantship in chemistry himself. He was turned down because of his grades, but he did so well in summer school that he won the assistantship anyway. Through one scholastic subsidy or another, he stayed with chemistry, and by 1929 had both M.S. and Ph.D. degrees.

Stanley was interested in chemistry as applied to medicine. In fact, the first paper on which he appeared as a co-author, with Professor Adams and others in 1927, represented one attempt to find a chemical cure for leprosy. His fourth paper—in 1929—was on the same subject. The authorship was illuminating—Wendell Stanley, Marian Jay, and Roger Adams. These three names appeared together on another paper in 1929—a marriage certificate. Stanley and Miss Jay were fellow graduate students and their professor stood up with them as best man. One can hardly ask more of biochemistry.

Germany was still the world center of chemical research. In 1930, Stanley obtained a $2,400 National Research Council fellowship and took his bride to Munich for a year of study. Wendell and Marian learned to ski, to enjoy grand opera, and to see Europe third-class. Stanley also learned to measure sizes in microns. It was possible, on their return, to measure their bankroll that way, too. The Great Depression was on. But it is a remarkable thing—people with book learning often thrive in bad times.

While still in Europe, Stanley had a letter from a physiologist at the Rockefeller Institute in New York—Dr. Winthrop J. V. Osterhout was looking for a bright young assistant, at $3,300 a year. How had this come about? It seemed Professor Adams had mentioned Stanley to a friend and fellow chemistry professor, James B. Conant, soon to become president of Harvard University. Conant had sent the name to Osterhout.

The young man of course knew the work of the great Rockefeller Institute and would have been glad, he said, to take a job there as an animal caretaker for its distinguished researchers.

The Institute was the world's foremost center of microbiological research, thanks to its director, Dr. Simon Flexner, assigned in 1902 to develop an independent research institute free of university conformity and dogma. In its heyday you could stand in the middle of its New York or its Princeton laboratories, throw a stone in any direction, and hit a man who had won, was about to win, or was meritorious enough to win the Nobel Prize.

Flexner was a slight, soft-voiced, gentle-mannered but severely self-disciplined and seemingly unapproachable man, the epitome of the impersonal scientist; he placed the Institute above friendship. He had an exquisite talent for spotting and hiring creative minds, including some individualistic geniuses who were not wanted in academic institutions. It was a rare man who amounted to anything in microbiology, or hoped to, who did not seek training at the Rockefeller Institute in those days.

In his seventeen years there, Stanley became the father of one son and three daughters, one revolutionary discovery that laid the foundation for virus chemistry, and more than one hundred studies dealing with the physical and the chemical structure of viruses.

The setting of the stage for all this was, if anything, inauspicious. Stanley worked in Osterhout's laboratory in New York for about a year. His first assignment from his chief was to see if he could build a model of the one-celled marine plant Valonia, with its unusual, semi-permeable membrane. This strange plant has the capacity to admit much more potassium salts than sodium salts from sea water, which, naturally, contains much more sodium salts. The plant's propensity for accumulating potassium salts is essential to its nutrition. Osterhout had had laboratory assistants working on the problem for several years, as a kind of research training device. Presumably, he didn't expect them to find the solution.

For the next month Stanley spent most of his time in the Institute library. This irritated Osterhout, who thought Stanley ought to be working in the laboratory. What he was doing, however, was examining the International Critical Tables. These give the properties of an almost endless list of chemicals. In another week or two he found what he was looking for, a nonaqueous material in which potassium salts would have greater solubility than sodium salts. The stuff was guaiacol, a smelly white crystalline compound related to creosote.

Stanley went to Osterhout and said: "This is the material you want." Faintly outraged, we suspect, his chief told him to prove it. Stanley did laboratory experiments the rest of the year and did prove it. Hence, he published two studies with Osterhout as joint author.

When the Institute in 1932 added plant pathology to its Animal Pathology Laboratory in Princeton, the young chemist went to Dr. Flexner and asked to be assigned there. This was a brash thing to do, particularly in view of the fact that Stanley had no better reason in mind than that Marian was pregnant and Princeton would be a far more pleasant and less expensive place to raise a baby than New York.

Flexner offered little encouragement at first, but after having a plant pathologist, Dr. Louis O. Kunkel, interview Stanley, Flexner called him in for another talk. The director briefly explained that the Institute needed someone to do research in the chemistry of plant viruses at Princeton, under Dr. Kunkel's direction, and asked:

"Are you interested?"

"I might be," said Stanley, "but what are viruses?"

"That is what you are going down there for," replied Flexner, "to find out what viruses are."

The man, virus, time, place, and method proved to be propitious choices. Stanley himself has said he couldn't help succeeding in crystallizing tobacco-mosaic virus in view of the groundwork that had been laid in protein chemistry. This estimate is too modest. He couldn't help succeeding because he was Stanley.

To investigate the nature of a virus, the scientist must single out an appropriate one for study. Usually he speaks of his selection as a research tool, or model. A good many plant viruses had been discovered since the time of Iwanowski and Beijerinck, but the tobacco-mosaic virus—commonly known as TMV in the trade—was Stanley's choice for a number of reasons.

For one thing, the virus is highly stable—in fact, one of the most indestructible. Stanley was interested in the fact that others had put it through a number of chemical manipulations, constituting rather rough handling, without killing its infectivity.

This was another reason for choosing TMV—it is so highly infectious. Rub a tobacco leaf with a solution containing viruses and it will be peppered with specks of infection within a day or two.

Dilute the solution a million or a billion times and it still can produce infection. Furthermore, as Dr. Francis O. Holmes of the Rockefeller Institute had established not long before Stanley came on the scene, the number of spots of infection are in direct proportion to the virus concentration of the solution, so the investigator can count the specks and estimate the quantity of viruses in the solution.

There is another, underlying reason for studying plant viruses. The study of animal viruses is sometimes complicated by the need for susceptible hosts. A virologist can waste a lot of time trying to infect an immune animal, and never be sure whether his failure was caused by immunity or a loss of vitality in his viruses. Some varieties of plant will resist diseases that will infect others, but any susceptible variety remains susceptible. It does not acquire antibodies.

For these reasons, as well as because of what Stanley was about to do, the plant virus TMV probably has been the subject of more fundamental chemical and physical research in virology than any other. Its nearest rivals perhaps are the cowpox virus, another stable character, and the bacteriophages, the viruses that live in bacteria found in our intestines, also known as bacterial viruses.

"It seemed to me," Stanley explained later, "that the biological activity represented by a given virus must belong to some tangible entity and . . . it should be possible by chemical methods to purify, concentrate and eventually isolate this entity. . . . I knew that Dr. Kunkel was firmly convinced, like most people . . . that viruses were merely still smaller living organisms, but I also knew that Dr. Kunkel, unlike many others, was nevertheless firmly convinced of the advisability of conducting chemical investigations of viruses."

It took Stanley two or three years to figure out what he wanted to do and how. He wanted to test the hypothesis that TMV is a protein molecule by methods of chemical fractionation. The result, if successful, would be a crystal such as Sumner and Northrop had produced. But it would be a crystal with the power to infect—hence multiply and perpetuate itself.

Often the scientist stumbles on his discovery by accident or chance observation. Stanley, however, did not just happen on TMV crystals while doing something else. Instead, he methodically and doggedly set out to get TMV out of infected tobacco leaves, and he did get it out. His tenacity matched that of Pasteur, and so did his luck. As Stanley explained, "This was a little luck and a lot of good chemistry—not superb chemistry—plus a proper attitude—a willingness to work hard."

Most commentaries on Stanley's crystallization of TMV skip the laborious part of it. Part of the time he looked less like a chemist than a farmhand at corn-cutting time.

In the winter of 1934–5 and the following spring he brought his experiments to a climax. He had to grow tobacco—in the Institute's greenhouse in the winter and on its farm in the summer. When his plants were still young, he infected them with the disease by rubbing a solution of the virus on their leaves with a piece of gauze.

After three weeks the now heavily infected plants were harvested and stored at a temperature of about ten degrees Fahrenheit. The freezing ruptured the plant cells. Then Stanley put the frozen plants through a power meat-grinder, catching his mash in five-gallon dairy pails. He now stirred in hot water and added one of the chemicals figuring in his plan of attack. He dumped this mixture into large gauze bags, and hung them up to drain. The process was completed by squeezing the bags in a fruit press to get out more liquid.

The tobacco juice—Stanley called it that—became the center of his attention now. He began a series of tedious operations—decanting, filtering, precipitating, and evaporating, while using still other chemicals to produce various effects.

This process is too complicated for the non-chemist to follow with any interest or understanding, but, in general, chemical fractionation involves a variety of manipulations that will produce known effects if the kinds of substances believed to be in the mixture are actually there. One manipulation is the addition of a chemical compound, such as one of the salts, that will readily combine with the substance sought, and then the extraction of this larger combination and its breakdown. It is a little like the problem of selecting the right hook and the right bait to catch a

fish believed to be at the bottom of a pond. If the chemist fisher-
man is successful, he pulls out his fish. But he still must remove it
from the hook.

Before he was through, Stanley used most of the primary tricks
in the chemist's tackle box. He poured pail after pail of his juice
through filters and funnels. It took twenty-four hours to filter one
pail of juice. It took that much longer to find out which way the
virus had gone. Had it stayed in the filter or passed through in the
clear brown filtrate? He rubbed specimens from each source on
the leaves of growing tobacco plants and watched for infection to
find out.

Gradually, Stanley eliminated the miscellaneous plant proteins
remaining his brew. Gradually also, this eliminated the color.
What had been a rich brown became a pale yellow after three or
four filtrations. Finally there was a filtration in which the virus
stayed in the stuff caking the filter instead of going into the solution. The plant-infection test proved it.

Now the young chemist was beginning to close in. He got his
filter cake containing the virus back into solution. He juggled its
electrical charge. Almost all extraneous protein now had been removed. He slowly stirred in some chemicals that would cause a
precipitation from all that was left of his tobacco juice.

A glistening sheen came over the liquid! The sheen proved to
be crystals of highly purified TMV. They could be seen under the
microscope, with low-power magnification. They looked like
needles, about $\frac{3}{25,000}$ of an inch long. Tests showed this substance
to be from one hundred to one thousand times more infectious
than the infected tobacco juice Stanley started with.

What this sane, solid, thirty-one-year-old, already bald Hoosier
chemist had done, in its total dimensions, was to reduce about one
ton of infected Turkish tobacco plants to less than a tablespoon-
ful of white, sugary, crystalline powder that was almost all protein
and almost all tobacco-mosaic virus.

The proportions of this task placed Stanley in the category of
the boy who said he wanted to do big things and who was therefore given a job washing an elephant. As a matter of fact, Stanley's actual job was something like capturing a flea in an elephant's ear by boiling the elephant down to a bit of caramel in the

bottom of a saucepan. There would be one difference, however. The flea no longer would be a flea, able to hop around and father other fleas.

Stanley's crystallized TMV, in contrast, did everything that a tobacco-mosaic virus in its natural state is supposed to do. When the crystals were dissolved in water and rubbed on the leaves of young plants, the plants broke out with the typical measles-like rash, and this infection could be transmitted from one plant to another. Obviously, the crystallized virus still was able to multiply as a one-celled germ does. But a germ would have been destroyed by such an elephantine chemical cook-out.

Discussing this unique achievement from the distance of nearly a quarter of a century, Stanley commented: "I feel foolish. It took more than two years to get the stuff out. A graduate student can do it in an afternoon today." But a graduate student would use the short-cut method Stanley later adopted—depending on an ultra-centrifuge, now one of the basic tools of virus purification. This instrument was developed by Dr. Jesse W. Beams, University of Virginia physicist, and Dr. E. G. Pickels, Belmont, California, physicist, following earlier invention of a centrifuge by the Swedish chemist and Nobel Prize winner Thé Svedberg. Viruses have a heavier molecular weight than plant substances. The machine, whirling at speeds up to sixty thousand revolutions per minute, throws the viruses to the outside, where they can be collected. Apparently the first biochemist to use a centrifuge in this way, to purify bacteriophage, was a German named Max Schlesinger, in 1933. He did not, however, produce crystalline material.

After Stanley's startling achievement, the great controversy of whether the crystal with the capacity for virus life was "organule or molechism" began. This delightful phrase has been attributed to Dr. Philip D. McMaster of the Rockefeller Institute. Another colleague, Dr. Thomas M. Rivers, then of the Rockefeller Institute and at the time one of the chief critics of Stanley's discovery, agreed: "We do not know whether to speak of the unit of this infectious agent as an organule or a molechism."

We now are able to recognize the virus as borderland form of life, both organism and chemical particle, depending on whether it is in its host cell or in transit. But in 1935 Stanley's crystals were a microbiological earth-shaker. His own associates did not believe his claim, and one of his superiors told him he was on his own if he published his study.

But Stanley was accustomed to publishing his findings—in fact, eager to do so. This is the way a young scientist makes a name for himself. Why do research if you can't tell the world what you find? If anything is wrong with it—well, it is true, a man must expect criticism. In the virus hunt, as in any other branch of science, one's colleagues will shoot his mistaken interpretations full of holes soon enough.

Stanley went ahead and published, taking the position that his crystals were protein and not living organisms but non-living molecules. His first short notice appeared in *Science* for June 28, 1935. It immediately caught popular imagination as a discovery involving the missing link between the living and the dead. In fact, the story made page one of *The New York Times*. Stanley wrote in a fuller report:

"Ever since 1898, when Beijerinck introduced his theory of a contagious living fluid, much discussion has centered around the question as to whether or not viruses are alive. The evidence presented . . . indicates that the virus of tobacco mosaic, the first to be described in the literature, is not alive. . . . The fact that this virus seems to be a protein may necessitate a fundamental change in the conception of the nature of other viruses."

What a wonderful story: an unknown, upstart chemist who talked about life as if it were nothing but protein molecules— some crystals dissolved in a test tube. He could not possibly have said anything more calculated to disturb pathologists and bacteriologists, but uninvolved people were delighted.

Some remembered that Pasteur had made his start as a twenty-four-year-old chemist studying the relation of a crystal's structure to its chemical nature. A few perhaps remembered that in his 1870–2 notebook Pasteur compared crystal development "in the germ of the chemical molecule" to the life "in the germ that has been in a state of transmission since the origin of creation."

We have no way of telling whether Pasteur, himself a tiller of new ground, would have applauded young Stanley or would have attacked him as a latter-day spontaneous-generationist who claimed life could spring from "rocks," so to speak. We do know that some latter-day Pasteurians did their gentle best to pick the pup chemist up with sterile forceps and deposit him in the specimen pan. Who had ever heard of an infectious disease that wasn't caused by a living organism?

A few outspoken physicians pounced on Chemist Stanley, just as their predecessors had on Chemist Pasteur. They were doctors of medicine and didn't much care whether tobacco plants had mottled skin or not. Some took a supercilious view of a man who worked with plant rather than human diseases. At a 1935 meeting of pathologists and bacteriologists, one twitted Stanley by pointing out that, unlike his plants, people have a vascular system, or circulation of blood. Stanley replied that he did have a *sap* system to work with, and it came in handy on some occasions. Though he is a man of dignity and restraint, somehow he left the impression that he had called his adversary a sap.

The old bacteriologists readily tended to move into the position that the viruses found in plants, a lower form of life, were different from the viruses causing diseases in higher animal life—some sort of chemical poison, perhaps. But for an infectious agent to multiply, it simply had to be alive, they insisted. Some charged that Stanley's crystals must be contaminated with the agent of the disease and were not the agent itself.

It is customary to picture the older professor who opposes the young hero's brilliant discoveries as the fossilized incarnation of a fiend, obstructing progress to achieve his own dark ends. But the organism-v.-molecule dispute was far more intellectual than personal. Stanley distinguished himself for life by taking the fight in good spirit and even, it appears, getting some fun out of it. Recently he observed: "It is good for the young scientist to learn he has an obligation to fellow scientists and to the public. If he doesn't learn that he must accept the burden of proof, he may turn resentful."

To establish his case, Stanley worked, wrote, and published like fury for the next five years, and he took to the stump. He appeared at every scientific meeting that would invite him to talk, and made a lecture tour of the United States and Great Britain.

To this day, as a result, Stanley's colleagues look upon him, with a mixture of awe and misgiving, as a man who "talks a lot" but "can usually back up what he says," who "has an opinion on everything" but has the "knack of getting results."

Every success in answering a scientific question raises a hundred more. The next question was: what other plant viruses could be crystallized? Stanley found that many could.

With others, such as Claude A. Knight, Frank Ross, and Dean Fraser, he went on to find that there were thirteen different strains of the mosaic virus, in tobacco, tomato plants, alfalfa, grass, cucumbers, and in other plants. These discoveries increased Stanley's burden of proof. He had to show that the TMV strain differences were true differences and not just the results of defects in his technique.

One of the nicest things about claims based on scientific experiments is that the experiments, if they are any good, are reproducible and other investigators can get the same results. Within a year after Stanley's original report, chemists in Great Britain, Australia, and Germany found that, as he said, TMV and other plant viruses could be crystallized. This confirmation meant that, whatever else might be found, no one could dislodge Stanley as the father of virus chemistry—or keep chemists out of the virus hunt from that time on. It also meant that in 1946, when it came time for the Swedish Royal Academy of Science to award a Nobel Prize in chemistry for protein-crystallization discoveries, Stanley would share in the award with Sumner and Northrop, who had turned the trick with enzymes.

But not all of Stanley's claims stood up. For one thing, he said his TMV molecule was protein—essentially carbon, hydrogen, oxygen, and nitrogen. It took two English biochemists to straighten him out on this. They were Frederick C. Bawden and Norman W. Pirie, both now at the Rothansted Experimental Station in Harpenden, but at that time both at Cambridge University. After Stanley crystallized TMV, they got busy and confirmed that it could be done.

But Bawden and Pirie also found in 1937 that TMV contained a little phosphorus. Analysis showed that it was due to the presence of nucleic acid of the same type as that previously isolated from yeast—ribonucleic acid (RNA). Stanley presently confirmed this fact himself: TMV is a nucleoprotein, a combination of protein and nucleic acid such as is found in the nuclei of living cells. The proportions in TMV are 94 per cent protein and 6 per cent nucleic acid. This seemed to move the virus a little closer to the land of the living than Stanley supposed.

Also, in 1956, Dr. Russell L. Steere, working in Stanley's laboratory at the University of California with the electron microscope, was able to photograph a natural crystal of TMV in a plant hair cell. Steere noted that it was not a true crystal but a crystal-like package of virus rods, each intact. They were packed together, side by side and end to end, in a herringbone pattern, and formed layers, like the layers of cloth in a bolt of good tweed. In true crystals, like molecules attach themselves to each other and extend outward in three dimensions. Being a mixture of protein and acid molecules, TMV forms in layers, or so-called para-crystals, crystals extending in one plane only. In other words, a virus crystal is similar to the inclusion body seen under the microscope by the early virologists, and made up of thousands of virus particles. This tendency toward crystallization keeps viruses well within the molecular domain of the chemist, particularly in his concern for purification, but does remove them from the bounds of biology as a system of life, or organism.

When the details were worked out subsequent to 1935, the virus of tobacco-mosaic diseases was found to be an amazing little rod with a coat of protein and a core of nucleic acid. It is 300 millimicrons long by 15 wide, or $^6\!/_{5,000,000}$ of an inch by $^3\!/_{5,000,000}$. It has a molecular weight greater than any protein molecule known—from 40,000,000 to 50,000,000 atoms.

As Stanley cheerfully conceded in a 1957 meeting of virologists, "I have had to swallow a lot."

This is a familiar situation in scientific progress and proves a number of things of importance to full enjoyment of our story. One thing is clear: a good virus tracker has to have a good swallowing apparatus, or else he will stand still.

Then, too, we see that Nature reveals herself a little at a time. Put another way: man is a better observer than explainer of nature. Stanley observed the crystals, but did not quite explain them. Jenner observed that cowpox protected against smallpox, but got into trouble with his horsepox explanation. The uncanny Pasteur had better luck explaining rabies, but Beijerinck was way off in explaining the nature of the virus that, as he correctly observed, had gone through his filter.

In any event, whenever a scientist, in the course of plowing a new furrow, buries an old principle, or simply casts doubt on it, the reactions of his colleagues and competitors are wonderful to behold. His superiors may try to slap him down; his inferiors, to pick him apart. Some authorities will denounce him.

But many will eagerly descend on his findings like blackbirds to pick up the grubs. Some are content simply to ask for proof of his claim, and expect him to be quiet if he lacks proof or if they refute him. A few will manifest plain alarm at the way he has disturbed the ground of existing knowledge, and some will point with horror at the crooked furrows where he went around the stumps. Whatever the case, the pioneer inevitably leaves much ground to be smoothed over.

As late as 1953, Sir Macfarlane Burnet, a Melbourne physician of strong character and strong words, as well as a world-renowned virologist and one of the most entertaining virus writers, said of Stanley's discovery: "This was work in the very best tradition of modern biochemistry—and yet there is more than a suspicion that it has not got us very far." [1]

Stanley might well have accused Burnet of beating Faraday's baby. Michael Faraday was the English physicist who discovered electric induction, the operating principle of electric motors and generators. When asked what good his discovery was, Faraday replied: "Of what use is a newborn baby?"

Stanley likes to tell this story in defense of "useless knowledge." The belittling of basic research—by physicians as well as laymen, we note—has been exposed in the last year or two as one of our grave human weaknesses, quite possibly costing us our lead in development of such things as rockets that might fly past the moon—or in missiles that will seek out our enemy.

As a matter of fact, since Stanley established his new Virus Laboratory in Berkeley in 1948, those working in his laboratory

[1] *Viruses and Man* (Penguin Books; 1953), p. 20.

have been able not only to answer his medical critics but also to show where the practical benefits may lie.

Among other things, they disposed of the argument that animal and plant viruses are different—that the chemist might be able to isolate, purify, and crystallize something infectious from tobacco or other plants but not from red-blooded animals or man.

The bridge from plant to animal viruses was crossed in 1955 when two men, working in Stanley's laboratory, crystallized the virus of poliomyelitis. They are Drs. Carlton E. Schwerdt and Frederick L. Schaffer. Their principal tools were the ultra-centrifuge and the electron microscope. Starting with two hundred gallons of polio-infected monkey-kidney tissue fluid from the Connaught Laboratory in Toronto, they ended with a crystal of pure polio virus!

The big difference between plant viruses and animal viruses, it became apparent, is simply that animal viruses exist in far lower concentrations, so low it's difficult to get enough together to form a crystal. Quite probably this is due to antibody defenses, always at work to knock out foreign invaders. Whereas it is possible to extract three parts TMV from every thousand parts of infected plant tissue, Schwerdt and Schaeffer found only about three parts polio virus per million parts of animal tissue.

By 1956 they had crystallized all three types of polio virus. Since then Drs. Carl F. Mattern and Herman DuBuy, working at the National Institute of Allergy and Infectious Diseases, have crystallized a Coxsackie virus responsible for a non-paralytic form of polio.

This isn't just work in the best biochemical tradition and of no earthly use. It is of immense importance in developing methods of producing purified vaccines to replace the protein-and-virus soups on which we have had to depend. These impure vaccines give protection, but they are more apt than the purified ones to produce toxic or allergic reactions.

So Wendell Stanley is being vindicated, if he needed any vindication. His pioneer playing around with plant viruses *has* got us somewhere. His crystallization of the tobacco-mosaic virus, falling like a heavy stone in a small pond of knowledge, started such a revolution in scientific thinking that the waves and ripples are still continuing. The possibilities are just beginning to emerge. Someday, on some distant shore, they may even splash up the secret of life.

"Viruses," says Stanley, "could have been the first type of life on earth." We should add that not all observers agree with this speculation. Some theorize, on the contrary, that viruses are a degraded form of life—a living thing that has gone downhill in evolution—reasoning that, as viruses are dependent on living cells for their own "borrowed life," cellular life must have preceded them on earth. At any rate, one could guess that some equivalent of cell protoplasm preceded them, for this vital juice (also known as cytoplasm) is their natural habitat. Indeed, further research has shown that the virtually complete lack of protoplasm and the membrane encapsulating it are features that distinguish viruses from bacteria. Lacking the conventional microbe's cellular integrity, the midget microbe is more akin to a cell nucleus than to the living cell as a whole.

12

WILLIAMS:
THE ASTRONOMER
WHO LOOKS AT VIRUSES

Not until the electron microscope was focused on a virus particle did virology really get to know viruses as physical beings. Indeed, it took more than the electron microscope; even with this powerful instrument, the essential problem remained the same: man's understanding of viruses progresses from the limitations of one tool or method to another. We are naturally more interested in what the scientist finds than in the special tools he requires to make his observations, but behind every man of science and his discoveries is a mountain of method, the techniques he invents to spy on nature.

For example we can take Dr. Robley C. Williams. Before 1944 he was an astronomer and, as he is pleased to admit, in his humorous, matter-of-fact way, "I didn't know a virus from my elbow." Then, within a week after making his first acquaintance with an electron microscope, he not only was looking at viruses but also gold-plating them!

But the first thing we need to do is get a firm grasp on the virus's place in the linear scale of things. Bacteria are measured in microns, mostly. A micron is about $\frac{1}{25,000}$ of an inch. A virus particle is so small that it can be measured conveniently only in millimicrons. A millimicron is one thousandth of a micron, or $\frac{1}{25,000,000}$ of an inch. Thus, if we call bacteria microbes, then we can regard viruses as millimicrobes. A polio virus, for instance, measures about twenty-five millimicrons, or one millionth of an inch, in diameter.

John Buist and others had been able to glimpse the 260-by-210-millimicron cowpox virus with the optical microscope, an instrument of magnification depending on the viewed object being big enough to block a wave of light. The electron microscope works much the same way, but substitutes a beam of electrons for the light wave.

Electrons are the smallest units of negative electricity. They can be focused on an object by the use of magnets. Hence, pictures—actually shadowgraphs—can be taken of microscopically invisible objects that scatter some of the electrons as the beam passes through them. That is what causes the shadows on the photographic film—scattered electrons.

The wave length of an electron is about $\frac{5}{1,000}$ of one millimicron. With the electron microscope—invented by German physicists in the early 1930's—it becomes a snap to take pictures of a virus only ten or fifteen millimicrons in diameter.

In fact, the electron wave is theoretically small enough to give us a look at single atoms. This is not actually possible because of technical difficulties. In practice, electron micrographs—the photographs made with the electron microscope—will portray particles two millimicrons in diameter. This is enough to disclose the interior of large molecules.

The first virus seen via electron microscope was reported in 1939. Three German physicists—G. A. Kausche, E. Pfankuch, and Helmut Ruska—made the picture. The latter's brother, Ernst Ruska, and Bodo von Borries were responsible for developing the electron microscope to this stage of practical application. The first virus pictured was—of course—our old friend TMV. It was a vague little rod, like a bit of straw.

In the next three years, virus hunters had their first electronic look at a dozen or more viruses. The cowpox virus, a reddish speck under the light microscope, now looked like a fuzzy charcoal briquette. The encephalitis virus, causing inflammation of the brain in horses and occasionally man, was like the first sprinkle of rain on a windshield. The ubiquitous influenza viruses were mere translucent blobs. The T2 bacteriophage, a virus that lives in a bacterium that in turn lives in our bowels, was more interesting; it looked like a tadpole, or a sperm cell, with a head and a tail.

It was a wonderful thing to see them all, in magnifications up to fifty thousand times natural size. This would make a six-foot man appear fifty miles tall! But still you couldn't see much.

A Robley Williams plus a Ralph Wyckoff were needed to clear up the picture.

Williams [1] is professor of biophysics in the Virus Laboratory of the University of California, in Berkeley. He is Scotch-Irish and looks it, thereby bracketing fairly well with Scotsman Buist, the first man to see a virus. Williams, fifty-one years old, and the father of a teen-age son and daughter, is moderately tall, square-shouldered, and slender. His hair is a handsome, wavy, sandy gray with a silver streak running back from his forehead. He has prominent "bumps of knowledge" and more prominent eyebrows, over rimless glasses. He talks lucidly, in a somewhat wry manner.

Williams describes himself as originally a spectroscopist. This means a scientist who manipulates the images reaching his eyes from the spectrum of radiant energy. Confessing that psychoanalysts might write him off as a sublimated Peeping Tom, Williams is the first to admit his voyeuristic drive, if we may lapse this once into unvirological, Freudian lingo. "My interests always have been visual," he says.

His earliest memory is of reading about the stars and wanting to be an astronomer; in fact, he believes his interest in astronomy extends into the unconscious memories of infancy. In 1910, when he was two years old, his father, Dr. William C. Williams, a physician in Santa Rosa, California, held him up to see the passage of

[1] The Williamses are a numerous people. The subject of this chapter and the author are not knowingly related.

Halley's comet. The father often recalled the incident when he found his son with his nose in a book on astronomical physics, or watched him in his early teens set up a ten-power telescope for inspection of the heavens. But describing the stars in mythological terms hardly excited Robley—whose mother named him for a California hero of the times, Admiral Robley ("Fighting Bob") Evans. Astronomical physics, the science of heavenly matter in motion, did interest him. Though Williams is a long way from astronomy today, he still follows the movement of the planets, and can tell you what Saturn and Jupiter are doing.

The elder Dr. Williams, who now lives in Hanford, California, was a restless man. He spent a good bit of time as a prospector, "looking for a gold mine on the other side of the mountain," his son said. The family of five moved about in the Golden state—Santa Rosa, Yreka, Placerville, Corona. So it was natural, perhaps, that the brainy son should wander far for his education. A scholarship took him to Cornell University in Ithaca, New York. Williams received A.B. and Ph.D. degrees in physics and mathematics, all at Cornell. Meanwhile, he won several letters as a track and tennis star.

Trained as a physicist, Williams in 1935 was now prepared to become an astronomer who never had taken a formal course in astronomy and eventually a virologist without a formal course in biology. His first appointment, at twenty-seven, was as an astronomy instructor at the University of Michigan in Ann Arbor. Here he pursued an earlier interest of his Cornell years, the developing of thin metal films for plating the mirrors used in telescopes. He and John Strong, now of Johns Hopkins University, independently developed the technique for applying the aluminum film used on the mirrors found in the largest telescopes, such as the ones on Mount Wilson and Palomar Mountain in California. Williams is also vice-president of The Evaporated Metal Films Company of Ithaca.

During World War II he was called into service by the Office of Scientific Research and Development in Washington. One of his assignments was to develop a metal film for the Navy that salt water would not corrode. It was an important mission, as the Navy is a great consumer of mirrors—for submarine periscopes, among other uses—but Williams could find no way to lick salt corrosion.

Back in Ann Arbor as an associate professor of physics, Williams one evening in September 1944 found his star in conjunction with that of Dr. Ralph Walter Graystone Wyckoff, also a Cornell Ph.D. Wyckoff is now a biophysicist at the National Institutes of Health in Bethesda. He had spent a good deal of time in virus research, had collaborated with Stanley in Princeton, and had worked important improvements in the ultra-centrifuge. He was then, at forty-seven, a resident lecturer in epidemiology at the University of Michigan School of Public Health. Williams was thirty-six.

Williams went down to the Physics Department basement, where an electron microscope recently had been installed, to have his first look at this instrument. Particularly, he wanted to photograph his aluminum film under an electronic beam. Also there, looking at this tall, massive piece of equipment, was Wyckoff. They introduced themselves. Wyckoff said he was mainly interested in viruses, and had just come over to see what an electron microscope would do.

Together the two physicists played with this $20,000 gadget with a potential magnification power of two hundred thousand times. Williams had wondered, he said, at the light and dark areas that could be seen in the aluminum film under an ordinary optical microscope. Was this mottling due to a thick-and-thin variation in the metal coating?

Taking some pictures and developing them, Williams and Wyckoff saw that the aluminum film was made up of rudimentary crystals of the metal. These, known as crystallites, produced the mottled effect. The film, they found, was actually of even thickness. Except for a new friendship, Williams and Wyckoff had not found much.

"Fortunately," Williams recalls, "there were two or three pieces of dirt on the specimen. If they hadn't been there, we *wouldn't* have discovered anything."

The two men fell to discussing how to measure the height of those untidy specks, and thus to tell what was high and low in an electron micrograph. How could you do it without a ruler?

"Well," pondered Williams aloud, "if it were a mountain on the moon, we could measure the length of the mountain's shadow and calculate the angle of the sun's rays. It is simple enough then to find the mountain's height."

But how might they force an object to cast a shadow at a known angle on the surface of their specimen screen? The way to do it came to them quickly enough. Williams was already an expert in the business of vaporizing metals at a high temperature so they would coat a mirror surface.

By the next day he and Wyckoff had developed a technique of gold-plating infinitesimally small objects in an oblique manner so that they cast a shadow when photographed under the electron microscope! The plating is done in a vacuum, inside a bell jar. They covered a tungsten filament with gold and placed the specimen to be coated under, but to one side of, the filament. Closing the jar and pumping the air out, they then heated the filament to an incandescent glow. The gold vaporized and was hurled in submicroscopic droplets in all directions. It took very little gold to cover the invisible speck they were studying.

The metal vapor strikes the surface of the object to be plated like a driving sleet storm. The metal vapor ices on the exposed side, leaving bare spots to leeward. Under the electron microscope, these bare spots become the shadows, in sharp contrast to the metal, which scatters the microscope's electrons when a photograph is made.

In a couple of days' time the two had the technique of metal shadow-casting, as they called it, worked out. "Everything we touched turned to gold," said Williams, meaning it quite literally. At least it was gold-plated.

They had to solve one unexpected difficulty. Surfaces that had looked perfectly smooth even under a microscope now proved to have uneven contours. When metal-shadowed, a "smooth surface" became in an electron micrograph like a rural landscape viewed from the sky under the long, slanting rays of an afternoon sun. They found that collodion film furnished the smoothest surface. On it, gold-plating produced a granular surface, resembling a choppy sea viewed from the air.

Within the first week the two physicists also tried aluminum, chromium, palladium, platinum, and uranium. In the end, Wyckoff preferred palladium, but Williams decided uranium was best for producing the thinnest and smoothest possible coating.

Using these metals, they plated every kind of surface and object they could find and get under a bell jar. A machined brass surface appears positively furrowed when shadowed for the electron microscope. The tip of a high-speed drill is as full of gulleys as the Dakota badlands. The surface of a used roller bearing, shadowed with chromium, looks like waves breaking on a Cape Cod beach. And the face of a polished diamond, when shadowed with gold, displays a number of mounds that look amazingly like the fine, firm, hemispherical breasts of a young woman.

"The thing to do," said Wyckoff, who knew how viruses ordinarily appear under an electron microscope, "is to shadow some viruses."

While waiting for a virologist friend, Dr. William C. Price, to send them some tobacco-mosaic and tomato-bushy-stunt viruses, they went to Professor Ernest F. Barker, head of the Physics Department, and told him what they had. Though Wyckoff was from the School of Public Health and Williams was rather off by himself in an astronomical research, Barker was enthusiastic. He got them an electron microscope of their own, and space to work in.

The pair now fell to experimenting with everything from blood molecules of the horseshoe crab to typhoid bacilli and staphylococci aureus, the germs that cause boils. The large molecules from the crab, under a chromium coating, are like a honeycomb. A chromium-plated typhoid germ looks like a washed-out breakfast sausage. And the staphylococcus germs are like dumplings floating in a dark gravy.

Soon they had a specimen of TMV. In an ordinary, unshadowed electron micrograph this virus had been a fuzzy gray rod. Now, with a coat of uranium, it looked like a round, firm, fully packed cigarette lying on the living-room rug under the light of a table lamp. The tomato-bushy-stunt viruses were like tiny round beads. The influenza virus, hitherto a vague, round blob, now stood out from its background, like a powder puff or a cotton boll.

You might think, of course, that the heat from melted and vaporized metal would fry or incinerate a virus into oblivion. True, there isn't much left of the virus, under its metal blanket. But the vapor condenses instantaneously as it hits, and thus takes the shape of its victim before the virus can burn up. A film of uranium about half a millimicron thick gives good results in bringing out the three-dimensional size and shape of what is underneath.

Williams and Wyckoff were scientific soul mates for two years before again going their individualistic ways. The *Journal of Applied Physics* published the news of their discovery in 1944, in a report signed by both. They wrote several more papers jointly before Wyckoff left the University.

Their technique attracted disciples. Dr. Robert C. Backus, who wanted to work with animal viruses, and Dr. Russell L. Steere, interested in plant viruses, joined Williams. He obtained the needed money from the American Cancer Society and the National Institutes of Health, both of which have the good sense to back basic as well as applied research.

For five years William and his shadow-casting teammates were a scientific attraction at Ann Arbor. The University of Michigan was not able to hold the line against the University of California, however. In 1950, Williams received a letter from Stanley inviting him to come out to Berkeley and study the physical structure of viruses there, with a full professorship in biophysics. Williams always had hoped to return to California; he had made thirteen trips back since leaving there for Ithaca.

Williams knew Stanley only by reputation, as a self-confident young chemist who had "stuck his neck out" and yet had survived the subsequent whackings. As a matter of fact, Williams had set out, he said, to prove Stanley wrong in estimating the tobacco-mosaic virus rod to be 300 by 15 millimicrons, but found himself proving Stanley right. Williams figured he could work for Stanley, so he went to Berkeley.

There he quickly became engaged in solving some of the technical problems arising from being able to see and learn so much more of viruses, but still not as much as he wanted.

Metal shadow-casting became the most popular way of looking at viruses while Williams was still at Ann Arbor. Its significance was obvious to every electron-microscopist as well as old-fashioned microscopists. As we have seen, the electron microscope is theoretically able to picture a speck far smaller than the smallest virus.

In practice, however, the user of an electron microscope finds it hard to separate an unshadowed particle of less than ten millimicrons from its background. Sometimes it is difficult to get a clear, accurate look at large micro-organisms whose size should make them easily visible with an optical microscope. They may be translucent and prone to absorb light waves or to scatter electrons more or less equally over their entire surfaces. This is why microscopists customarily stain their specimens, in an attempt to achieve contrast. Metal shadow-casting serves much the same purpose, by producing sharp contrast, and its introduction had the effect of getting the visualization of viruses "out of the fog."

The electron microscope, with the aid of shadow-casting, established the size of viruses as in the general range from about 15 to 300 millimicrons. This is a remarkable fact in itself. If man came in such a variety of lengths, we would have one-foot midgets and twenty-foot giants. We have enough problems as it is.

The smaller viruses, mainly though not exclusively inhabiting the plant world, are quite uniform in shape and size. It is the large ones, mostly from the animal world, that vary so much. The first four shapes Williams described were spheres, rods, ovals, and tadpoles.

Williams wanted to know a great deal more than that, but he was a sufficiently apt student of psychology to take care not to get carried away by his passion for seeing things. As a matter of fact, he became a student of the shortcomings of both the technique and the technician.

He is prompt to point out that, despite his own and his fellow scientists' reverence for complete objectivity, the interpretations they make are frequently subjective—particularly when looking at sub-microscopic objects. In fact, he finds it as truthful to say "Believing is seeing" as "Seeing is believing."

For instance, if one takes a specimen of virus-diseased cells and a control specimen of normal cells and looks at them in that order, he will far more often see virus-like particles in the diseased spec-

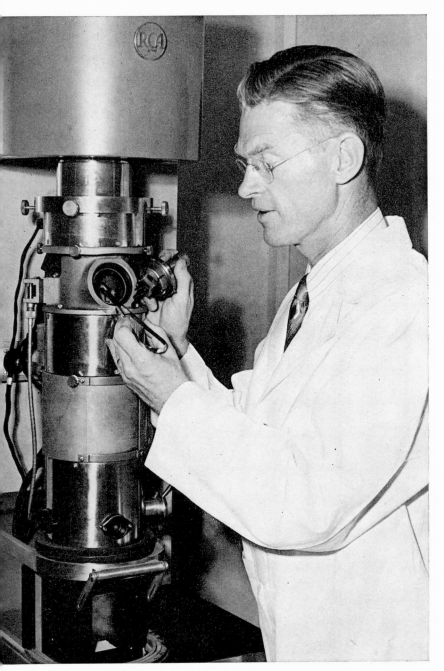

Robley C. Williams places a specimen in an electron microscope
at the Virus Laboratory of the University of California.

PLATE 3

Wendell M. Stanley, first man to crystallize a virus. Few deeds of pure science have caused more excitement—Stanley fanned the flames of controversy over whether a virus is living matter or dead. (*Black Star Photo*)

PLATE 4

imen than in the normal specimen. *Naturally,* you might say, for the diseased specimen contains the virus. But wait. Williams found that if you look at the control specimen first and see no virus particles there, you are much less likely to see them in the diseased specimen! In either case, there could be psychological bias.

In any case, the particle one sees may not be a virus—or the virus that caused the disease. The biggest drawback to the study of viruses under the electron microscope, particularly when they are singled out for shadowing and other manipulations, is that "we don't see them when they are behaving like viruses," says Williams, in his characteristically deflationary manner. Viruses are "at home" only in living cells.

One of the many problems Williams and his associates were faced with was the "serious danger that our observations of a necessarily limited field will give us false impressions."

Consider this: the electron microscopist places a drop of fluid supposedly containing the virus on a copper-mesh, collodion-coated disk one eighth of an inch in diameter. Then he dries it. Each mesh is $\frac{1}{200}$-inch square, and itself much larger than the field of a single photograph. There are 400 of these squares on a single disk. Thus the drop would have to contain 2,000 virus particles to supply each square with an average of five. It would be extremely hard to find as few as five particles in so large an area. But the electron-microscopist can't be sure of even one virus in every square.

He can scan the specimen with the aid of the electron microscope's fluorescent viewing-plate, the equivalent of an ordinary microscope's eyepiece and illuminating mirror. And he can select the most interesting squares, but rarely will he photograph more than twenty out of a possible 400. It would be too tedious, wasteful, and expensive to study and photograph all 400.

But this leaves him in the dark as to precisely what was in the other 380. Thus, as Williams says: "It's like looking for a needle in a haystack with a hay-cutter."

His group, with Dr. Renato Dulbecco of the California Institute of Technology, demonstrated the fact with poliomyelitis. They tried to find the polio virus in monkey-kidney tissue in which the polio virus was growing—they knew the tissue was infected. Still, they could not find the virus! It simply was not abundant enough to be found in any bit of infected tissue chosen at random.

When one finds the needle in the haystack, there is another problem. Williams points out that there is no visible difference between many of the spherical viruses causing diseases as widely separated as those of humans and plants. "The biological woods are full of viruses we don't know anything about," he says.

So, when someone hops up and says he has found a virus in a cancer cell, our number-one man of electron microscopy is inclined to raise his shaggy eyebrows and say: "Prove that the particle under study is the cause of the disease under study." In the face of claims based on lesser evidence, "we must proceed with tongue in cheek—but don't press too hard against the cheek," Williams advised at a meeting of the Biophysical Society, founded in 1957, of which he was the first chairman.

The imaginative scientist doesn't just stand around scratching his head about these difficulties. Backus and Williams developed a method whereby they could spray their specimen fluid through an atomizer onto the collodion screen, so that individual droplets could be studied wherever they hit. These, when dried, were only about $\frac{1}{2,500}$ of an inch in diameter and therefore furnished a more concentrated photographic field.

Looking at viruses in such a restricted area, it is feasible to count them, a particle at a time. The total might be anywhere from six to five hundred in a spray drop. Now, if the scientists knew the volume of that spray drop, they could estimate the concentration of viruses in a given amount of specimen.

The idea of counters came to them—indicator particles of a known size and number. They chose polystyrene latex spheres 270 millimicrons in diameter.

A given number of these counters were suspended in a given volume of specimen fluid. They sprayed a series of drops, counted the counters in each, and arrived at the average per drop. Assuming a uniform distribution of the counters in suspension, they could now estimate the volume of the average drop. Then, by counting and averaging the virus particles in a series of drops, they could estimate the total number of virus particles in the known volume of the original suspension.

As a dividend of perplexity, we may add that another question is whether the viruses are present in numbers that would constitute an infectious dose, thus making them the likely cause of the disease at hand. Finding either too few or too many particles in diseased tissues may well mean they are something other than viruses.

In another direction, it occurred to these scientists that drying a specimen exposes a spherical virus to evaporation pressures that might deform it. So Williams adapted a freeze-drying technique as a means of preserving the original shape. Now he placed his copper disk in a flask containing liquid air and sprayed it with a virus suspension. Then he closed the flask and pumped out the air. This had the effect of bringing the temperature down to forty or fifty degrees below zero Fahrenheit. The spray droplet freezes in about $\frac{1}{10,000}$ of a second, and dries without losing its shape.

The virus particles, frozen and dry, were coated with metal and examined. The old drying technique had indeed distorted some spherical viruses. It had caused them to pancake.

This was most exciting: viruses thought to be spherical were in some cases found to be polyhedral—that is, many-faced. The head of a T2 bacteriophage, for instance, had previously looked round, like a tadpole's. Now it turned out to be shaped like a hexagonal prism, six-sided, with a pyramid at each end.

The influenza virus, hitherto thought to be oval, proved to be quite round. The turnip-yellow and rabbit-papilloma viruses still looked like spheres, but had a pebbly surface like a raspberry.

But, although a sphere remained the most common virus shape, the most astounding finding was the variety of angular forms, some as complicated as anything to be found in a solid-geometry book. Not long ago, Williams got interested in insect viruses. One virus inhabiting the crane fly (*Tipula paludosa*) proved to be a perfect icosahedron. To save you a trip to the dictionary, an icosahedron is a solid with twenty faces, each an equilateral triangle. Life, if we can call it that, comes in strange shapes.

There are ways of studying the physical structure of a virus that place it closer to home—in the infected cell. One is to look at the virus inside cells whose walls are so thin that the electron beam goes through and picks up interior details. Another is to embed the cells presumably containing viruses inside some sort of material that can be sliced in ultra-thin sections.

Steere, in 1956, developed a new technique that wrapped several of these techniques into one. He took a mass of virus-infected cells, quick-froze them, and then planed one surface of the frozen block. He exposed this surface in a vacuum, causing the cell surfaces to elevate to a height of about ten millimicrons. The surface was then coated with uranium vapor, producing a shadowed replica, or mask, of what was underneath.

This system worked particularly well in determining the structure of virus crystals such as TMV. More recently Steere has been slicing up polio-virus crystals and the chromosomes of the fruit fly—the source of most of our knowledge of genetic mutations.

Meanwhile, Williams and Dr. Dean Fraser had worked on techniques of virus smashing, in order to get a better look inside of viruses. They found that they could disintegrate a virus by alternately freezing and thawing it in water.

They broke open the hexagonal heads of the T2 bacteriophage and found the contents arranged in distinct, closely intertwined strands of a nucleic acid. Looking into the tails of these millimicrobes, they found a central core ending in a tuft of fibers arranged in a V. They measured the tail and found it to be 130 by 6 millimicrons!

They also observed something that others had noted before: that the bacteriophage attacks a bacterium with its tail; and that when the virus loses its head, the head does nothing, but the tail goes right on sticking cells.

Others have observed evidence of internal and external structure in viruses. The viruses that cause parrot fever and cold sores look, after drying, like derby hats. Something of softer structure may have collapsed inside the stiff outer coat. The viruses of cowpox and smallpox are shaped like loaves of bread or, some say, bricks. They showed definite signs of having opaque insides and transparent outsides. In contrast, particles of the medium-sized and smaller viruses, such as influenza and polio, do not show this characteristic.

Williams had a hard look at the oldest subject of virus research, the tobacco-mosaic virus. Bombarding TMV with sound waves beyond the range of the human ear, he broke the rods into short fragments. These chunks looked six-sided, leading him to conclude that the most likely form of the intact rod was that of a hexagonal prism, more or less the same as a lead pencil in appearance. Others have regarded the TMV rod as more like a series of lock washers strung on twisted wire core. The photographs "resist unambiguous interpretation . . . a hard way of saying they don't amount to much," says Williams. Others have suggested that the outside structure of TMV is wrapped around the core helically, like a coiled spring spiraling around a metal rod.

The Williams wit more or less resolves the argument in his own favor for the moment. When exhibiting his own clearly hexagonal findings, he dryly observed: "You could conclude that this rod was helical in shape, thanks to poor photography."

In sum, virology has been able to show that viruses infect every living thing of one cell or more in size—bacteria, higher plants, insects, animals, man. And the electron-microscopist in each case has furnished a picture, plus the fascinating discovery that life —at least, virus life—comes in many-angled, geometric forms. For example, as this book was going to press came news that two University of London scientists, employing X-ray diffraction, had determined the structure of a polio virus, hitherto simply put down as a spherical particle. This virus, like certain animal and plant viruses previously mentioned, resembles a raspberry. It has a nucleic-acid core and a coat made up of sixty pebbles of protein. These are arranged not in a perfect sphere but in an icosahedron, the same as the insect viruses pictured by Robley Williams. Each of the twenty triangular faces consists of three protein pebbles. Quite likely other small viruses will prove to be equally fantastic in shape.

TRACKING VIRUSES
BY THEIR ANTIBODIES

To DISCOVER its nature, virologists have subjected the infinitesimally small virus particle, alone and in all its multiplications, to
a staggering variety of manipulations. They have squeezed,
frozen, and spun it. They have shook, shocked, sliced, and
stained it. They have heated, treated, dried, fried, dissolved,
crystallized, and embalmed it. In these ways they have learned
many of its secrets.

Yet, from the standpoint of understanding and controlling the
viruses within us, the main concern of us human beings, medical
science has had to depend mainly on the signs and symptoms that
different virus infections produce. These are generally unmistakable in clear-cut cases of the so-called classic virus diseases, such
as smallpox, rabies, yellow fever, measles, and paralytic poliomyelitis.

On the other hand, the viruses causing these diseases and the
150 and more other viruses that may infect us don't always produce symptoms. Even when they do, virus infections have a tendency to resemble one another, or at least begin the same: fever,
inflammation, extreme weakness, a cough, aches and pains, loss

of appetite, vomiting, diarrhea, or other common ills, such as rash, ulcers, or itch. Often there isn't even this much for a physician to go by. Even the most dangerous viruses do not sicken, cripple, or kill us, or even redden our tissues every time we are exposed to them.

As a matter of fact, modern microbiologists have quite a different slant on the relationship of parasite and host, or virus and victim, than did the early disciples of Pasteur and Koch. The old microbe hunters thought of man and germs as at war, of the microbe as a "foreign invader" engaged in attack and forcing man to "mobilize his defenses." There is some truth in this viewpoint, as we can see from the way that influenza rose in Asia and swept the world in 1957. But aggression from outside is not the whole story.

One of microbiology's leading thinkers, Dubos, prefers to look upon the host and its unwanted microbes and millimicrobes as involved in more or less "peaceful coexistence." [1] In fact, he distinguishes between *infection* and *disease*. Some physicians will argue that there is no difference, pointing out that an invasion of a living cell by a virus, for instance, must involve some injury to the cell. The microbiologist replies that disease involves symptoms of sickness, some overt departure from a state of health, whereas the presence of viruses (infection) in a few millions of our billions of cells doesn't necessarily result in any noticeable discomfort or injury (disease). In short, "inapparent" or "sub-clinical" infection is the normal state of affairs, according to this view; the parasite tends to dwell within the host in a relative state of harmony or —to borrow from *McCall's*—togetherness. Only occasionally do virus and victim fall out, owing to some alteration in this "balance of nature" which permits the virus to get the upper hand. What this somewhat novel dictum takes into account, of course, is something we know to be statistically true even in the worst epidemic: in virus infections, crippling disease and death are usually exceptions rather than the rule.

The reason viruses do not harm us more than they do is that

[1] René J. Dubos: *Bacterial and Mycotic Infections of Man*, chapter ii, "The Evolution and Ecology of Microbial Diseases" (Philadelphia: J. B. Lippincott; third edition, 1959).

our bodies do not take these infections lying down. Nature equips us with a series of defenses in depth which neutralize, or almost neutralize, the virulence of most of the microbes and millimicrobes that disturb our physiological peace. These defenses fall under the general heading of resistance or immunity, natural or acquired. Generally, fresh infection tends to build fresh resistance and hence restore the balance mentioned by Dubos. Therefore, our "perfect parasite," the virus, survives only by a continual uphill struggle and by the fact that we are, from our own selfish viewpoint, an "imperfect host"—that is, our defenses are not perfect. Some susceptibility remains or returns at some times in some people.

Our skin, mucous secretions, white blood cells, and fever and inflammation themselves are all germicidal defenses. But possibly the most important—or, at any rate, the best known so far—are the antibodies that circulate in our blood. They constitute specific bodily reactions to what, in this sense, is truly "foreign invasion." Hence, if 150 different viruses infect us, our bodies produce 150 different kinds of antibodies in an effort to protect ourselves against them.

Antibodies are of primary interest in our story at this point because, next to the general symptoms of illness itself, they are the most important sign of a virus's presence. Furthermore, they furnish a means of diagnosing or identifying a virus infection, inasmuch as each kind of antibody is the result of a specified kind of virus. As a matter of fact, an immune serum from the blood—that is, a serum containing specified antibodies—has been one of the most useful of all laboratory tools not only in virus detection but also in the testing of vaccines.

Indeed, the virus hunters have needed to work out only about four big ideas in order to prevent human diseases via vaccination. The first big idea, at least two thousand years old, is that people who recover from certain infectious diseases are safe from a second attack. The second is that a scientist can find a suitable animal host, susceptible to the infection, that will manufacture virus for him in quantity. The third idea is that in such a host, or through some laboratory maneuver, the scientist can find a way of taming, stunning, or killing the virus so that it will still produce disease resistance but not the disease. The fourth idea is the use of antibodies in an immune serum—or antiserum, as it is also called—as a quantitative index for virus presence. This is called a virus-neutralization test.

Here, those who pass out the laurel wreaths and hall-of-fame niches appear largely to have overlooked a man named George M. Sternberg (1838–1915). It was Sternberg who originated the neutralization test that remains today, sixty-seven years after its discovery, as the backbone of virus-disease prevention.

Robert Koch, himself known as the father of bacteriology, called Sternberg the father of American bacteriology. He was that and more. The son of a Lutheran minister, Sternberg became an Army medical officer and was captured by Confederate soldiers at Bull Run, but escaped. He rose to be Surgeon General of the Army under President Cleveland.

The Army probably dissipated a great deal of Sternberg's creative energy by treating him as a body rather than a brain and moving him about the world from pillar to post, in contrast to Pasteur, who stayed put in his Paris laboratory, and Koch, who remained in his in Berlin.

But Sternberg found time for a number of original experiments, despite his military handicap. He anticipated Elie Metchnikoff, the "mad Russian" scientist who came to Pasteur's laboratory and discovered phagocytes, the type of white blood cells that act as "eater cells"—scavengers of foreign substances floating in the blood stream. In 1881, three years before Metchnikoff's popular discovery, Sternberg suggested that white blood cells ate bacteria.

He developed modern microphotography, and he organized the Yellow Fever Commission, headed by Walter Reed, that went to Cuba and found the yellow-fever virus and the means of controlling the disease through controlling the mosquito carriers. But when Martha Sternberg, his widow, came to write the general's biography in 1920, she neglected to mention the experiment for which virologists remember, and the world might well honor, her husband.

In 1892 viruses as such had not yet been discovered, and the cause of cowpox or smallpox was therefore still unknown. In Germany, Emil A. von Behring two years before had performed the crucial experiment resulting in the discovery of antibodies. What Behring, an army doctor like Sternberg, did was mix virulent diphtheria germs with serum from immune guinea pigs and inject it into susceptible animals. They did not die, but lived, protected by something in the immune serum. Behring called it "antitoxin," leaving the elaboration of the theory of antibodies to another Koch disciple, Paul Ehrlich.

Sternberg pondered this new knowledge that blood serum— the clear, straw-colored part of the blood—contained this strange germicidal power when it came from immunized animals. He decided to make an experiment and, in his choice of diseases, became the first to show that what Behring found to be true for bacteria was also true for viruses. He selected cowpox, in the hope that he could find a serum that would neutralize the smallpox "poison" immediately after a person was exposed to it.

Sternberg, a year before he became Surgeon General, visited Dr. William E. Griffiths, who for years had been cultivating smallpox-vaccine virus on calves in Brooklyn as a business venture. Sternberg looked stiff and proper in his uniform, but he was a gentle, unassuming man. From Dr. Griffiths he purchased a calf that was not immune to cowpox. He had no difficulty interesting the enterprising doctor in the experiments he wished to perform.

From a vaccinated calf Sternberg obtained a specimen of blood. From it, twenty hours later, he drew off clear blood serum into small, sterilized glass tubes, four drops of serum per tube. From another calf with fresh vaccination ulcers, he obtained three quills of vaccine matter. He placed these in one serum tube, removing them an hour later. In the second tube he placed a fresh vaccination scab from a child's arm. Sternberg then inoculated the non-immune calf he had purchased with the contents of the two tubes.

Looking for a vaccination ulcer nine days later, he found no sign of one. It appeared that the immune serum, mixed with the virus, had neutralized its infectivity.

He now thought of an objection to the experiment. Perhaps the blood of any calf, even though not vaccinated, would have this neutralizing effect when mixed with the vaccine matter if the blood were allowed to stand for twenty-four hours. He repeated the experiment with blood from a normal, non-immune calf, plus the virus, thriftily vaccinating the same experimental calf used in the previous experiment. He made this inoculation on the calf's left thigh. On the right thigh, he again vaccinated the animal with the virus mixed with serum from the immune calf.

Eight days later he examined the calf and found the regular vaccine ulcer on the left thigh. No neutralization had occurred with normal serum, in other words. He found nothing at all on the right thigh. Here, neutralization had occurred with immune serum.

Sternberg concluded, when he wrote up his report for the Association of American Physicians: "The result of the experiment made is, therefore, very definite, and shows that the blood serum of an immune calf contains something which neutralizes the specific virulence of vaccine virus. . . ."

Sternberg hoped to go on and isolate this "antitoxin," he said. He didn't do this, for he would have had to isolate not only the filterable virus but also its specific antibody. However, he did draw some critical fire during the discussion of his paper. He was cautioned against jumping to the conclusion that this knowledge might be of any specific benefit to humanity. One discussant, pointing out that surgical operations even so small as vaccination scratches might affect the course of disease, recalled that there had been a great craze about circumcision as a cure for epilepsy, but that the operation was no longer performed for that purpose. This man also brought up the distressing fact that Koch had claimed that tuberculin was a cure for tuberculosis but it had proved to be a provocative agent of tuberculosis (and, indeed, had killed a great many persons). Still another physician said he didn't think medicine was as near to disease prevention as some enthusiasts thought.

Sternberg, certainly no crank, made a masterful and prophetic reply:

"I admire conservatism and scepticism, but . . . I am very free to say that I think the future of scientific medicine is in this direction, and that we have entered upon a field that . . . will give you results that will knock the conservatism from under your feet before many years. I believe that there is something in the blood of the immune calf that neutralizes the . . . virus. . . ."

He was dead right.

As we shall see later, the Sternberg neutralization test, with modern improvements, was the key tool in the detection of the different types of viruses which cause influenza and poliomyelitis, and in testing the antibody-producing potency of the vaccines developed against these two diseases.

This is a strange, circular affair—a kind of science enabling the serologist, or serum expert, to raise himself by his own bootstraps. It may be easier to keep in mind if we think, by analogy, of our virus hunter deducing what kind of gun fired a shot by examining the hole in the target. Detecting viruses by the specific antibodies they produce, in fact, is a sort of biological ballistics. A crime-laboratory ballistics expert can tell what gun fired the bullet he is examining if he can find the gun and fire a test shot from it. The serologist doesn't look at the bullet (virus), however, but only at the effect of the shot (antibody). The virus-neutralization test, therefore, is a cross-matching procedure, fitting the shot's effect to the gun used. This, of course, requires the firing of many test shots—that is, the production of standard immune serums by infecting susceptible animals with known viruses.

Serology and, by extension, immunology might strike an engineer or mathematician as pretty crude science. It is; yet, the expert in this field can tell an amazing amount. He can start with a virus and tell you whether you have antibodies against it, or start with your antibodies and tell you what viruses they should protect you against. And he can do these things without ever seeing a virus or an antibody!

To be sure, the neutralization test has certain limitations that make it unhandy for routine laboratory diagnosis of a virus infection, so it is not of much use in telling your doctor what virus you have at the moment. It is expensive, because it requires test serums and test animals or tissue cultures, used in a series. It is time-consuming, for it takes about two weeks to complete. This is the length of time needed for antibodies to develop to an easily detectable level. Most virus infections are over in that time.

Here, Dr. Albert H. Coons, Harvard Medical School immunologist, has scored a notable advance. Coons has developed what might be described, in its widespread diagnostic uses, as a Sternberg neutralization test with neon lights. He makes antibodies fluorescent, or self-illuminating, so that when he looks at them under a microscope with ultra-violet light they glow in a colorful way—yellowish green. This test reduces what took two weeks to two hours.

Nobody ever has seen an antibody, in the singular, but Coons's discovery has brought him closer to this achievement than any other man to date.

This much, in sum, is now known about antibodies, thanks to the diligence of a large number of immunochemists: They are proteins, among the thousands formed in our bodies. They are all found in the gamma-globulin fraction of blood serum. They form in reaction to a variety of foreign invaders, known as antigens (antigens include viruses and any other substance that will produce an antibody). Whenever the antigen enters the body again, the remaining antibodies—or whatever mechanisms have filed the antibody blueprints away—go to work making more antibodies. These combine with the fresh antigen and neutralize it, by forming various so-called precipitates, agglutinates, and aggregates.

The idea of labeling or tagging antibodies to trace their whereabouts was not original with Coons, but he was the first to accomplish the feat, in 1941. His success, he points out, depended on the help of two Harvard chemists, Drs. Hugh J. Creech and R. Norman Jones, and on knowledge borrowed from chemistry.

Certain naturally fluorescent compounds will attach themselves to protein molecules—combine with them chemically. Antibodies being proteins, the problem was to find just the right fluorescent compound to hook on to them. The scientists' choice, as a means of distinguishing their marker from other types of fluorescence common in nature, such as blue and orange, was fluorescein, the simplest of the fluorane dyes. It emanates a greenish light. Some have called it apple green.

They were able to show that fluorescein attached itself to the antibody molecules at two points—making it a boat with two green running-lights, so to speak—and they also demonstrated that these attachments did not destroy antibody specificity. Fluorescent antibodies continue to behave like antibodies.

World War II interrupted this work, and Coons was not able to report any further developments until 1950. Since then, however, all immunology seems to be turning green with envy and emulation, we might say.

Many scientists now use the Coons technique to tag antibodies and with them trace antigens in infected tissues. The experiment begins with the selection of an antigen to be studied and with the production of an immune serum. The antibodies are tagged by mixing fluorescein with the serum. The antibodies and dye combine.

Now, if one takes an ultra-thin slice of tissue from a laboratory animal that has been infected with a virus and covers the tissue with the immune serum, the fluorescent antibodies in the serum seek out the antigen. And, under the ultra-violet-lighted microscope, they show the virus's location in or around the cells. What the immunologist sees is the aggregate of antibody with antigen. If there is no antigen-antibody reaction, due to lack of specificity, there is no concentration of green light.

How many antibodies does Coons see in one of his aggregates? He cannot say. Undoubtedly it is a large number. The big point is that immunologists at last can locate, and put a fluorescent finger on, the source of specific antibody formation.

Coons and others, using this new technique, now have begun to clear up the mystery of just where in the body antibodies are made. They are probably formed, it appears, in the plasma cells. These are not just any cells that make up blood plasma, but peculiar cells that, it long has been known, appear normally in mucous membranes and lymph glands and frequently show up in the vicinity of disease. Immunologists now know why. When an antigen enters the body, plasma cells are sure to come on the scene to make an antibody against the disease. The plasma cells themselves appear to be formed in the bone marrow, the spleen, and perhaps the lymph glands.

It seems strange, perhaps, that virologists have been able to see and measure single virus particles before they have been able to do as much with single antibodies produced by viruses. But it is not so strange when one realizes that the antibody is smaller than the smallest of viruses. Immunochemists have been able to deduce that a typical antibody molecule may be about sixteen millimicrons long by five wide. This places it a few millimicrons under the smallest animal virus, that of encephalitis, but well within electron-microscope range, if someone can find a way of singling it out for photography.

PART THREE: FIRST BIG BREAK-THROUGH IN VACCINES

GOODPASTURE
HATCHES AN EGG

BEFORE the 1930's there were only two virus vaccines—one against smallpox and the other against rabies. Jenner introduced the first smallpox vaccine in 1798. Pasteur came along with the first rabies vaccine in 1885, nearly a century later. These were ingenious stabs in the dark, because the causes of the diseases were then unknown.

There the vaccine business rested, as far as viruses were concerned, for another half-century. Today about twenty virus vaccines have been developed for human use. About fifteen of these can be described as chick-type vaccines, cultured in hatching eggs.

The reason that virus-disease prevention had its Dark Age, while in the same years bacteriology produced many immunizing agents against bacterial diseases, was the virus's stubborn refusal to reproduce outside of the living cells of specified hosts. Bacteria are content to propagate in some lifeless medium, on a plate of blood jelly or in a cup of insipid broth. Nothing but the interior of a living cell is good enough for viruses.

This created a serious impasse. To make a vaccine for a widespread disease, a virologist must have an abundant source of live virus, whether he uses a mild strain that will produce immunity but not the disease, or uses a dangerous virus and kills it first.

The problem went deeper than mere virus production. To learn to prevent an infectious disease scientifically, the virologist must know he is working with the virus in question. If he cannot see the virus itself, he must be able to see signs of it, and to read these signs correctly. In general, he must be able to work with the germ in captivity to find out how to tame it. To cook rabbit, first catch the rabbit, it has been said.

Before 1931, scientists had varying luck in transmitting viruses to experimental hosts. Jenner's animal host was already available in the barnyard—the cow with cowpox. Later, others found that cowpox would "take" in many different animals. Pasteur and Roux caught their "rabbit" in nerve cells of real rabbits, infected with rabies from dogs. They passed the virus from rabbit to rabbit, ground up the spinal cords, and mixed them with water to provide a source of vaccine. It wasn't anything like pure virus, of course, but really a nerve-protein soup seasoned with the virus.

Fairly early in the game the laboratory people found that monkeys and chimpanzees were heir to many of man's virus ills. Karl Landsteiner infected Rhesus monkeys with poliomyelitis in 1908. But infected monkeys do not make a good source of vaccine. The expense is great; the virus yield, meager.

Then came the mouse era. Dr. Max Theiler established yellow fever in the mouse brain in 1928. Dr. Wilson Smith and his British co-workers in 1933 put human influenza in an experimental animal for the first time—ferrets. A few years later influenza and polio-myelitis were transmitted to mice. This was progress.

Ferret flu had not helped matters much, however. Ferrets are as bad as monkeys. They are expensive, require a lot of care, and bite vigorously. Bacteriologists have died from the bites of infected monkeys.

Mice are much better. They breed fast, grow quickly, and live only about two years. They are fairly cheap, even today: fifty to seventy-five cents for a standard laboratory mouse, as against as much as sixty-five dollars for a Rhesus monkey.

It's possible to produce mouse-brain vaccines fairly efficiently, but there are drawbacks. Viruses grown in brain cells may de-

velop a special propensity for attacking the brain. A worse danger
is presented by the nerve protein. Such a brain vaccine, while
protecting man from some other disease, may produce an allergic
encephalitis—an inflammation of the brain. It doesn't happen often, but it doesn't need to, to turn everybody against a vaccine.

Then came the egg. Few developments in medical research
have been of more practical benefit to mankind than the use of
hen's eggs to produce vaccines. The technique was an important
turning-point. Hatching eggs today cost about twelve and a half
cents apiece, or $1.50 a dozen. They hatch after about three
weeks of incubation, under a hen or in an incubator. The fertile
egg is our cheapest experimental host; it has the further advantage of being free from confusing latent infections, and a large
harvest of viruses can be produced in it. A chick-type vaccine is
hazardous only to persons allergic to eggs. Few are.

The people responsible for this discovery were Dr. Ernest W.
Goodpasture and his associates in the Pathology Laboratory at
the Vanderbilt University School of Medicine, in Nashville.

This quiet, unassuming, Tennessee-bred pathologist is, at the
age of seventy-three, a serene, scholarly, silver-haired, self-sufficient but easily approachable man. He contemplates the world
through pale horn-rimmed glasses and sees himself at peace with
it. The world scarcely knows him, but it is deeply in his debt.

He was born in 1886, one of five children of Albert and Jennie
Goodpasture. They lived in an octagonal house built by his maternal grandfather, a physician, on an ancestral four hundred-acre
tobacco farm in Montgomery County, Tennessee. Dr. Stephen W.
Dawson, whose family originally came from Montgomery County,
Maryland, was a memorable figure, and undoubtedly influenced
his grandson's choice of a career. After Dr. Dawson obtained his
diploma at Jefferson Medical College in Philadelphia, he went
west in the Gold Rush of 1849, was robbed by his partner, but
eventually returned with $15,000 in gold and took over the family
farm in Tennessee.

Part of the gold went into building what had been described by
its original designer, Orson Fowler, as "The Perfect House." The
two-story, eight-sided building was surfaced with grout—a sand,
gravel, and cement plaster—and capped by a cupola and a wid-

ow's walk. One flaw in this perfect house was that it was inflammable; it burned while Ernest still was a boy.

Albert Goodpasture, Ernest's father, was a lawyer. When he was appointed clerk of the Tennessee Supreme Court, he moved his family to Nashville. Ernest was graduated from Vanderbilt in 1907, where he had worked as an assistant in the biology department, and contemplated going to medical school, for he already felt a pull toward medical research.

The Johns Hopkins Medical School recently had come into prominence as the first American equal of the great European medical centers. Essentially, the idea was to seat the medical school in a large hospital and use its charity wards and laboratories as combined instruments of instruction and investigation. When Goodpasture spoke to Nashville doctors about it, they told him: "You don't want to go there; it's too theoretical. Go some place where you can get a practical education." "That's what decided me on Johns Hopkins," Goodpasture recalls. "I already had decided that I didn't want to be a practitioner, but a medical scientist."

In Baltimore the mild young man from Tennessee presently fell under the spell of Dr. William Henry Welch (1850–1934), one of the "Big Four" doctors who made Johns Hopkins great. The others were Sir William Osler, William S. Halsted, and Howard A. Kelly.

Goodpasture, a friendly yet scrupulously reserved man, carefully refrains from telling anecdotes about his illustrious teacher—a prudent man would hardly know what to say about Welch. Known as "Popsy" among his students, Welch was an out-size personality in medicine, an imposing chunk of *homo medicus*, neckless, with a bald head, fat jowls, white mustache and goatee. He was brilliant in both bacteriology and pathology and, like all great teachers, can be measured by the impressive number of distinguished doctors who trained under him. He was a huge eater and, it is reported, paid only official respects to the germ theory of disease as far as personal tidiness went.

Welch had been trained in Berlin, in the tradition of scientific pathology established by Rudolph Virchow. Inasmuch as the

Johns Hopkins Hospital was organized around the pathology laboratory and the Medical School became an early pace-setter in
American medicine, Welch, probably more than any other single
man, set the pattern of modern laboratory medicine in this country. A few students of medicine also suspect him of being one
agent of transmission for an air of superiority commonly characterizing academic pathologists of the old school.

In the case of his student Ernest Goodpasture, the superiority
is genuine. Indeed, it is possible to make a case for Goodpasture
as perhaps the most creative research pathologist since Virchow.
The latter founded the whole science of diagnosing diseases by
studying cells in dead tissues from patients. Goodpasture founded
the science of studying living infections and their behavior without patients—or guinea pigs, mice, rabbits, or monkeys. All he
needed was a live chick embryo.

Goodpasture obtained his M.D. degree in 1912 and stayed on
under Welch as a research fellow and instructor in pathology for
three years. Caring nothing for pills or the bedside manner, he
found the pathology laboratory much to his liking. Pathology is
not a popular specialty, but it is a good place for a fellow interested in the scholarly side of medicine. A pathologist commands
respect. He is the hospital's expert witness on disease and death.
He is the specialist assigned the privilege of second-guessing the
doctors who attend patients, bearing frank witness for or against
his colleagues on every laboratory and autopsy report. Perpetually, he asks: "What is this disease? What killed the patient? This
disease? *This doctor?*"

The things a pathologist looks for in the specimens under his
microscope are patterns of disease processes in the tissues and
their cells. He often can distinguish infected cells, or cancerous
ones, from normal cells almost at a glance.

In 1915, when he was twenty-nine, Goodpasture went home
and married Sarah Catlett of Clarksville, Tennessee. He took her
to Boston, where he became an instructor in the now world-famous
Peter Bent Brigham Hospital at Harvard Medical School. Mrs.
Goodpasture, who died in 1940, bore him a daughter.

World War I—he served in the Naval Medical Corps as a lieutenant—gave Goodpasture an opportunity to witness the world-wide 1918 influenza epidemic as it first struck the naval base in Boston, to study the lungs of the first sailors who died of influenza-pneumonia, and to report, in one of his earliest studies, a peculiar membrane that obstructed the air passages. He blamed an unknown virus.

The war also made him something of a job-hopper for a time. He went to the Philippines after the war, and then returned to direct a Pittsburgh research laboratory in association with Dr. Oscar Teague, a well-known bacteriologist. Teague, who had been to Vienna to study some of the new work with viruses being done there by Dr. Benjamin Lipshutz, got Goodpasture excited about viruses. Their association was abruptly ended, however, when Teague was killed in an automobile accident within a year or two.

When Vanderbilt in 1924 offered Goodpasture a chairmanship in pathology, he accepted. He was then thirty-eight. First, however, he took a trip to Vienna and learned a few things for himself about viruses. At this time Goodpasture's main research interest was how the rabies virus, with its affinity for nerve tissues, made its way to the spinal cord and brain. He concluded that, like the herpes-simplex (cold-sore) virus, it passed along the axis cylinders, or pathways, of the nerve cells.

In 1927 a promising husband-wife team came to Vanderbilt. They were C. Eugene Woodruff, a Yale University medical graduate, and his bride, Alice M. Woodruff, who had taken her Ph.D. degree in physiology at Yale. Woodruff began training as a pathologist in Goodpasture's new pathology department in The University Hospital. The following year Alice Woodruff came into the pathology department as a research fellow, working with Goodpasture and her husband on investigations of fowlpox. After three years she resigned to become a mother, six months after publishing a report that was to raise the name of Woodruff to the virus hunters' hall of fame.

Goodpasture first set Eugene Woodruff to work on fowlpox, a disease known to chicken farmers as "sorehead" because of the ulcerous nodules that appear around the beak. Fowlpox is caused by one of a dozen animal viruses related to the virus causing small-

pox in humans. Unlike cowpox, however, it doesn't produce either
infection or cross-immunity in humans.

Eugene Woodruff's particular assignment was to study the so-
called inclusion body found in cells infected with fowlpox. Inclusion bodies had been seen many times over the years, but their
nature was poorly understood. It is now known, largely as the result of the observations of Woodruff, that an inclusion body is a
conglomeration of viruses, walled off inside the cell in which they
have multiplied. The body may sometimes be of crystalline structure, along the lines of the crystals Wendell Stanley produced. To
the Vanderbilt men they looked more like microscopic potatoes.

Woodruff did some fantastically delicate experiments, using a
microdissection needle, a fine capillary tube of glass with a sharpened end. With this instrument, also known as a micropipet, he
was able to pick a single inclusion body from an infected chicken
cell. Thence, he transplanted the inclusion body into a follicle, or
hole, left by plucking a pinfeather from a chick. Within a few
days a typical fowlpox sore appeared at this spot, demonstrating
that Woodruff was indeed dealing with the agent causing fowlpox.

Furthermore, Woodruff was able to break a single inclusion
body down and with the use of a stain, much as John Buist had
done it, show under the microscope that the inclusion consisted of
as many as twenty thousand virus particles—called "Borrel bodies" or "elementary bodies," just as the inclusion body was often
called a "Paschen body," in each case after its earlier discoverer.
Goodpasture, in fact, admired Amédée Borrel so much that he
classified all pox viruses as *Borreliota*, or "little particles of Borrel." They are not so small, as viruses go, and Goodpasture and
Woodruff had no difficulty in seeing them with an optical microscope.

Now that they had mastered fowlpox virus itself, Goodpasture
felt obliged to do something with it. As he has remarked, "Everybody was wondering why viruses couldn't be cultured." So was
he. He decided to put Alice Woodruff on this problem, among
others, when she came into his laboratory in 1928.

Laboratory animals—chickens, monkeys, mice—are messy at
best. They have diseases which the scientist does not want to

study, but which confuse his results. They have unsuspected immunities that waste his time. Even when the animal is stricken on schedule, it is not always possible to isolate the infectious agent. The bacteriologist infinitely prefers to work with a microbe that will grow in a test tube or plate in "pure culture"—that is, in a sterilized medium containing colonies of nothing but the microbe's own offspring.

There were two ways of attacking the problem of virus cultivation outside of an animal host. One was tissue cultures—the use of bits of tissue kept alive in test tubes or their equivalent. The other was to inject the virus into a fertile egg and then incubate egg and virus together. Neither was a new idea.

The first man to grow living tissues outside of the body was Dr. Ross G. Harrison of Yale University, who accomplished the feat in 1907 while at Johns Hopkins. He was able to produce an outgrowth of nerve fibers in a hanging drop of blood plasma. His technique was to place a drop of plasma on a glass slide and lay a tiny fragment of nerve tissue in its center. He then inverted the slide so the drop hung in a hollowed-out spot in a thick glass slide underneath. Harrison sealed the two slides together. The drop formed a clot when kept in an incubator at body heat. The tissue within it put out new fibers. Dr. Edna Steinhardt and her associates at Columbia University usually receive credit as the first to cultivate virus in a tissue culture, in 1913. Using Harrison's hanging-drop method and bits of cornea from the eyes of guinea pigs and rabbits, they kept cowpox virus alive for several weeks. They did not prove, however, that the virus multiplied.

Tissue culture became a lively research subject in the middle 1920's, owing in large part to Dr. Alexis Carrel, the French-American surgeon who won the 1912 Nobel Prize in medicine for discovering a method of sewing severed blood vessels together end to end. At the Rockefeller Institute for Medical Research he became, as everybody called him, the "high priest of tissue culture." As early as 1911 Carrel showed that it was possible to keep organs removed from an animal—a bit of chicken kidney, for example—alive and functioning in a good-sized glass flask, containing various vital juices and kept at body heat. Later he introduced an important modification, the so-called roller-tube method. Sealed test tubes, containing the tissue under cultivation plus a thin layer of plasma and various mineral salts, tissue extracts, and nutriment fluids, are placed horizontally in a machine that rotates in the incubator room. The tissues are alternately submerged and exposed to air as they roll along the walls of the tube. In this way, they can be kept alive and growing for months or years.

The big problem Carrel faced was bacterial contamination of his tissues. The warm, nutritious environment he established was as fine for microbes as for living tissues; the germs could rapidly destroy his tissue specimens. To maintain sterile conditions before the era of wonder drugs, Carrel developed a complicated ritual of scrubbing, gowning, and masking, such as is followed by a surgeon in preparing for an operation, and would reveal his technique to only a chosen few. His colleagues at the Rockefeller Institute joked about his "secret rites" and "tissue cult." But in 1926 Carrel did report that he had been able to culture the virus causing a cancer of chicken known as Rous sarcoma. Still, this didn't get the would-be science of virus cultivation very far.

Drs. Frederic Parker, Jr., and Robert N. Nye, working at Boston City Hospital in 1925, produced the first conclusive evidence that viruses could be passed from one tissue culture to another and made to multiply in each. In a series of eleven passages, using Harrison's method and the tissue of rabbit testicles, they increased their volume of cowpox virus by fifty-one thousand times. They also cultivated the cold-sore virus.

But the most valuable virus tissue-culture method to emerge— prior to the 1948 discovery that brought a Nobel Prize to John Enders of Harvard—was that introduced in 1928 by Dr. Hugh B. Maitland and his wife, Mary, at the University of Manchester, shortly after their marriage. (The Maitlands have one of those colorful English home addresses: Oaklands, Swann Lake, Cheadle Hulme, Cheshire.) The Maitlands simply put cowpox virus in one- or two-ounce glass flasks containing enough minced chicken kidney, chicken serum, and a mineral-salt solution to cover the bottom. They demonstrated that the virus multiplied when incubated, and boldly but incorrectly reported this feat in *Lancet* as "cultivation of vaccinia virus without tissue culture." Others later demonstrated that the tissue cells as well as the viruses did multiply; the Maitlands had not cultivated virus in a lifeless medium after all. The Maitland technique was later used in the original experiments that yielded 17D yellow-fever vaccine, and also was the jump-off point for Enders's tissue-culture discoveries.

However, the Maitlands did not solve the contamination problem—by Carrelian or other rites. The usefulness of their technique remained limited for some time to come. The only way they could keep their cultures from being overtaken by bacteria was to make transfers of the virus-infected fluid to freshly prepared flasks every third or fourth day. Except for the always accommodating cowpox—and, as it turned out, yellow fever—few viruses of any importance could be persuaded to grow under this circumstance of rapid turn-over.

Meanwhile, running parallel to these pioneer explorations of virus production *in vitro,* or under glass, were a variety of experiments seeking to exploit the embryonic growth of chicks. The fertile egg, which the hen from time to time rotates in the nest during the three-week hatching period, is nature's equivalent of a roller tube, one might say.

Nosy scientists have been cutting windows in hatching eggs and spying on the contents since the eighteenth century at least. This often has been done in the name of embryology, the science of how embryonic tissues grow and develop. The idea of putting a glass window in the hatching egg is nearly 150 years old. A nineteenth-century German scientist went on to invent an embryoscope, a cumbersome tube-like instrument that he attached to the egg. It had a glass hatch at its top. Here, he could look in, through his microscope, and watch blood circulate through the embryo. Goodpasture, commenting on its awkwardness, observed: "The embryoscope apparently did not become a very popular instrument of research, and I count it a blessing. . . ."

As time went on, one person or another performed all kinds of operations on the chick embryo, in answer to the age-old question: "What would happen if—?" Borrel seems to have been the first to use *des embryons de poulet*—chick embryos—as a host for experimental infection, though he apparently didn't publish anything about it. He left the whole matter to Dr. Constantin Levaditi, a Rumanian bacteriologist, who continued Borrel's experiments of inoculating eggs with a variety of one-celled animalcule called a *Spirillum,* responsible for a blood poisoning in chickens. In 1906 Levaditi reported that, providing the egg was fertile and contained a growing embryo, the microbe would multiply.

The next assault on the egg appears to have been that of the great tumor-virus pioneer, Dr. Peyton Rous of the Rockefeller Institute, who discovered the virus that causes a malignant tumor in chickens. In 1910 Rous and James B. Murphy took six- to sixteen-day-old hatching eggs from the incubator, cut a small window in each shell and its lining, and then put fine bits of the Rous chicken sarcoma in the plainly visible chick. Opening the eggs a week later, they found a growing tumor mass in each.

Detailed surgical techniques for operating on chick embryos without killing them were spelled out by Eliot R. Clark from the University of Missouri department of anatomy, in 1920. The object of keeping the embryo alive was to perform experimental operations on it—removing the spinal cord, heart, tail, a blood vessel, or a limb bud. Sterile surgical technique had to be maintained throughout.

Goodpasture suggested that Alice Woodruff see if she could cultivate the virus of fowlpox in a tissue culture. This should have been possible if Parker and Nye and the Maitlands were right, but—perhaps luckily—she had no luck. He then suggested that she try fertile eggs.

They could see that the egg should be an ideal place to grow viruses, in theory at least. If kept dry, clean, and uncracked, it's essentially a bacteriologically sterile medium. And the embryo inside should meet the virus's requirement of a living host.

Furthermore, Goodpasture had an idea that nobody else had given much consideration to. Different viruses not only favor different hosts but also different cells in those hosts. The pox viruses dwell mainly in the skin, where they form ulcers. So he felt that the virus should be injected at just the right place—in the ectoderm, or outermost layer of the chorio-allantois, the membrane sac that envelops the chick and provides a breathing-passage into its body. Happily, this is the first thing one comes to after cutting a half-inch window in the shell and turning back a flap of the tough shell lining.

Alice Woodruff used the Clark surgical technique, with modifications as the experiments progressed. She removed the egg from the incubator, candled it to determine fertility, and pencil-marked the location of the air sac and embryo. An egg cup was the operating-table. The window was cut with the point of a small scissors blade (others later substituted the tiny emery wheel of a dentist's drilling machine as the cutting instrument). After she inoculated the egg with the virus, she closed the window with a piece of glass fixed upon a ring of vaseline. Then she put the egg back into the incubator, keeping an eye on developments through the egg's window.

She worked in what she hoped was a completely sterile room, kept closed to prevent air currents, and did everything she could think of to avoid the chronic problem of bacterial contamination. Her room was in the University Hospital's Pathology Wing, several doors down the hall from her husband's laboratory and some distance from Goodpasture's office. Goodpasture came every day to see how she was doing, and together they would look over the infected chick embryos. For some time they saw nothing but dead embryos, usually overgrown with molds or other bacteria. In other words, simply putting in a tiny droplet of fowlpox-virus solution was enough to open the way to contamination, and this killed the unborn chick.

Alice turned to "Gene," her dexterous husband, for help. He came down the hall and helped her work out a variety of techniques for moving fowlpox virus from a soreheaded chicken to a chick embryo and meanwhile keeping it free of the annoying bacteria. The source of the virus was pox nodules on the heads of chicks. Eugene Woodruff shaved the head of a chick and bathed the surface with alcohol, then sliced off the nodule with a sterile cataract knife. After washing the nodule in a sterile solution, he cultured one fragment of it in yeast broth to see if it would produce bacteria. If not, it was suitable for injection into a hatching egg.

He also tackled the problem in other ways. One was to go back to his use of the microdissection needle in picking out single fowlpox inclusion bodies, working under a microscope. The chicken tissue around the inclusion bodies was digested away with the enzyme called trypsin. This was an incredibly painstaking approach, but Woodruff showed it was technically possible to deliver pure virus to his wife's chick embryos in this manner.

Still the reward of such efforts was nowhere in sight. Alice Woodruff was growing tired of cutting windows in eggs and, in the end, seeing nothing but dead, unborn chicks through them. Together, she and Dr. Goodpasture and sometimes her husband, too, sat in conference. Gene Woodruff was certain it was possible to accomplish the technical feat of transmission of the virus without bacterial interference, and Goodpasture agreed, for they already had done this in proving that the inclusion body was the cause of fowlpox. Goodpasture also agreed with Alice that it was pointless to go on much longer with her experiments. Perhaps the egg was not a good medium.

Then, one morning when she peeked into the window of an egg that had been incubating for about a week after she had inoculated it with the virus, she saw something different. This chick embryo was still alive, whereas the others had died. She removed the embryo from the shell and examined it. It had a swollen claw. "Could this be due to fowlpox infection?" Alice Woodruff asked herself. She went to Goodpasture and put the same question to him. As she now recalls:

"I can't forget the thrill of that moment when Dr. Goodpasture came into my lab, and we stood by the hood where the incubator was installed and I showed him this swollen claw from the inoculated embryo. . . . One might say it represented the Achilles' heel of virus resistance."

That was their first success in cultivating fowlpox virus in hatching eggs. Soon Gene Woodruff's sterile techniques brought bigger pay-offs, and the first consistent series of infections was noted in a thickening of the chorio-allantoic membrane, at the point of inoculation. Once they had established virus growth in the egg, the contamination problem was behind them, because it was possible to move pieces of this infected membrane from one egg to another and maintain "pure" virus through this serial transmission. They did not make quantitative tests for virus multiplication, as now is commonly done, but they could see they had multiplication from the fact that one minute droplet of virus solution was enough to produce an area of infection many thousands of times larger than the droplet; further, this expansion could be repeated indefinitely from egg to egg. They still had to prove they were working with the same virus they had started with—namely, that of fowlpox. But that was simple enough, both by microscopic examination and by experimental infection.

When they were satisfied that they had Borrel bodies in their infected eggs and could induce infections in adult hens with them, Goodpasture and Alice Woodruff diffidently concluded: "The preparation of non-contaminated concentrated virus in fairly large quantities is made possible."

The implications of such a statement were far-reaching if other viruses would take to hatching eggs as fowlpox did. A good source of the virus—the prime requirement in the preparation of a vaccine—would now be available.

Later Goodpasture reflected: "Even at the beginning of our experiments we were able to appreciate the great potential usefulness of a living host so easily obtained, so cheap and so uniform as the developing egg and at the same time free . . . of all those uncertain conditions which represent the response of animals that have led an independent existence. . . ."

First news of their success was published in the *American Journal of Pathology* for May 1931, in an article entitled: "The Susceptibility of the Chorio-Allantoic Membrane of Chick Embryos to the Infection with the Fowl-Pox Virus." There is one nice thing about a good scientific article: its title tells you what's in it. The authors were "Alice Miles Woodruff, Ph.D., and Ernest W. Goodpasture, M.D."

Meticulous in deciding the matter of senior and junior authorship on the basis of work done, rather than seniority in position, Goodpasture put the lady's name first, as he also had put Eugene Woodruff's name first in the inclusion-body reports. Alice Woodruff recently commented on this:

"My name should not have been first. . . . Dr. Goodpasture was over-generous in this. The work started as a result of his suggestion and continued under his expert guidance, but he did leave much planning and action to the individual initiative of his

staff. His extensive knowledge of viruses was an inspiration to us
all."

After one more report, her name disappeared from the literature because she had a baby. Now a mother of three, she hopes
that, when her children are all educated, she may someday return
to research. Eugene Woodruff's name ceased to appear in virus
research because he became interested in tuberculosis, a bacterial
disease. Since 1935 he has been pathologist and laboratory director of the Maybury Tuberculosis Sanitorium in Northville, Michigan, where the Woodruffs now live.

Alice and Eugene Woodruff look back on their work with
Goodpasture as wonderful days. "Our life, my husband's and
mine, was centered closely around the laboratory. Though we
never took time to go home for lunch, we sometimes tired of hospital diet, and used the facilities of my lab to warm up some pot
roast and cook some fresh spinach on my Bunsen burner. I don't
think we ever invited Dr. Goodpasture to partake of this menial
fare, but we did 'entertain' other members of the lab in this
way."

The news that Goodpasture's laboratory at Vanderbilt had
grown viruses in hen's eggs excited the microbiological world,
though it was to pass virtually without public notice for some
years. Somehow, this scientific attack on the unborn chick lacked
mass appeal—it may even have displeased morning-newspaper
editors who concern themselves with the fare of their breakfast-
table readers. Nevertheless, as we shall see, Ernest Goodpasture
has done more than any individual since Pasteur to bring us vaccines against viruses, even though he himself makes it clear that
vaccines were not in his mind when he turned to the problem of
cultivating viruses in the chick embryo. Indeed, he still insists:
"The contribution of my colleagues and me was in pathogenesis,"
meaning how disease develops. But this is the way the true pathologist would look at the matter.

Among the first to confirm the Goodpasture discovery that
viruses can be induced to multiply in a hatching egg was Sir
Macfarlane Burnet of Australia. A quarter of a century later he
said, in retrospect: "Nearly all the later practical advances in the

control of virus diseases of man and animals sprang from this single discovery."

Virologist Gilbert Dalldorf of the National Foundation (formerly "for Infantile Paralysis"), also looking at Goodpasture's achievement in retrospect, put it in a different way. He held that the rapid development of virology in recent years has resulted mainly from three technical advances in the 1930's. He put the chick-embryo technique first. The others, he said, were the introduction of the ultra-centrifuge in virus purification and the use of the electron microscope in virus detection.[1]

Goodpasture had his method of growing viruses; it remained for him to put it to work in immunology. A Netherlands-born, Michigan-bred medical student in his mid-twenties now joined the group, becoming so interested in what might be done with chick embryos that he dropped out of medical school to become a laboratory assistant. He was Gerritt John Buddingh. Later, Goodpasture persuaded him to finish medical school and Buddingh went on to become first a professor of bacteriology at Vanderbilt and now head of the department of microbiology at the Louisiana State University School of Medicine in New Orleans.

Within the year, Goodpasture, Alice Woodruff, and Buddingh reported that the cowpox and cold-sore viruses also could be grown in chick embryos. This was an important observation. Whereas fowlpox is a natural disease of chickens, cowpox is only slightly infectious in adult chickens and the herpes virus will not touch them at all. Yet they grew in chick embryos.

The group now foresaw the possibility of making a smallpox vaccine completely free of contaminating bacteria, and got busy at it. In 1933 Goodpasture and Buddingh reported the first success with a chick vaccine. They had obtained a three hundred-egg incubator from Sears, Roebuck, and some tried-and-true, calf-grown vaccine virus from the New York City Board of Health. In fifteen months they successfully passed this one line of virus through a series of eighty-five generations of hatching eggs. Each time, of course, the virus multiplied by millions.

They also showed—and subsequently backed up their position

[1] Gilbert Dalldorf: *Introduction to Virology* (Springfield, Ill.: Charles C. Thomas; 1955), p. 7.

with a 1,074-case study—that chick vaccine against smallpox
worked as well in human beings as calf vaccine. They pointed out
that the egg was a much purer, simpler, cheaper source of vaccine. The calf vaccine is produced, rather crudely, by shaving the
skin of calves, scratching their skin with cowpox virus, and waiting a week for lymph matter.

But it's hard to get anywhere with a product just a little better
in a field long occupied by an established success. Except in Germany and for a time in Texas, the Goodpasture chick vaccine
did not catch on. Generally, when we are vaccinated against
smallpox, we still receive calf and not chick vaccine.

One thing was cinched, however. A virus could be grown in a
hatching egg and a vaccine made from it. Goodpasture, always
the student, more interested in finding things out than applying
them, was happy to leave further vaccine-making to others and
get back to his first love, pathogenesis. Other associates soon
joined him in years of study of the process of various human infections in the chick embryo.

Notable among these persons was Dr. Katherine Anderson, a
bacteriologist who was to become the second Mrs. Goodpasture
in 1945. They and their colleagues gave diphtheria, "strep throat,"
cold sores, boils, meningitis, shingles, rabies, rabbit fever, undulant fever, plague, typhus, mumps, whooping cough, and a venereal disease to unborn chicks.

Often, they observed, the germ selected the same organ for
attack in the chick that it did in humans—rabies the brain, and
whooping cough the bronchial passages, for example. Dr. Anderson also showed that it was possible for two different viruses—
herpes and cowpox or rabies, for instance—to occupy the same
cell. A cell could hardly be more miserable.

Or an unborn chick, for that matter. Actually, it is a fairly rugged individual, capable of withstanding all manner of insults to
its integrity. According to Goodpasture:

"Chick embryos twelve days old and more sustain a variety of
severe operative treatments surprisingly well. . . . We have at
times left an egg containing a developing embryo on the laboratory desk at room temperature for two or three days with a large
window in the shell exposing the chorio-allantoic membrane,

without observing infection [or] apparent injury to the embryo."

In all, chick embryos have been found susceptible to more than thirty viruses.

Within ten years after Goodpasture's and Buddingh's 1933 preparation of the first chick vaccine, new virus vaccines began to emerge. Dr. Joseph W. Beard, now of Duke University, Dr. Ralph W. G. Wyckoff (who collaborated with Robley Williams in metal-plating viruses), and their associates at the Rockefeller Institute made a chick vaccine against horse sleeping sickness. Max Theiler, also at the Institute, perfected a yellow-fever vaccine in a tissue culture made of minced chick embryos and then switched the virus to hatching eggs for vaccine-production purposes. Dr. Thomas Francis made and tested a chick vaccine against Influenzas A and B.

Now we have chick virus vaccines against a variety of influenzas (including Asian-A), three kinds of encephalitis, Colorado tick fever, and rabies. The new and probably safer rabies vaccine developed by Dr. Hilary Koprowski is grown in duck eggs in preference to hen's eggs; as duck eggs take four weeks to hatch instead of three, they give the slow-moving rabies virus a longer time to multiply.

The triumph of the egg in immunization against rickettsial diseases such as louseborne typhus, fleaborne typhus, Rocky Mountain spotted fever, Q fever, and parrot fever extends the good work of Goodpasture well beyond the limits of true viruses.

Dr. Herald R. Cox, then of the United States Public Health Service, now of Lederle Laboratories, got busy with typhus in eggs, following development of the chick-embryo technique. Cox produced a chick vaccine that was given to millions of troops during World War II. Typhus—also known as camp, ship, famine, or jail fever—is a classic disease of war, and a big killer. Whereas epidemics struck in various parts of the world in the war years, with high death rates, there were only sixty-four mild cases and no deaths among immunized American troops. Later, Cox made a good chick vaccine against spotted fever.

The story is not yet complete. Only in penicillin and other antibiotics is there anything that compares with the unborn chick in protecting us against infectious diseases.

For thirty-one years Goodpasture was professor of pathology at Vanderbilt and from 1945 to 1950 also dean of the School of Medicine. He was due to retire in 1952, but obtained a three-year extension and did not become an emeritus professor until 1955, when he was sixty-nine. He then became director of the Department of Pathology, Armed Forces Institute of Pathology, at the huge Walter Reed Army Medical Center in Washington. He continued there nearly four years, and at this writing actually was on the point of retiring to a cottage in the hills and hollows in Williamson County, not far from Nashville.

Never much of a man for vacations, it would appear, Goodpasture holds: "I look at science as a career like fishing. If you can make a living out of it, it's a fine thing. You are making a living out of a pleasure—the satisfaction of your curiosity." In fact, Goodpasture insists he has spent his whole life having fun. "Science is a luxury," he said. "The old idea that you have to make a sacrifice is the bunk."

THEILER:
YELLOW FEVER'S
SECOND EXIT

TODAY, thanks to what has been done, yellow fever is a rare disease in humans, even in its two great natural reservoirs, the African and South American tropics. But in these places, beyond any chance of complete extinction, the virus persists in the monkeys and mosquitoes that live in the treetops.

Jungle yellow fever has been known in recent years to wipe out every howler monkey in Central America for a hundred miles around, nature having slipped up in not providing these animals with the same immunity that monkeys in Africa and South America have.

Mosquitoes in the jungle canopy carry the virus from monkey to monkey. When an unvaccinated man cuts down a tree, the mosquitoes come down with it and carry the virus to him, too. Thus, a spattering of human yellow-fever cases occur from one year to the next in the tropics. In the last year or two the disease —absent from the United States for more than a half-century—

has broken out of the Amazon River Valley and made its jaundiced way to the southern border of Mexico.

So now you read reports that yellow jack is back, or nearly so.[1] People love to call the disease that, perhaps because it evokes a connotation of impending terror and panic. A yellowing of the skin and eyeballs is characteristic of severe cases; however, the name "yellow jack" came not from jaundiced men but from the yellow quarantine flag flown to warn of the presence of infectious disease aboard ship or in port.

Most people who have yellow fever get well and become immune to it, but, in roughly one tenth of all cases—the death rate varies from five to fifteen per cent—the disease follows a malignant course and kills in four or five days. Severe yellow fever is fearfully dramatic. One striking feature is the *vomito negro,* or black vomit. This is the result of hemorrhage from erosions in the mucous membranes of the stomach, the blood being blackened by the action of gastric juices. Doctors watch for Faget's sign, named for the French physician who first noticed the curious phenomenon of a gradual slowing of the heartbeat as the fever mounts. One would expect the opposite. This isn't what kills, however. Death, if it comes, usually is owing to a functional failure of the liver or kidneys, more rarely from virus damage to the heart.

No drug will cure yellow fever (you get well or die). However, the North American who would like to make a safari into "darkest" Africa or take a trip up the Amazon has nothing to worry about if he has had yellow-fever vaccine first. As a matter of fact, the Public Health Service may not let the traveler back into the United States unless he has done so. The rule is that anyone coming from or passing through the yellow-fever zones of Africa or South or Central America must show a valid yellow-fever vaccination certificate upon entering the United States, if he's headed for any of thirteen Southern states. Such a certificate is good for six years, or twice as long as the one for smallpox.

This is one indication of what a good vaccine we have against yellow fever. It wears well. Six years is actually the minimum;

[1] Steven M. Spencer: "Yellow Jack is Back," *The Saturday Evening Post,* October 19, 1957.

protection endures far longer than that in most cases. The reason for its durability, in theory, is that some yellow-fever viruses remain alive in living cells of the body, to be periodically released and thus to stimulate new antibodies—in effect, providing a built-in booster shot. There is no proof of this, for the virus cannot be detected in an immunized host.

The Rockefeller Foundation spent $14,000,000 from 1916 to 1949 in a majestic effort to help the yellow-fever countries wipe out this disease. The Foundation, established in 1913, went into yellow-fever control with the idea that the whole business could be cleaned up in a few years. It undertook its research program, culminating in the vaccine, only after discovering that scientists didn't know as much about yellow fever as they had thought.

The immediate impetus for the Rockefeller program was the opening of the Panama Canal in 1914. Yellow fever, a New World disease, had shown a liking for travel, having migrated from the tropics to almost every Atlantic shipping-port. It was two or three centuries before anybody knew that this was due to a fondness of *Aedes aegypti* for man. This mosquito bred in his rain barrels and came into the house at night to bite him.

Unfortunately, the yellow-fever virus utilized this mosquito as a common carrier and, for a long time it seemed, used this one species of mosquito alone. As far as is known, the virus never destroys the mosquito, but depends on its bite to get from one bloodstream to another. Sailing-ships carried the mosquito larvae throughout the Western Hemisphere in their water casks.

With the new short route to the Far East through yellow-fever country, it appeared only a matter of time before yellow fever would be killing Asians by the hundreds of thousands, as smallpox already was doing in India.

The Rockefeller Foundation took its cue from the work of Major Walter Reed and General William C. Gorgas, and hired the latter to head its own Yellow Fever Commission. History books will tell you that Reed, Gorgas, and their colleagues in the Army's Yellow Fever Commission (appointed by Surgeon General George M. Sternberg, who discovered the virus-neutralization test) conquered yellow fever by fighting mosquitoes and thus made possible the completion of the Panama Canal. The

French had started construction in 1882, but yellow fever and malaria killed their workers. The United States took the job over in 1904, after Gorgas made the Canal Zone livable.

The story is true as far as it goes. These pioneer virus hunters did conquer urban yellow fever, but they knew nothing of the jungle type. Before 1900, doctors had laughed at the mosquito-bite theory of Dr. Carlos J. Finlay of Havana. When Major Reed went to Cuba that year, he took Finlay seriously and proved three things. *Aedes aegypti* was the culprit there. The epidemics spread in a man-mosquito-man cycle. All you had to do to wipe out the mosquito and the yellow fever it carried was to dry up household breeding-places.

It made a colorful story, because of the human experiments Reed conducted. Dr. Jesse W. Lazear, a member of the Commission, died of yellow fever, and Dr. James Carroll was at death's door, but recovered. Reed died in 1902 of appendicitis, an equally dangerous infection in those days.

The last yellow-fever epidemic in the continental United States was in New Orleans. This city had been yellow-jacked to death for three centuries. In 1905 there were 3,384 cases and 443 deaths, nearly all of them in New Orleans's "old town," a pestilential breeding-ground of long standing.

The Walter Reed story, one might say, depicted yellow fever's first exit.

Our main interest is in the second exit, thirty-odd years later. The second exit of this disease of the Torrid Zone was ushered from an outpost in the North Temperate Zone at 66th Street and the East River, in New York, by a Westchester County resident of Swiss parentage and South African birth who holds a British medical license and Sweden's highest scientific honor, who likes Scotch whisky and American baseball and regards himself as a world citizen.

Dr. Max Theiler, a five-foot-two-inch, 130-pound giant of virus research, is the Westchesterite in question. In 1937 he discovered what fellow microbiologists appraise as the best virus vaccine. Actually, Theiler (pronounced "Tyler") did the basic work on two vaccines against yellow fever—the so-called French-strain, or Dakar, mouse vaccine; and the 17D chick vaccine. The Dakar is the more potent, but the 17D is safer and, at the same time, a reliable one-shot protection in ninety-five of a hundred cases, perhaps more. It is not probable that anyone will ever surpass this vaccine made from live but attenuated virus.

In any event, one Theiler vaccine or another has been used in an estimated hundred million persons of all races, colors, and creeds. The general result has made Theiler a kind of light-hearted Albert Schweitzer who never left home (home being Hastings-on-Hudson).

Theiler, now sixty years old, is the director of the Virus Laboratories of the Rockefeller Foundation's Division of Biological and Medical Research. This Division shares buildings and facilities with the great Rockefeller Institute for Medical Research, at 66th Street and the East River. The one is not otherwise a part of the other, though their philanthropic and financial parentage is the same.

Dr. Theiler's laboratory is presently engaged in "pure fact-finding," as he puts it, on the nature and behavior of approximately seventy other insect-borne viruses, some of them with exotic names such as Rift Valley fever, West Nile fever, and Bwamba fever. Some may be identified as responsible for fevers presently listed as PUO—pyrexia of unknown origin. Others may continue as "orphan viruses," unconnected with any known disease.

Theiler is something of an oddity among modern, go-getting virologists. He would far rather read than write—many researchers publish as much in a year as he does in a decade—and would rather stay home than attend a scientific meeting. In short, he would rather not waste his time on minor or irrelevant observations and social pleasantries.

One of the stranger aspects of Theiler is that he has no academic degree as a doctor of medicine or science. However, his colleagues call him "Doctor" and he is too polite to object. It is true he did go to college, in Capetown, and to medical school in London. He is licensed as a physician by the Royal College of Physicians in London, is a member of the Royal College of Surgeons, and does hold a diploma from the London School of Tropical Medicine and Hygiene.

But, academically, he doesn't have so much as an A.B. This is remarkable in these days of accreditation and certification of everybody from baton twirlers to proctologists. Theiler could be the prototype the onetime dean of Yale Medical School, Dr. Milton C. Winternitz, had in mind when he remarked: "We ought to give them all an A.B. at birth, a Ph.D. at puberty and then teach them something." Yet this astute observation doesn't quite fit Max Theiler, whose own opinion is "You can't educate a person; you can only create an environment in which he can educate himself."

A superficial inspection of Theiler's environment finds him still hard at work educating himself. The central feature in his rather plain office, amid the laboratories on the fifth floor of the Theobald Smith Building, is a long worktable. When the discoverer of yellow-fever vaccine—a tiny man with an angular face, strong nose, dark-brown eyes, uncontrolled, faded brown hair, and a fine profile—sits down to think—and perhaps write a little—he has at hand a good supply of well-sharpened pencils, a pad of ruled paper, a fountain-pen set, four metal ashtrays vaguely shaped like hollyhocks, a pack of Chesterfields (regular), and a Zippo lighter.

There's an artless warmth about Theiler that surprises and pleases his visitors, as for example when he mentions that he for a time was known to fellow commuters from Hastings-on-Hudson as The Man Who Lives Next Door to Alvin Dark. Dark was then a Giant baseball-player and, Theiler emphasizes, a good neighbor. Presently, we gather, Theiler became known on the station platform as the Nobel Prize Winner Who Lives Next Door to Alvin Dark.

The one thing Theiler does have that most scholars do not is a Nobel Prize in physiology and medicine. He won the $32,000 prize singly and unshared in 1951. On this occasion he got out the grammar-school report cards his dead mother had so carefully saved. He had done best in English and history, but not too well in anything and worst of all in Latin. There didn't seem to be anything here that would predict a Nobel laureate.

This startling evidence that one doesn't necessarily need a Phi Beta Kappa key and a brace of degrees to be intelligent and well educated may come as a source of hope and inspiration for some persons, as well as of dismay for degree holders. It even bothers Theiler a little. The man who, when asked by a reporter what he was going to do with his Nobel Prize money, replied: "Buy a case of Scotch and watch the Dodgers" occasionally displays genuine alarm that his whimsical side will somehow disgrace unbending colleagues. Theiler appraises himself in this way:

"Basically, I look upon myself primarily as a very serious student who likes a few of the frills of life. I would have liked to have lived at the time of the Renaissance. In those days it was still possible for an individual to be thoroughly familiar with all spheres of learning. This is impossible nowadays."

Long residence in Westchester County makes Theiler eminently respectable, in any event. He has lived there twenty-nine years with his wife, Lillian Graham Theiler, Boston-bred and formerly a laboratory technician, whom he married in 1928, and his daughter, Elizabeth, a Radcliffe College student. A son was killed in an automobile accident at the age of eight.

To anyone reviewing his life, excepting possibly Theiler himself, it seems logical enough that he wound up as an internationally famous scientist. He was raised in an atmosphere of bacteriological laboratory research and field studies.

Theiler was born in 1899 on a farm near Pretoria, in what was then the South African Republic and is now the Union of South Africa. He was the youngest of the four children of Sir Arnold Theiler, who had come with his wife, Emma, from Switzerland, taken a post as state veterinary bacteriologist, and had risen to be director of the Union's veterinary services to farmers.

Sir Arnold was among the earliest to take an interest in filterable viruses. He discovered a virus causing horse sickness, a deadly disease transmitted by a bloodsucking fly.

The elder Theiler was not only a brilliant man but also an exacting one. His stern tactics evoked a strong desire in little Max to leave home, become independent, and be as unlike his father as possible. Max went to public school—in the American sense— and had no difficulty (except with Latin), but loved to go off by himself, roam the fields, and collect insects.

His father did stimulate his curiosity by giving him a compound microscope when he was twelve. Max became familiar with his father's large laboratory, but didn't spend much time in it. He was a little afraid of the man.

Entering the University of Capetown at eighteen, he took a two-year pre-medical course being offered for the first time. To become a physician, he would have to go overseas to finish his education; this was an inviting prospect. He wanted to go to London, become a general practitioner, and return to South Africa not as a bacteriologist but as a doctor of medicine.

Sir Arnold lectured his son about applying himself in mathematics, chemistry, and physics, and thus acquiring a sound basic education. Theiler exposed himself to the grind courses just enough so that he could hold his father to his promise to send him to the University of London.

In 1919, immediately after World War I, the youth made the long voyage that was to deprive South Africa of his talents. He received a setback, however. The University wouldn't recognize his two years of pre-med at Capetown. Rather than start over, he chose to prepare for a medical licensing examination by taking a practical course in one of London's teaching hospitals—St. Thomas. "I didn't learn anything, and I decided I wasn't cut out to be a doctor" is the way Theiler summarizes his four years in the hospital, spent mostly in examining and attending patients.

He found the wards rather depressing. Most of the patients had typhoid fever, nephritis, or tuberculosis. "There was almost nothing the doctor could do for them then, and to me all this pill-giving was hogwash," recalls Theiler. Internal medicine then meant making a correct diagnosis and letting nature take its course. Surgery was "too mechanical."

"I went through medical school doing a minimum amount of work, and taking in a maximum number of theaters and art galleries," he says. "I read Shaw, Wells, Chesterton, and Ibsen. It was a gay life."

The gaiety was suitably enhanced by a monthly allowance of twenty pounds from his father. In London, Theiler learned not only to enjoy life but also to know his father. Sir Arnold came to visit him; they did the beer halls and restaurants together, and went to Switzerland on vacations.

This new side of the "old man," as Theiler calls his father in the back-country way, without disrespect, delighted Theiler. Sir Arnold had given up smoking and drinking to set his children a good example, he said. When he found it did no good, he told his son: "Damn it, why shouldn't I enjoy life?"

When he finished his medical schooling, Theiler couldn't have a medical degree. But he could, as was customary, take the examination to become a licensed practitioner. He did so, and also took a four-month course offered by the London School of Tropical Medicine and Hygiene.

This was a decisive move. He chanced to pick up a slender little book called *Infection and Resistance* by the great American bacteriologist Dr. Hans Zinsser, then at Columbia. Zinsser, the man who later wrote *Rats, Lice and History*, was imaginative and stimulating. "My gosh, this is for me—this is *science*" is the way Theiler reconstructs his reaction.

Also, Theiler found himself no longer among callow medical students but doctors of all ages. One man who sat next to him in class, and who walked with him to the laboratory, particularly impressed him. He was Dr. Oscar Teague, the American bacteriologist who first interested Goodpasture in viruses. They listened to lectures on African sleeping sickness, yaws, malaria, and yellow fever together. One day Teague asked:

"How would you like to have a job at Harvard Medical School?"

"Sure, fine," said Theiler agreeably. He had barely heard of Harvard at that time.

Teague explained that the School of Tropical Medicine at Harvard had asked him to keep an eye out for a likely young assistant for one of the professors. Theiler got the appointment and came to the United States in 1922, when he was twenty-three. He has been here ever since, not as a citizen, oddly enough, but as a permanent resident. He explains that he has no intention of going back to South Africa—"I am not a nationalist"—but that he never applied for American citizenship "due to inertia." He finds his status handicapping only when he leaves the country, as he has several times. He must apply for a re-entry permit. Otherwise, "nationality never has played a part in my life. I find congenial people everywhere."

With a British colonial upbringing, Theiler found only one

thing disturbing about life in America, he says. This is the general American disrespect for laws—such as Prohibition. It amazed him that we should have a law against the manufacture, sale, and transportation of intoxicating liquors and disobey it.

Happily, he found that there was no law against home-brew. In fact, the malt could be legally purchased. In his eight years in Boston, Theiler found several occasions to make beer for home consumption, and to exchange recipes with the delightful Dr. Zinsser, who had come on to Harvard. It was a puzzling experience, but not an unlawful or unhappy one, he found.

In the meantime, Theiler settled down to a career as a research bacteriologist, under Dr. Andrew W. Sellards, associate professor of tropical medicine. Our young maverick was a long, long way from pill-pushing now.

Within a short time Theiler and his chief found themselves in the middle of the big debate then going on regarding the cause of yellow fever, and it fell to them to help straighten the issue out.

An Italian named Giuseppe Sanarelli was the first to specify a cause of yellow fever. It was a bacterium, he said in 1897. Walter Reed studied the question and dismissed Sanarelli's microbe as a secondary invader. At the suggestion of the great Johns Hopkins pathologist Dr. William H. Welch, Reed and Carroll looked for a filterable virus. In 1901 they found one by injecting clear, filtered serum from yellow-fever patients into three volunteers; two came down with the disease. Reed called it an ultra-microscopic organism, as postulated by Pasteur. It was the first virus to be isolated as the cause of a human disease.

Many other able bacteriologists confirmed this finding, but, for reasons still not clear, the evidence was not acceptable to Dr. Hideyo Noguchi, a Rockefeller Institute bacteriologist of Japanese descent, and a historic example of both the physical and intellectual perils of being a scientific investigator. In 1919, while working in Guayaquil, Ecuador, Noguchi found what he believed was the cause of yellow fever. His bacterium, taken from patients, produced something in guinea pigs resembling yellow fever. Noguchi called it *Leptospira icteroides,* meaning a slender coil causing jaundice.

Theiler refuted the greatly mistaken Noguchi. This young fellow was heard from for the first time in 1926, when he was twenty-seven. Theiler and Sellards reported having studied *Leptospira icteroides* and found it to be nothing more or less than *Leptospira icterohaemorrhagiae*, the already discovered cause of Weil's disease, or spirochetal jaundice—not related to yellow fever at all.

Meanwhile, the Rockefeller Yellow Fever Commission had been investigating the first reports that yellow fever was native to central Africa as well as tropical America. There was no sign of Noguchi's microbe in Africa. But in 1927 came news from a group of Rockefeller scientists working on the Gold Coast—news that was both good and bad.

In Accra, Dr. A. H. Mahaffy had drawn blood—in the laboratory sense—from a black-skinned, fez-wearing, twenty-eight-year-old black African named Asibi, mildly sick with yellow fever. Dr. Adrian Stokes and his associates injected the blood into African and South American monkeys without much luck. Then they tried a Rhesus monkey from India, a country that has no yellow fever. Mr. Rhesus became critically ill.

Now, for the first time, yellow-fever workers had an experimental animal! Soon they were passing yellow fever around from monkey to monkey. They proved conclusively that the disease was caused by a virus. It would pass through a bacteria-tight filter. It could not be cultivated. Yet it could be transmitted serially. What else could it be?

This was a setback for Noguchi. It was also a setback, in one way, for the Rockefeller Foundation. The yellow-fever problem was getting bigger. Many African monkeys had antibodies against the disease—and so did African man. It was not an urban disease exclusively, and *Aedes aegypti* was not its exclusive transportation agent. How do you wipe the mosquitoes out of a thousand miles of jungle? The more Rockefeller scientists learned, the more their hope of ridding the world of yellow fever receded. The disease was a built-in feature of life in the jungle.

And now yellow fever served tragic notice, as it had on Lazear, Carroll, and others, that it was no laboratory plaything. It killed five scientists in less than two years' time, all from accidental infections.

The much-liked British pathologist Dr. Stokes, forty years old, was the first in this group to go. He fell victim to the Asibi virus and black vomit and died in Lagos, Nigeria, in September 1927. Apparently, infected monkey blood had got on or under his skin —the virus, it has been shown, can make its way through unbroken skin.

A native laboratory boy got yellow fever accidentally the following February, but recovered. The disease typically runs a milder course in the African Negro.

Prophetically stating: "I will win down there or die," Noguchi went down to Accra from New York. A handsome, dark, curly-haired man, then fifty-two, Noguchi looked for his leptospira bacterium in this jungle yellow fever. But it wasn't leptospira that infected him in May 1928. It was the virus of yellow fever.

At the end, "funny Noguchi," as he called himself, now aware that he was dying of yellow fever but ignorant of how he had become infected, seemed to find insight at last. "I don't understand"—these were his last words.

Microbiologists often speak of Noguchi. They say he "almost won the Nobel Prize for a mistake." He was considered for it at one time. Some have said that Noguchi, sensing that the evidence was running against him, went down to Africa and committed a bacteriologist's hara-kiri. His tragic story has a fascination for scientific investigators, who know how easy it is to err, and how deep runs a scientist's wish for recognition. Perhaps some unconsciously feel: "There, but for the laws of probability, go I."

Next to go was a Gold Coast government pathologist, Dr. William A. Young, a man of forty. He died of yellow fever at Accra a few months after Noguchi. Dr. Paul Lewis of the Rockefeller Institute went to Bahia, Brazil, to try to repeat Noguchi's findings; he died at fifty. The fifth was Dr. Theodore H. Hayne, a thirty-two-year-old entomologist who in 1930 died of a mosquito bite in Lagos, Nigeria, the place where Noguchi apparently acquired his infection.

These scientist sacrifices were among thirty-two laboratory infections with yellow fever enumerated in a 1931 report by Dr.

George Packer Berry, now dean of Harvard Medical School. The other twenty-seven laboratory workers all recovered.

Following the big break-through in infecting monkeys at Accra, Sellards went to Africa for Harvard in 1928, and brought back the so-called French strain from a Syrian patient in Dakar. He carried the virus in frozen monkey liver.

Sellards and Theiler had a difference of opinion about what to do with the monkey livers. Sellards, still very much the Old Bacteriologist, wanted to try to cultivate the yellow-fever organism—whatever it was—in a lifeless medium. He agreed with Noguchi about the cause being a bacterium, but thought that Noguchi just hadn't found the right one.

Theiler, in contrast, believed that the cause of yellow fever was certainly a filterable virus and that it never would be cultivated in a lifeless medium. He was right, but being right isn't necessarily the best way for a young assistant to get on with his chief. Nonetheless, Sellards let Theiler do what he wanted.

Theiler reasoned like this: the monkey, as an experimental animal in yellow fever, was a great discovery, but not too useful a one. Karl Landsteiner had established poliomyelitis in the brains of monkeys twenty years before, but this hadn't advanced polio knowledge much. A Rhesus monkey cost seven dollars, almost a day's pay for a young scientist in those days (at sixty-five dollars, the same monkey today costs considerably more than a day's pay for a young scientist). On the other hand, you could breed white mice for a few cents apiece.

Theiler noted that others had tried to inject a yellow-fever patient's blood under a mouse's skin or into its abdomen, without results. He likewise knew that Pasteur and Roux had had no luck with rabies in a laboratory host until they put it in the brain— first in dogs and later in rabbits.

So why not try yellow fever in the brain of a white mouse? Theiler delicately injected a solution containing fine bits of infected monkey liver into the heads of mice. In several days they were all dead. Autopsying his dead mice, Theiler found no sign of yellow fever—no liver or abdominal organ damage at all. But their brain tissues were highly inflamed. The virus was neurotropic—in other words, had some affinity for nerve cells.

Theiler was lucky—to have made a discovery that proved a turning-point in the prevention of yellow fever, and to survive the case of yellow fever he soon acquired from one of his mice. This occurred in June 1929, while Paul Lewis was dying in Brazil. Fortunately, Theiler—he was Case No. 17 in Dr. Berry's list of thirty-two laboratory infections—had a mouse-sized case of the French strain of yellow fever. For him, it was about the same as a bout with Asian influenza—fever, bed rest for two or three days, and then back to work, a little weak but willing.

The happiest part, as blood examinations later revealed, was that Max Theiler was now immune to yellow fever. What had happened, unintentionally, was that he had made himself the first recipient of the first of two kinds of yellow-fever vaccine he was to discover.

The thing was this, thought Theiler: "When you give a mouse yellow fever, he gets not jaundice but encephalitis, not a fatal bellyache but a fatal headache."

What could you make of that? You could make a report in *Science*, for one thing. He did so, in 1930. In it he laid the foundations for his momentous work to come. You could pass yellow fever from monkey to mouse. In a mouse it was an inflammation of the brain, purely and simply. And you could pass the disease from mouse to mouse and back to monkeys, and in them it became yellow fever again. It was unbelievable.

The thirty-one-year-old South African had his neck way out. He and Lillian, his lab-technician bride of two years, who helped him write his paper, knew it. Sellards said that he wanted no part of such nonsense—probably due to some slip-up and unknown contamination. The mighty medical faculty of Harvard, bristling with great names, neither knew nor cared what young Theiler was doing. As for bacteriologists who read his articles, "Everybody attacked this new concept," Theiler recalls. "There was harsh criticism."

But Theiler's evidence, a little sketchy at first, accumulated fast. That's the thing about mice: you can use a lot of them and develop a series of experiments promptly. Theiler found that yellow-fever virus introduced in mice and passed from the brain of one to another became more virulent for mice, after a series of passages, but less so for monkeys. Pretty soon the relative virulence became fixed, or stabilized.

Now Theiler had a virus that would uniformly kill a mouse with encephalitis if injected into the brain, but would barely give a monkey a fever if injected into his body, in contrast to a strain taken from nature. This fit Pasteur's concept of an attenuated virus. Within a year Theiler was in a position to talk back to the doubters. He developed a "mouse protection test."

Theiler knew all about the Sternberg neutralization test—the backbone of virus immunology. He mixed his virus with immune serum from a patient or an animal that had recovered from yellow fever, and then injected it into a mouse. If the animal presently keeled over, it meant the virus did not match up with yellow-fever antibodies. If the animal lived, it would indicate that the antibodies in the immune serum neutralized the virus and therefore that virus and antibodies were related to the same disease—yellow fever.

Theiler obtained immune serum from ten laboratory workers who had recovered from yellow fever. In all cases, the serum neutralized the virus and protected his mice, whereas serum from persons who'd never had yellow fever did not. Let the critics talk now! What he had put into mouse brains and passed from mouse to mouse *was* yellow-fever virus, surely enough.

A scientist doesn't have to prove himself right in major claims more than once or twice in his whole life to receive general acclaim. One thing that came of Theiler's discovery was the offer of a job in New York. The Rockefeller Foundation International Health Division, forerunner of the present Biological and Medical Research Division, had opened a yellow-fever laboratory, under the direction of Dr. Wilber A. Sawyer, for the express purpose of convincing the unconvinced that African and South American yellow fever were one and the same virus disease. Here was young Max Theiler with the means of doing it.

Theiler already had concluded that he hadn't much future at Harvard. In eight years he had risen from assistant to instructor, at $3,000 a year. There was still no professorship in sight.

Sawyer offered Theiler $6,000 a year, and Harvard lost a future Nobel Prize winner, right at the time he was getting ready to do his most important work. Theiler's findings up to that moment, in 1930, were of great importance to the Rockefeller program in two ways.

His mouse protection test made it possible to launch a world-wide survey of the distribution of yellow fever, for one thing. Take a sample of the people's antibodies in any locality. If they neutralize the mouse virus, yellow fever has passed that way— and may still be there. As time went on, these findings cleared the air and made it possible to bring about a united front in the fight against yellow fever, jungle and urban, African and South American.

Secondly, Sawyer used Theiler's mouse-adapted French strain to put a stop to laboratory infections. Sawyer is sometimes held to have developed the first yellow-fever vaccine, though the credit unquestionably belongs to Theiler. What Sawyer did, actually, was step Theiler's mouse-protection test up to a human level. He and his associates mixed the Theiler-tamed virus with human immune serum and inoculated ten laboratory workers who thus far had escaped yellow fever. It worked. Seemingly, the immune serum neutralized much, but not all, of the virus, permitting it to produce antibodies but no alarming reactions. In view of what was to come, Sawyer might have knocked on wood.

The measure did mark the end of laboratory infections, but Theiler didn't approve of it. Nor did he approve when the French government went ahead in 1934 to develop his mouse-adapted French strain into what is now known as the Dakar scratch vaccine.

The French strain is highly neurotropic in mouse-brain cells, where it produces encephalitis. It does the same thing in a monkey's brain, if injected there. Put under the skin, however, it doesn't hurt brain or liver, and in a week or so, monkeys are solidly immune, no matter how virulent a dose they receive.

This knowledge was enough for the French, who had a huge native population on their hands and now realized that there was yellow fever in the treetops. Occasionally there were outbreaks in native towns. Within a few years the French had a huge vaccination program rolling, using a combined yellow-fever and smallpox vaccine that can be quickly scratched into the skin. This "scratch vaccine" is simply made of ground-up, infected mouse brains, combined with cowpox virus.

Theiler always has considered the method dangerous. Indeed, several human deaths have been attributed to the scratch vaccine. The French, however, rely on the facts that the scratch infection is superficial and that yellow-fever infections don't seem to hit the African Negro as hard as the white man.

From 1939 to 1953, fifty-six million persons received this crude but effective vaccine, made at Dakar. According to a World Health Organization report, "Human yellow fever has practically disappeared from the territories in which vaccination was performed."

Thus, the people of west and equatorial Africa have vastly benefited from a virus originally exported to Harvard and then imported again after a South African had passed it through some white mice!

The French health authorities report severe reactions as "very rare. . . . Fatal cases have been exceptional." Quite a number have mild reactions—fever, headache, and stiffness—but *c'est la guerre.*

In 1934 Theiler set out on an intensive program of trying to produce a safer strain for vaccine purposes. One alternative already had been eliminated, and that was the production of a killed-virus vaccine. It's no problem to kill the yellow-fever virus. You could do that almost by looking at it—if you could see it. One of the smallest of the viruses, in a class with those of poliomyelitis and encephalitis, the yellow-fever virus has not been examined under the electron microscope at this writing, nor has it been crystallized. It never has been seen. Passage through filters with pores of various diameters has established its general size—from seventeen to twenty-five millimicrons. This is one millionth of an inch or less.

Its students call the yellow-fever virus "labile," meaning it is unstable. Strangely enough for a virus that makes its home in the tropics, it can't stand much heat. And it's so sensitive to chemicals that you can kill it with salt water. Alive and virulent, the virus can outrun the susceptible body's defenses faster than the body can produce heat, salt water, or antibodies, however. When killed and injected as a vaccine, dead yellow-fever virus won't stimulate antibodies.

Theiler wanted to work with the virus in some other medium besides the living mouse brain, in the hope that he might get rid of the neurotropism and produce a mild but living virus resembling Jenner's cowpox virus. Fundamentally, and with only a few exceptions (such as in poliomyelitis and influenza), what the virologist wants in a vaccine is a live virus that will produce lasting antibodies without signs of the disease itself and without danger of toxic effects. That's the ideal.

Theiler and his Rockefeller laboratory associates—Wray Lloyd, Nelda I. Ricci, and Hugh H. Smith—turned from monkeys and mice to the tissue culture of the virus.

The cultivation of virus in living tissues kept alive in a glass flask was then in a primitive state, as compared to modern methods, but the British husband-wife team Hugh and Mary Maitland had showed it could be done with cowpox, if one subcultured the virus from flask to flask every three or four days and thus stayed a jump ahead of bacterial contamination.

Suiting the Maitland technique to their own needs, the Theiler group found that yellow-fever virus also would multiply in tissue cultures. They performed seventeen different series of tissue-culture experiments.

In the seventeenth series Theiler decided to work with a wild strain of Asibi virus so virulent it would kill monkeys one hundred per cent of the time if merely injected under their skins. It attacked their livers, mainly.

It was a rugged virus and, they found, willing to multiply in all kinds of tissue cultures—mouse brain, mouse embryo, mouse testicle, chick embryo, and other tissues. The Theiler team passed this virus from culture to culture hundreds of times. They kept it alive and in continuous cultivation for more than three years without an intervening passage through a living host.

The Asibi flasks were labeled "17" with letters added at random to indicate the particular kind of tissue used in a given series. In the matter of the 17D strain, where there was a pay-off equal to any discovery in the history of laboratory research, students of yellow fever-research find an indication of Theiler's carefree spirit; they search his writings in vain for the A-B-C-and-D explanation of what happened in "17" flasks up to and including "D."

When pressed on this question, Theiler confesses that he did not arrive at the D designation in any systematic way, hence the confusion in the minds of people who expect system from their scientists. But if the alphabetical details mystify, the outcome is brilliantly clear, from A through Z.

Theiler and Smith, unimpressed by anything that had emerged from their experiments thus far, took an Asibi virus line that had been multiplying in mouse-embryo tissue and put it into cultures made of whole chicken embryo minced up. The virus multiplied, as before.

After fifty-eight uneventful passages in these chick-embryo cultures, they subdivided this particular line into three. They continued the whole-chick cultures, later designating them as 17D(WC). They started a second line of Asibi virus in chick-embryo brain alone, and this became 17D(CEB). Their third line of attack involved Asibi virus in chick embryo *with the brain and spinal cord removed.*

Generally speaking, then, the 17D series concerned Asibi virus grown in a variety of chick-embryo tissue cultures. But they also had this third line of cultures, using the Asibi strain in chick-embryo tissue with the brain and spinal cord removed—a sort of 17D-minus-CNS (for central nervous system), one might call it. But this line became known—in fact, famous—simply as 17D.

There was some point to the refinement of experiments in this way. The passage of the Asibi virus through chick-embryo tissues had produced an attenuation, or weakening, of its capacity for destroying the liver of a live monkey, but it still gave a monkey a rough time when injected directly into his brain. They were interested in seeing what influence the presence or absence of the brain and spinal cord might have on the virus.

Theiler and Smith continued the brainless, spineless chick embryo through another 118 subcultures, or a total of 176 since they first introduced the Asibi virus into chick-embryo tissue cultures. From time to time they tested the pathogenicity, or "wallop," of their virus. For example, in subculture No. 89 the virus killed three out of three monkeys receiving injections in the brain. That was in January 1935.

The routine continued—a subculture every third or fourth day, as a rule. In April 1936 they came to No. 176 and decided to make two more monkey tests. This time, they were pleased to see, both animals lived. Furthermore, the animals subsequently proved to be immune when challenged with the highly lethal wild Asibi virus.

"From this," remarks Theiler, "it is quite apparent that we had the desired mutant in our hands for quite a long time, although we were not aware of it. The fact of the matter is that we were more interested in other things at the time."

In October 1936 they found the opportunity to retrace their steps as far as they could. At irregular intervals they had dried samples of their various cultures and had stored them. Following No. 89, still lethal, the next one that they had saved was No. 114. Testing this one in the brains of monkeys, they found that all four monkeys lived!

All four were found to have enough virus circulating in their blood on the second or third day to kill a mouse, and yet one month later all were well and completely immune to the wild Asibi virus. One of the four had a little fever, that was all! The virus didn't bother their livers either.

When the two scientists tested this 17D virus in the brains of mice, they found that the mice took longer to die. As Theiler and Smith would report in the *Journal of Experimental Medicine,* six mice died from Culture No. 176 in an average of 9.5 days, whereas the average had been 7 days with Culture No. 114. This gain of 2.5 days looked big to them. It meant appreciably less neurotropism.

Theiler assumed that the removal of the brain and spinal-cord tissue from the chick tissue culture had turned the trick—"in all probability," he said. But Theiler is by nature a skeptic; he trusts people but not their facts—not even his own.

As soon as he had the time, he repeated his tedious serial experiments, using chick embryo with brain and spinal cord removed. But there was no loss of neurotropism this time. This was perplexing, though quite characteristic of the inexactness of biological research. What had seemed a rational cause-and-effect relationship proved to be none. Theiler was left with an effect lacking any cause, at least of a kind he could produce at will. "There is no explanation," he said.

His statement was truly that of a humble man. He exhibited no need whatsoever to seek any theoretical explanation of his observation that his virus had changed character. What seemed to be the case, as we might interpret it, was that an accident of nature had taken place in his laboratory—a spontaneous mutation, the emergence of a new breed. Natural evolution had occurred—so it appeared—in a bare-looking laboratory in a big building overlooking the East River. It was some time in the winter of 1935–6.

Who could say just when, on what day, at what hour, or in what tissue culture? Not Theiler. Not an assistant named Smith. It occurred somewhere between the 89th and 114th passage of the virus, some time perhaps within a period of three or four months. That is as close as we can pinpoint it. So we cannot go back and look at the Weather Bureau records and establish what kind of a day it was—whether the barometer was falling or there was rain on the windowpane or a touch of spring in the air. Nature, in her greatest moments, seems to elude her stage manager.

But there was a mutation in one of Max Theiler's Maitland-type flasks—it surely must have been a mutation and must have been there, in that brainless, spineless juice of an unborn chick.

In November 1936, Theiler, Smith, and Lloyd tried the 17D virus on themselves, and on Dr. Thomas Francis, Jr., then at the Rockefeller Institute Hospital and also having some luck with an influenza virus. All were already immune, from accidental infection with yellow fever or from the Sawyer vaccine. But 17D did raise their antibody level, as shown by comparing the virus-neutralizing power of their blood before vaccination and a few weeks afterwards.

Next they tried 17D on eight non-immune persons, from twelve to forty-five years old. After a few days five developed slight temperatures, headaches, and backaches, but these quickly passed. Two weeks later they had good antibodies against yellow fever.

Now Theiler and Smith were ready to report, in March 1937, that they had produced an attenuated virus, similar to Jenner's cowpox and Pasteur's fixed rabies virus. It was "an efficient immunizing agent," and they recommended it for "more extensive trial."

All that remained to be done to put 17D vaccine into shape for mass production was to transfer it from the chick tissue culture to the hatching egg itself, a much handier instrument for assembly-line methods. This Theiler was able to do, using Goodpasture's technique.

The 17D vaccine was field-tested in Brazil from 1937 to 1940. Certain serious bugs had to be overcome. For example, one subcultured line of 17D varied for some unknown reason and exhibited neurotropism; it produced several cases of encephalitis in vaccinated persons. One child died. Another batch failed to produce immunity. The troublemakers were eliminated.

While 17D wasn't as strong an antibody producer as the French strain, it conferred immunity on most people and proved much safer, especially for sensitive white people. It became the standard yellow-fever vaccine in South America and everywhere in the world except Africa.

From 1940 to 1947 the Rockefeller Foundation produced 28,104,420 doses of 17D vaccine at a cost of 2.2 cents per dose. The Foundation gave it all away free, to thirty-three different tropical countries or agencies, including the United States Army and Navy.

It was a wonderful demonstration of good-neighborliness. The Foundation wound up its yellow-fever program in 1949 in the knowledge that, thanks to its efforts, nobody need suffer from yellow fever again. Confirmation came in 1951 when the Caroline Institute of Medicine and Surgery, administrator of the Nobel Prize in medicine, made the award to Max Theiler not on the basis of the originality of his idea, it said, but in the recognition of his two vaccines' benefit to mankind.

There was one small—well, not small, but passing—cloud overhanging the Rockefeller-Theiler story. It is the oldest bugaboo of the vaccination business—contamination. This is another chapter in human efforts to make peace with the ultra-microscopic world.

HEPATITIS
AND HELL TO PAY

WE COULD say that the hepatitis virus seems to have been put on earth to make virologists look bad—were it not almost certain that it was here before they were. This hardy perennial of the submicroscopic world functions to keep them humble—"jaded and despondent" is the way one of them put it—amid widely acclaimed progress against more accessible, less exasperating viral infections.

Many a competent virus hunter has blunted his lance tilting with this virus. It put one great research administrator in the scientific doghouse. It menaced the American Red Cross's wartime blood-plasma program. We shall come to these events, and also to one victory scored over this disease by an inquisitive young surgeon who is not a virologist at all.

The highly regarded British team Drs. G. M. Findlay and Fred O. MacCallum were the first to put the finger on a virus as the probable cause of hepatitis, in 1939. But it required the World War II epidemics of infectious hepatitis and the work of investigators such as Dr. W. Paul Havens of Jefferson Medical College to bring out its transmissibility and filterability. The virus's usual route through the body is in one end of the gastrointestinal tract and out the other. But a possible detour into the liver produces one of humanity's most miserable ailments.

The passage of the virus through bacteria-tight filters has shown it to be something less than fifty millimicrons, or one half-millionth of an inch, in diameter. This makes it a little bigger than the polio or yellow-fever but smaller than the influenza virus. Like the yellow-fever virus, the agent of hepatitis never has been seen.

Hepatitis went into the war as a commonplace disturbance of the liver called catarrhal jaundice (by doctors) or yellow jaundice (by laymen). Jaundice means yellow. It emerged as two diseases, infectious and serum hepatitis, or hepatitis A and B. The mighty nineteenth-century German pathologist Dr. Rudolf Virchow introduced the term "catarrhal jaundice," believing the disease to be due to a mucous inflammation obstructing the common bile duct that runs from the liver to the small intestine (the gall bladder is a storage tank along the way). Virchow was mistaken, of course. The virus somehow disturbs the liver's secretion of bile, but every patient doesn't turn yellow. So now it's "hepatitis," the Latin way of saying "inflammation of the liver."

Scientists somewhat arbitrarily set serum hepatitis (B) apart from the common epidemic type (A). Hepatitis B, strictly speaking, is a doctor-induced disease resulting from the virus's contamination of a vaccine, blood, or plasma transfusion or any biologic medicine that is injected by hypodermic needle. Soldiers have been known to get serum hepatitis while having a sweetheart's name tattooed in a heart on their chests. The connection between the A and B viruses has not been definitely established, but one good guess is that the B is simply an A virus that has given up its wandering ways and adapted itself to life in the host's blood stream, or in the circulation of someone to whom the host gives blood.

Infectious hepatitis moves about the world in periodic epidemics, most of them in the late fall or early winter. It's mainly a disease of children, and often gains its foothold through contamination of drinking-water or food. In an institution for the mentally defective, the least intelligent, being the least sanitary, will have the most hepatitis.

But this does not explain why British officers have more hepatitis than their troops. The British pathologist Kenneth R. Hill said: "Although it is tempting to believe that the virus of infectious hepatitis and genius is found more frequently in officers . . . the real explanation is probably that the use of single, personally cleaned mess kits by ordinary troops is much more sanitary than the communal mess arrangements of . . . officers!"

The epidemic virus incubates from two to six weeks, apparently multiplying in the intestines and blood-forming organs. The disease begins with a fever of 100 to 103 degrees, combined with marked loss of appetite, terrible tiredness, headache, chills, vomiting, and awful itching, among other things.

Many people struggle to stop smoking, give up alcohol, or take off weight. Hepatitis is one way of doing all three, but it is not recommended. Tobacco tastes vile to the hepatitis victim; whisky makes him shudder; rich, fatty foods drive him from the table. But most likely he already is in bed, or should be. Any exertion aggravates the liver and delays the eventual day of recovery. Bed rest is the only treatment known, but the doctor who keeps the patient down until his liver is well has earned his fee.

One of the worst features of hepatitis is that people may suspect the patient of being neurotic, or of gold-bricking—at least until the jaundice appears. If it does, it will be after about a week of fever, and will remain for a week or two. The victim turns a gruesome mustard yellow.

Hepatitis is a disease of high morbidity and low mortality—long on sickness, short on death. About half of one per cent die, in a coma. Others may wish they were dead; mental depression and a dragged-out feeling are common features of a slow recovery that may take weeks or months. Usually a sudden return of appetite, often with the jaundice still at its deepest, is the first signal of recovery. Fortunately, the liver has a tremendous capacity to restore itself without permanent damage.

Hepatitis is exceeded, some authorities say, only by the common cold, influenza, and measles as the most prevalent virus disease. Dr. Cecil J. Watson, University of Minnesota internist, described infectious hepatitis as "probably the most important

viral disease still unconquered." Presumably he would include
serum hepatitis.

The National Office of Vital Statistics lumps infectious and
serum hepatitis cases together, apparently surmising that the
latter may be reported as the former. There were 50,000 cases
in 1954. That was the post-war peak. By 1957 the total had
dropped to 15,000, about the same as it had been in 1951. A rise
in reported cases early in the year indicated that 1959 would be
another big hepatitis year.

The annual total is only what physicians report. While hepatitis
is a quarantinable disease, health experts are aware of some
medical tendencies to diagnose and report in keeping with current scientific fashion. Virus hepatitis came out of World War II
as a "new disease," and attracted considerable attention. It is difficult to say whether the 1954 and 1959 increases are apparent or
real. A great many people seem to have acquired some sort of
immunity to hepatitis.

In any event, the serum-hepatitis problem has definitely grown.
The experience of the University of Chicago Clinics, better
known as Billings Hospital, one of the country's top medical-re-
search centers, is typical (we single it out here only because this
institution has had the courage to report its experience). About
fifteen years ago one of every two hundred Billings patients who
had blood transfusions acquired serum hepatitis—usually a long
time following the transfusion. Today, in this same hospital, despite anything its top-notch staff can do, the rate is more than two
per cent, or four times as much as it used to be. This seems to
indicate that voluntary blood donors carry more hepatitis virus
in their blood than they used to. It doesn't necessarily mean that
they have had more hepatitis, inasmuch as the hospital seeks to
screen out all who have had the disease.

Clinically, serum hepatitis can scarcely be distinguished from
the epidemic form, except that there may be less fever with the
serum type and the disease incubates slowly, taking two to five
months to appear. On the other hand, the viruses may be different
strains, as judged by antibody production. Gamma globulin (the
part of the blood containing antibodies) from a person who has

recovered from hepatitis A will to some extent protect another person from attack. However, it will not keep him from getting hepatitis B. And gamma globulin from a B patient apparently has no effect against A. The situation is most confusing.

One may now begin to appreciate what an insidious villain this virus is. According to another theory, the B virus represents a carrier state following exposure to A. The carrier may or may not have had the disease—often there is no history of it. The virus and host get into some kind of balanced relationship. If the host becomes a blood donor, he can pass the virus along, through his pint of blood, to a susceptible patient. The only good thing about it is that patients show some resistance, too. Three of four exposed to contaminated blood or plasma will not get hepatitis—only one does. The hardiness of the virus, it seems, is exceeded only by the hardiness of prospective victims.

As far as a vaccine goes, the hepatitis story is about where yellow fever was before Adrian Stokes found the Rhesus monkey to be susceptible—not so far as when Max Theiler introduced his mouse-brain adaptation of the virus in 1930.

First, a test animal has to be found. The hepatitis people don't have one as yet. A number of animals, including dogs and pigs, get hepatitis, but not human hepatitis. The only test animals presently available are human volunteers. They present a "perpetual stumbling-block," as the British hepatitis expert MacCallum points out. Undetected virus, antibodies, or both may be present in the blood of these volunteers and produce contradictory results during experimental infection.

Secondly, a vital medium, such as a chick embryo or tissue culture, is needed to grow the virus in. Thirdly, the researcher needs some way of detecting and measuring the presence of the virus. Research seems to be stymied on all three points.

One ray of hope has emerged from the laboratory of Parke, Davis and Company in Detroit. There a group headed by Drs. I. William McLean, Jr., and Wilton A. Rightsel have, at this writing, isolated a hepatitis virus in a tissue culture of human bone marrow, known as Detroit-6 cells. In one series the virus was passed through these Detroit-6 cells some forty-three times. It was difficult, however, for the group to tell whether they were transmit-

Upper left: Richard E. Shope, whose medical detective work provided an explanation of the 1918–19 influenza pandemic, which killed an estimated 21,000,000 persons. *Upper right:* Thomas Francis, Jr. The first to develop a workable influenza vaccine, this epidemiologist became the No. 1 expert on scientific mass-testing of vaccines. *Lower left:* Max Theiler. He discovered the 17D yellow-fever vaccine; many virologists regard it as superior to all others. *(By Pach Brothers, New York) Lower right:* J. Garrott Allen, who found a way to kill the hepatitis virus that wrecked the Red Cross blood-plasma program. *(By Lewellyn Studio, Chicago)*

PLATE 5

Many aspire but few are summoned to Science's Mount Olympus in Stockholm. Here, D Sven Gard presents Drs. John F. Enders, Frederick C. Robbins, and Thomas H. Weller fe the 1954 Nobel Prize in medicine, in recognition of their discovery of a test-tube metho of cultivating polio virus. (*By Hans Malmberg, Black Star*)

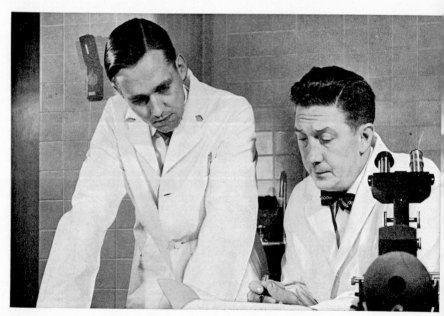

Wallace P. Rowe and Robert J. Huebner, discoverers of a strange group of viruses found i adenoids and tonsils—the adenoviruses.

PLATE 6

ting the virus as the result of multiplication—that is, its reproduction—or by division—that is, by diluting the fluid containing
the virus and "spreading it thinner."

Their big problem was spontaneous degeneration of the virus,
blamed on antibodies in the human serum the culture required.
McLean was frank to say: "We cannot be sure the virus is being
cultivated."

This leaves us where we were in the problem of safe human
serum. Contamination is one of a physician's sorest trials, undoing
his wish to heal and making him, against all intention, a violator
of the Hippocratic injunction against doing the patient any harm.
Microbial contamination, whether due to carelessness, ignorance,
or simply helplessness, has pursued doctors ever since they began
puncturing our skins for the purpose of adding substances to or
subtracting them from the body.

You will remember that during Edward Jenner's first experiment, when he gave his infant son swinepox, the doctor produced
an extraneous infection—he said it was erysipelas. Then, when
smallpox vaccination became popular throughout the world after
the James Phipps experiment, contamination rose to embarrass
the Father of Vaccination.

The human body is heir to few blood-stream infections that
were not at times passed along in the name of vaccination. In
fact, German doctors traced an 1883 outbreak of catarrhal jaundice to contaminated smallpox vaccine, then made from humanized lymph taken from a vaccination ulcer. Contamination
remained a bugbear until human serum was eliminated by transferring virus production to the skin of calves.

Again, serum hepatitis contaminated yellow-fever vaccine after
Max Theiler discovered the 17D virus. The ensuing tragedy
ruined the record of an otherwise able research administrator,
Dr. Wilber A. Sawyer, then director of the Rockefeller Foundation's International Health Division and Theiler's chief. The
episode was neither the first nor the last of the vaccine scan-
dals.

In 1940 the Surgeon General called on the great Rockefeller
Foundation to mass-produce Theiler's 17D vaccine for the Army.
Since 1937 it had been field-tested on nearly two million Brazil-

ians and, in fact, was undergoing further testing in Brazil at the time.

The Foundation decided this would be its major contribution to the war effort. It entered into a rather novel war contract for a capitalistic country—it agreed to make all the vaccine the Army, Navy, and Public Health Service wanted without charge! The prospect of making a yellow-fever vaccine for military use alarmed as much as it pleased Theiler, for he was still trying to work certain bugs out of his discovery. Here was the problem:

In 1937 Findlay and MacCallum had reported on twenty-two hundred persons vaccinated against yellow fever by the method Sawyer had introduced in 1931. That was a mixture of Theiler's mouse-adapted French strain of virus with human immune serum. The Britishers saw fifty-two cases of jaundice, all about two to three months after vaccination. Without coming to a definite conclusion, they mentioned five possible explanations for the contamination; a virus in the human serum was one possibility.

The Rockefeller scientists and public-health officers of Brazil had a somewhat similar experience in the course of vaccinating the two million Brazilians. They used a 17D virus grown in chick embryos and suspended in blood serum from non-immune persons. At that time the serum generally was thought to be necessary to keep the attenuated virus in the vaccine alive. Human serum was preferable to animal serum because of a lesser danger of vaccinated persons having toxic reactions to foreign proteins.

There were three outbreaks of jaundice in vaccinated persons, as well as one of encephalitis. Some 1,072 cases of jaundice and 32 deaths were traced to certain lots of vaccine, on the basis of circumstantial evidence.

This did not amount to a great deal statistically, but Theiler was concerned. He tried producing a new 17D vaccine without human serum, which he believed to be the source of the trouble. He made his new vaccine out of clarified chick-embryo juice containing the virus, plus distilled water, in the same simple way Pasteur had made his rabies vaccine. The virus seemed to keep all right. Brazil resumed its vaccination program in 1940 with the water vaccine, and two hundred thousand more were vaccinated that year. No further jaundice appeared, but it was in this two hundred thousand that some cases of encephalitis and the death of a child occurred. Vaccination had to be halted while the trouble was ferreted out and the offending substrain of virus replaced with the original strain of 17D.

But meanwhile, to meet the Army's request for vaccine, Sawyer had to make a choice, and he did so. It was to stick with the vaccine made with human serum. The Rockefeller Foundation had had longer experience with it, and at the time for decision it was not clear to him what the outcome with the water vaccine would be, though Theiler recommended that the water vaccine be adopted. The only alternative would be to keep an Army preparing for war waiting for yellow-fever vaccine. At the time, that seemed unthinkable.

Sawyer arranged for a continuous supply of white Leghorn hatching eggs from a New Jersey poultry farm. The laboratory at the Rockefeller Institute grew the 17D virus in these eggs and suspended it in human serum. As a precaution, the serum was heated to 132–134 degrees for one hour (as others later determined, the hepatitis virus may not die in this short period).

The Foundation had been obtaining human serum for the Brazil-bound vaccine from the Blood Transfusion Betterment Association of New York. Now it required an additional source of supply. Sawyer arranged to have Johns Hopkins Medical School students, interns, nurses, and lab technicians become paid donors.

Between January 1941 and April 1942 the laboratory produced seven million doses of this vaccine, half going to the Army. It was not an easy time for either pure scientist, pure administrator, or pure military preparedness. The first six months of 1942 were one of the United States Army's weakest periods—MacArthur retreated from the Philippines, Bataan and Corregidor fell, American soldiers made the Death March.

Meantime, in Stateside training camps, recruits were falling ill with hepatitis following vaccination against yellow fever. Jaundice first appeared in California camps in March, and then mounted rapidly. The Surgeon General ordered use of Rockefeller yellow-fever vaccine stopped, pending an investigation, and assigned his Committee on Tropical Diseases, headed by Sawyer, to conduct it.

When you make a mistake involving the Army, as many have, there's no end of explaining to be done. The Sawyer committee —the great San Francisco virologist Dr. Karl F. Meyer also was on it—sent out questionnaires and counted cases for months to come. In the end, the addition was rather staggering: 28,585 soldiers were stricken and 62 died.

It was easy to distinguish the serum hepatitis from the epidemic variety, also present in the Army. The serum kind came in bunches, following vaccination by thirteen to sixteen weeks, whereas infectious hepatitis was scattered throughout the year, irrespective of vaccination. Nine lots of vaccine were responsible for most of the serum cases, the attack rate per lot being from 13 to 95 per 1,000 vaccinated.

Checking back to Baltimore, Sawyer found that the contaminated lots contained serum from Johns Hopkins donors who previously had had catarrhal jaundice. In those days nobody thought to ask them this before they gave blood.

Sawyer blamed contaminated human serum unequivocally in his report, published in the *American Journal of Hygiene* in 1944. He assumed that there was a virus in the serum, though attempts to isolate it had failed.

The report was a masterpiece of objective investigation, solid and complete, but nowhere in it did Sawyer acknowledge an error in judgment or state that he had guessed wrong. Rather, he appeared to rationalize his decision on the scientific grounds that "earlier evidence suggesting that human serum may harbor the causal agent of the infective hepatitis was not at all convincing." He pointed out that Findlay, in Great Britain, had continued to use human serum in yellow-fever vaccine despite his 1937 finding of an associated hepatitis, and that the English did not discontinue the human serum until 1943—well after the Americans. Sawyer said:

"Serum was eventually omitted from the vaccine in Brazil, but the issue there at the time was further confused by the preliminary reports regarding occurrence of post-vaccination encephalitis which coincided with the omission of serum and which necessitated discontinuation of vaccination altogether for several months in 1941."

Others—Theiler among them—found early evidence against use of human serum more convincing than did Sawyer. Indeed, human serum is well flagged with danger signals in the history of vaccination, beginning with Jenner's humanized lymph, though it does take the investigator time to read and interpret the signs correctly.

Sawyer did not seek to justify his decision from an administrative, or command, standpoint. Administratively, he was in a pretty solid position.

He had reacted in the same laudable manner as thousands of other war-production chiefs who got to work when the Army orders came through. He had his design—17D virus grown in chick embryos and suspended in blood serum from non-immune persons. Generally, it had been effective as a vaccine against yellow fever. Some problems remained.

Sawyer froze his design, so to speak, and went into production. This is the way of management, as contrasted to research—you go with what you have and take a calculated risk.

Production on time, and not perfection, becomes the primary measure of success. If the product fails in any important way— well, that is the chance one takes. Sawyer took it and lost.

After trouble arose in the Army, human serum was unmistakably incriminated as the source of the hepatitis and abandoned. The Foundation laboratory soon resumed production of vaccine bottled in water instead of blood serum; it supplied the Army and, in fact, the world with twenty-eight million doses by 1947. There were no further setbacks. Theiler's 17D virus in water, many believe, is the best of all virus vaccines available today, Nonetheless, after publication of his report, Sawyer retired. He died a few years later.

In 1956 the world's hepatitis hunters gathered in a symposium at the Henry Ford Hospital in Detroit to discuss the poor hunting. The veteran Dr. Joseph Stokes, Jr., from the University of Pennsylvania, recapitulated the serum-hepatitis situation as it applied to the use of blood plasma in first aid and surgery:

It became clear to many in England and in the United States quite early in World War II that pooled plasma was responsible for the relatively high rates of serum hepatitis (hepatitis B) in the casualties from all theaters who were transfused with this pooled blood fraction. Whole blood in certain theaters, such as the Mediterranean, when it was obtained from men in that area apparently increased the rate of viral hepatitis considerably above that caused by pooled plasma alone. This was probably because of the relatively high incidence of epidemic hepatitis, and therefore blood-borne virus, among the men who were donating the blood. . . .[1]

MacCallum added: "One fact that still amazes me is that physicians and surgeons throughout the world continue to inject untreated pools of serum or plasma from a large number of donors for some quite unnecessary procedures, in addition to unnecessary transfusions."

Sitting in the audience, waiting to give his report, was a surgeon who was equally amazed. He was Dr. J. Garrott Allen, of the University of Chicago, a tall, well-built, youthful-looking man in his early forties, with a large amount of chestnut hair and a sensitive face.

Allen seemed to be the only man present who had run up any kind of score in the prevention of serum hepatitis. Dr. Isidor S. Ravdin of Philadelphia, chairman of the board of the American College of Surgeons and perhaps the most powerful voice in American surgery, once commended Allen as "a voice crying in the wilderness." The general dimensions of the wilderness and the voice crying in it are as follows:

The American surgeon, at his best, is capable of incredible feats. In terms of training, technique, daring, and success, he is the best in the world. It is worth noting, for instance, that neither Dwight Eisenhower nor John Foster Dulles went to Europe for their major surgery, whereas Anthony Eden did come to the United States for his second and third operations following a surgical accident to his common bile duct at home.

The master surgeon, wherever he is from, can remove a part of the brain, a lung, stomach, kidney, or several feet of bowel, or

[1] *Hepatitis Frontiers.* Henry Ford Hospital International Symposium (Boston: Little, Brown & Company; 1957).

open the heart, and increase the patient's chance of longer life
thereby. Most frequently, these big operations are heroic maneuvers against cancer. The result is not all that we might hope in
many cases, but it would be almost one-hundred-per-cent hopeless without the operation. This kind of surgery may increase
the patient's chances for several more years of life from zero to
one in twenty, or one in ten, or fifty-fifty, or sometimes six or
seven out of ten.

The surgeon fights an uphill battle to raise his percentage of
"cures." Most of the ground he gains inch by inch, from paying attention to many details beyond excision of the malignant growth
itself. He concerns himself with the preparation of the patient and
his post-operative care, building up the patient's strength with
various infusions, such as the proteins found in blood plasma.
The clear plasma, without the red blood cells, is also excellent for
warding off surgical shock during the operation.

We need not run through the surgeon's entire armamentarium
here. Most important in a big operation, however, is his ability to
replace the patient's blood—replace it as rapidly as it is lost. Such
an operation takes at least three or four pints of whole blood, or of
blood and plasma combined. Sometimes the need is for ten or
twenty or even thirty.

The blood bank, therefore, is one secret of the cancer surgeon's
success—blood freely given, typed, bottled, stored, cross-
matched, and finally brought up from the bank and swung from
a standard over the operating-table and dripped, through tube
and needle, into the patient's vein.

Now and again, in about one case in fifty, the virus that makes
doctors look bad passes down through that tube and causes hepatitis. If a patient is exposed, there is a one-in-four chance that
three or four months later, when he is well on the road to recovery, the disease will hit him. If it does, he and his doctor have
lost some ground. Hepatitis will not only make convalescence
miserable, but will kill fifteen per cent of the time.

This is his risk, the price he must pay for life-saving blood
(over and above the usual charge of thirty-five dollars a pint).
Obviously, it's a worth-while risk. What infuriates surgeons such
as Garrott Allen is also obvious: serum hepatitis. At present they

cannot do anything about it—except re-examine the question of whether a patient really needed whole blood.

There are various blood substitutes, but none as good as blood. The loss of much red blood requires replacement with much red blood, to avoid a severe anemia. None of the substitutes supplies red cells. Otherwise, the natural plasma is best, probably. It works as well as blood itself in simple prevention of shock and protein deficiency. It has one advantage over whole blood in that it can be stored indefinitely, whereas blood is good for no more than two to three weeks at the very most. In fact, over-age blood is the chief source of plasma. The red cells settle in each bottle, so the clear plasma can be drained off and pooled in large containers with that from other donors.

Plasma, to be frozen or dried, was the main object of the American Red Cross's blood-procurement program early in World War II. But contamination with serum hepatitis was so troublesome that the pooling of plasma eventually was abandoned. There was a great store of pooled plasma at the end of the war, and it was pretty thoroughly contaminated with hepatitis.

Of all the surgeons in the country, the one who became most exercised about the loss of plasma was West Virginia-born, Harvard-educated Allen. According to his friends, Allen is a man of some spirit and candor, capable of sustaining a high state of moral indignation. The medical literature itself shows some signs of this.

Allen had begun looking into the serum-hepatitis problem while still in resident training at Billings in the mid-1940's. By 1950, with the help of his associates, he had collected seventeen case reports in the hospital and thirty-seven that had appeared in medical journals.

Now he made a simple observation, one that Dr. Warren H. Cole of the University of Illinois, a leading surgical scientist, later was to class as "one of the most important contributions . . . since the discovery . . . that blood is so useful in the operative and postoperative phases of surgery."

The observation was this: not a single case of serum hepatitis had occurred in patients receiving liquid blood plasma that had been pooled and stored at room temperature for several months (the minimum safe period later was fixed at six months). The patients who got serum hepatitis were the ones who had whole-blood transfusions, or a combination of blood and liquid plasma, or dried plasma, or plasma preserved by freezing and refrigeration.

It had been pure happenstance that the Billings blood bank had stored liquid plasma at room temperature, on a top shelf near the ceiling, where the temperature ranged from 76 to 96 degrees and averaged 89 the year around. This was largely due to steam sterilizers in the room. Sufficient refrigeration space was not available when the blood bank opened in 1942. So, when fresh blood became outdated, twenty-five or thirty bottles of it were pooled, as plasma, in large, sealed flasks and just put away to age. About a fourth of it spoiled; when it did, the technicians threw it out.

Allen now sought the explanation of the hepatitis hazard to be found in dried, frozen, or refrigerated plasma. Again, it was a simple observation. As any virology textbook will tell you, a good way to keep a virus alive is to dry and freeze it. We've seen that before. Whereas viruses resist cold, they are generally susceptible to heat.

The hepatitis virus is so hardy, however, that it takes heat of 140 or 150 degrees for ten hours to quick-kill it for sure. That much heat is ruinous to the therapeutic qualities of plasma.

When some people involved in the blood-procurement programs read Allen's 1950 report in the *Journal of the American Medical Association*, they sniffed and turned up their noses. They would not have done it, surely, had they known what a determined young man he was. Before he was through, he probably could have sold them martinis with plasma aged at room temperature substituted for the vermouth.

It is understandable perhaps why the blood authorities found Allen's position on plasma unappealing. It was such a homely little idea, for one thing—just put the plasma on some dusty old shelf and the virus goes away! Then, too, it wasn't tactful of him to say that their previously recommended methods for preserving plasma "are also the most suitable means available for the preservation of virus activity." Plasma had given the Washington blood people a lot of trouble, and they were in a once-burned-twice-shy mood. So, following Allen's report, they condemned use of plasma in *any* form.

For the next four years he argued and piled up evidence. As he revealed in one report in the *Annals of Surgery,* he ran into questions that any scientist must face when he makes a claim, but also some that indicate his critics may not always have been as scientific as one would expect.

For example, someone had rebuffed him with a statement that a blood bank in Sydney, Australia, had a serum-hepatitis attack rate of 2.5 per cent after storing pooled plasma for several months at room temperature. Allen ran it down and found that the plasma actually had been stored at about forty-three degrees and later frozen.

There were other objections, including the legitimate concern that the proteins Allen so dearly prized in plasma had deteriorated with age. He worked that one out, too. It wasn't so; others confirmed him.

The Public Health Service Laboratory of Biologics Control at Bethesda ran a rigorous experiment. The Laboratory took fresh plasma from persons actively sick with serum hepatitis and injected some of it into human volunteers; 52 per cent got hepatitis. Some of the same plasma was stored for six months at room temperature and then given to another group of twenty volunteers. Only one got a full-blown infection, six and one-third months later, an unusually long incubation period. Some said this appearance of one infection was evidence against aged plasma—Allen didn't have as air-tight a case as he claimed.

It is a good rule never to make a good man angry. Allen made two points about this attempted evaluation. One is that if you propose to test a man's claims you are bound to duplicate his conditions. The Laboratory of Biologics Control had stored its deliberately contaminated plasma at an average 72 degrees, a full 17 degrees lower than the average he specified! Nevertheless, he pointed out, in the Bethesda study even this cooler state had reduced the attack rate in hepatitis-loaded plasma from 52 to 5 per cent.

In 1954 this redheaded surgeon mustered convincing survey

data from 124 hospital blood banks. From 25,207 infusions of dried, frozen, or refrigerated plasma, there had been 259 reported cases of serum hepatitis. From 1,248,439 blood transfusions, there had been 544. From 191,887 units of properly aged plasma, *there had not been a single case reported.*

In 1955 he threw a direct challenge at official foot-draggers. "The National Research Council, the National Institutes of Health, and the British Ministry of Health have been reluctant . . . to approve the safety of six months old liquid plasma which they must do if the physician is to be reassured or the manufacturer encouraged in his plasma production. . . .

"If the fears of the disapproving agencies are well founded that many cases of serum hepatitis occur from liquid plasma and are unrecognized these bodies should by now be able to produce records of multiple cases of serum hepatitis in recipients of plasma from the same pool."

Nobody met this challenge. In fact, Drs. Paul I. Hoxworth and W. E. Haesler, Jr., of Cincinnati repeated Allen's work and confirmed it. They got serum-hepatitis cases with whole-blood transfusions and not a one with pooled plasma stored and aged according to his directions.

In early 1958 the NRC, under a certain amount of pressure from the Armed Forces to say how plasma from outdated blood should be handled, quietly but definitely reversed its opposition. It was a complete victory for Allen, who was privately telling colleagues in his peppery way what a handicap it was to be a surgeon and not a virologist: "I have to admit that as a surgeon I don't know anything about viruses and it is only since I upgraded my glasses from Woolworth's to Kresge's that I have been able to see one!"

Most hospital blood banks now regard the Allen formula as the only dependable way to process plasma, having found that other methods, such as ultra-violet irradiation, are not as good.

Allen emphasized that the plasma-aging process is not applicable to whole blood—in its natural form, it deteriorates after about three weeks. Furthermore, one obvious drawback to aged plasma, he said, was the risk to the patient of bacterial contamination. The University of Chicago Blood Bank had been able to avoid the problem by being careful, but the resultant "losses of plasma pools from bacterial contamination represent an ill-afforded extravagance of a product not readily available," said Allen.

Therefore, he turned his attention to other possible methods of sterilizing blood and blood plasma. Many a good man has done likewise, among them Dr. Gerald A. Lo Grippo, Henry Ford Hospital microbiologist. Others have tried heating and formaldehyde, classic methods of killing micro-organisms, but these methods denature the blood proteins to an undesirable extent.

Lo Grippo used a drug called beta-propriolactone (BPL) in plasma administered to 672 patients. None suffered any ill effect. In tissue cultures, BPL kills bacteria, viruses, and fungi, but not the cells of the tissues; therefore, it appeared most promising as a blood-sterilizing agent. On the other hand, tests on five volunteers who received slightly more than a pint of plasma containing both hepatitis virus and BPL indicated that treatment of the plasma with the drug did not solve the serum-hepatitis problem. Four of the volunteers got hepatitis.

Furthermore, Lo Grippo emphasized that BPL cannot be injected directly into a patient's blood, even though it is safe to mix with plasma in a bottle. Beta-propriolactone is a "potent carcinogen," meaning it can cause cancer unless chemically changed before being given to the patient. Lo Grippo reported his seven years' experience to the New York Academy of Science in April 1959, and left it an open question whether BPL would contribute anything to the ultimate solution of the serum-hepatitis problem.

The same might be said at this point for the blood-sterilizing drug that Allen hit upon. He chose monochloracetate, a close relative of the acid in vinegar. Allen also made his first report in April 1959, but on the opposite side of the continent, in San Francisco, before the American Surgical Association.

When a tiny bit of monochloracetate is mixed into a pint of heavily contaminated plasma or whole blood, "a surprisingly high degree of antibacterial activity" results, he said. The MCA, as we might call it for short, killed a considerable number of different disease bacteria, including the notoriously hardy *staphylococcus aureus,* the cause of boils and many post-surgical infections in hospitals.

Allen said this first cousin to vinegar was "hopefully virucidal," but stopped right there, for lack of evidence. At this writing there seems to be some indication that MCA will kill certain viruses in both plasma and whole blood, but this had not been claimed as yet.

The interesting thing about monochloracetate, in addition to its promise as a blood sterilizer, is that experiments over the past three years indicate that it can be injected directly into the patient's blood without harm. Allen and his University of Chicago colleagues (Drs. Donald Dawson, Wynn A. Sayman, and Ross S. Benham, and Miss Isabelle Havens) put the vinegary drug into both animal and human as well as test-tube tests.

Dogs, forced to depend on plasma injections for all the proteins in their diet for periods of twenty-eight to forty-two days, thrived on large daily injections of plasma containing MCA. They ran no fevers and lost no weight. Their blood, bone marrow, and vital organs remained normal in every way. It was apparent that the drug does not denature proteins. It was equally without harmful effects when injected into eleven debilitated patients dying of cancer; in fact, they showed some nutritional benefits.

But, as Allen reported, the most exciting question about monochloracetate still stands: "Its potential as a virucidal agent for the hepatitis virus remains to be demonstrated."

The hepatitis story is therefore an unfinished one; indeed, at this stage it is of the type known as a "cliff-hanger." We do not know how it will turn out. But we can find some reason for optimism in the fact that people like Garrott Allen are working on the problem.

Allen takes the word *work* rather literally. He often begins his day at 3:30 a.m. and does not go home to his equally energetic family of five until 6:30 p.m. This permits him to carry a full schedule of surgery and hospital rounds and still leaves ample time for reading, writing, and research. In June 1959 he transferred the scene of his strenuous pursuits to the Stanford University School of Medicine in Palo Alto, California, where he became chairman of the department of surgery.

LAST GREAT PLAGUE,
1918 MODEL

INFLUENZA owes its name to Italian astrologers of long ago who blamed the disease's periodic appearances on the *influenza,* or influence, of the heavenly bodies. This remained almost as good an explanation as any other until 1918.

Then this usually mild, almost friendly disease that seems always to be with us fooled us. It suddenly turned into a murderous psychopath. It forswore its reputation as a mere killer of babies and old ladies, and strangled people in their prime.

In the fall of 1918, influenza became a great killer. It teamed with pneumonia to produce the worst pestilence civilization ever has experienced. It seems incredible that the most terrible epidemic of all occurred within the lifetime of anyone forty-one years of age. But it is so. Other epidemic diseases produce far higher death rates—smallpox, yellow fever, typhus, bubonic plague. In an absolute sense, however, on the basis of total deaths, the 1918 pandemic, or world-wide epidemic—Dr. Fred M. Davenport calls flu "the last great plague"—surely was the worst.

The middle estimate of the number of influenza-pneumonia deaths in 1918 and 1919 is 21,000,000. The total sick were esti-

mated at 500,000,000, or, some said, "half the world." In the
United States the toll was an estimated 20,000,000 cases—twenty
per cent of the population—and *850,000 dead!* The Army hospi-
talized more than 1,000,000 soldiers; 44,000 died. In other words,
of every four Americans lost in World War I military service, one
was killed in bed by the one-two punch of influenza and pneumonia.

The pandemic came at the close of the war. It was as if Nature
had suddenly grown bored with man's savage but puny efforts to
destroy himself, and had decided to teach him a lesson—or give
him a hand.

Though often explosively contagious, the 1918 flu actually remained fairly mild in the majority of cases. Compared to some
diseases, its death rate was low—about four per cent of those
stricken.

But there was a peculiar virulence about this flu which caused
it to do considerable damage in robust people's lungs. In one year,
1918, it reduced the average life expectancy of young Americans
in their twenties and thirties nearly twenty-five per cent!

We should make one thing clear. There was no panic, mass
flight, mob rule, or disruption of law and order, as in the four-
teenth-century plague or the nineteenth-century yellow-fever epidemics. Nobody burned down houses to stop the epidemic.

This is one of the chief characteristics of flu—it doesn't scare us.
Every winter this virus disease turns up somewhere in local outbreaks. It had done so the two winters before 1918. Every few
years there are real epidemics. And once every generation or so,
influenza becomes a world traveler.

Flu is taken for granted and soon forgotten. People forget the
last epidemic and greet this morbid visitor the next time around
as a "Newe Acquayntance." The Elizabethan English called it
that. It's really an old, old acquaintance, of course, and a modern
physician wouldn't describe it too differently from the 1557 one
who observed:

". . . It began with a roughness of the jaws [we would call it
sore throat], small cough, then a strong fever, with a pain of the
head, back and legs; some felt as though they were corded over
the breast and had a weight on the stomach; all which continued

to the third day at the farthest; then the fever went off with a sweat, or bleeding at the nose. In some few, it turned to a pleurisy, or fatal peripneumony."

Here we see the essential insidiousness of flu. You have it and you get over it, and if you don't, pneumonia gets the blame. Pneumonia became our number-one killer in 1900 and remained so until 1921, when heart disease overtook it. Its inflammation of the lungs strikes swiftly; it can be so lethal that in pre-penicillin days doctors and nurses used to call it—a little callously—"an old man's friend." It put him out of his misery rather promptly.

Reading *The New York Times* day by day, you would have had no clear impression that a great catastrophe, greater than the war itself, had struck humanity—that 400,000 Americans died of influenza-pneumonia during the month of October 1918.

As a matter of fact, both the *Times* and Dr. Royal S. Copeland, New York City health commissioner, adopted the traditional attitude toward flu epidemics: that there was nothing much to get alarmed about. (In terms of what anybody could do about it, there wasn't.) Only once during October did influenza make page one, largely occupied by news of the Allied advance, Germany's imminent surrender, and the Liberty Bond drive. Doubtless there was a patriotic motive for burying the epidemic deep inside, usually beyond page nine. As October wore on, however, the reported sick and dead in New York City alone exceeded the current war-casualty lists.

The six-week epidemic was much lighter in New York than elsewhere, as Dr. Copeland repeatedly pointed out. Still, the reports of influenza-pneumonia sick and dead issued by the Health Department each morning at ten o'clock showed a gradual rise from 1,000 or so new cases a day, with 100 new deaths, at the beginning of the month to more than 5,000 new cases, with 600 dead, reported on the last day of the month. While acknowledging that the reports were not complete—many doctors were too busy to report—the health commissioner's view was consistent throughout: "no reason for alarm," "epidemic under control," "crest of wave will break in a few days," "disease on wane," "still no cause for undue alarm." Never in American public-health history have disability and death been met with more optimism.

Granted, the situation wasn't as bad as the Germans reported. They said the bodies were being piled in heaps on the streets of New York. Two thousand bodies did remain unburied in Queens cemeteries for a few days, until city workers gave the gravediggers a hand. In some instances, families buried their own dead and sometimes more than one: a mother and her two children all died on the same day.

Delving inside, the diligent *Times* reader got the story: GRIP NOW SWEEPING 43 STATES. San Francisco passed a law compelling everyone to wear a gauze mask. Illinois health authorities prohibited all sports events and public gatherings; Philadelphia postponed the Dempsey-Levinsky fight. There was a shortage of coffins in Baltimore. An Army general denied that people were being executed for spreading germs, and the government scotched the idea that influenza had been brought in by enemy agents and therefore should be called "German plague." Americans, having got first news of the pandemic from Spain, called it "Spanish flu."

New York City fined people three dollars for spitting on the sidewalk. The Red Cross undertook to make fifty thousand flu masks. The bride and groom wore masks when one flu-stricken soldier and his girl insisted on going through with the ceremony. Forty per cent of the workers in a Staten Island shipyard were out sick, as were twenty thousand telephone operators and many hundreds of subway workers in Manhattan. Authorities said the number of persons home sick might solve the problem of crippled transportation services. Sing Sing refused to accept new prisoners after a flu epidemic broke out in the penitentiary.

The hardship was staggering. Whole families were bed-ridden with flu. There was a fuel shortage; landlords had to be ordered to furnish heat or face fines. Women volunteers made hundreds of gallons of chicken broth to take to the homes of the sick, who were often without food. There was a shortage of nurses for both home and hospital service. Hospitals were overcrowded; private mansions were converted to hospital use. In late October the Health Department announced that, while the work was actually outside its province, it would take care of children left without parents, as many were.

Surgeon General Rupert Blue of the United States Public Health Service and Dr. Copeland did not agree on anti-flu measures. Dr. Blue recommended the closing of all schools and other public buildings, to keep people out of crowds. Copeland was right in refusing, but for the wrong reasons. He said conditions were different in New York. The truth is, isolation and quarantine don't work against flu. He did urge people to stay out of crowds, avoid coughers and spitters, and go to bed and take a dose of castor oil or salts when they got sick—an order of events not designed to give them immediate rest.

At the time when the first wave of the pandemic became evident in the spring of 1918, many doctors thought they knew the cause of influenza—*Hemophilus influenzae*. Richard F. J. Pfeiffer, German bacteriologist, found this bacterium in flu patients but not in normal persons in the great but not so deadly 1889–92 flu pandemic. Some doubts began to arise about Pfeiffer's bacillus when later it turned up rather commonly in the air passages of people without flu, and also in measles and whooping-cough patients.

The first wave of the 1918–19 pandemic, following small epidemics the year before, appeared to be the spitting image of the 1889 one. It spread fast and far, but remained quite moderate. Many doctors thought of Pfeiffer, of course, but his bacillus at first could be found in only a small portion of the cases. The microbiologists looked for a filterable virus. They didn't find that either.

In November and December 1918 three Public Health Service workers in Boston tried to transmit the disease to sixty-two human volunteers, thirty-nine of whom had no history of flu. Filtered and unfiltered secretions from the noses and throats of flu patients were sprayed and swabbed into the noses, throats, and eyes of the volunteers. No one developed flu.

Ten of these volunteers were required to visit each of ten patients with acute flu, shake hands, chat for five minutes, receive the patient's breath in their faces five times while inhaling, and finally let the patient cough five times directly into their faces. Not a single volunteer got the flu! Similar experiments were car-

ried out in San Francisco with fifty volunteers and equally negative results.

But while the agent of flu remained a mystery, some facts
were observed in the United States Navy, the British Grand Fleet,
and at Camp Shelby, Mississippi. Shelby tied with Boston for the
honor of being the first place hit by virulent flu in the second
wave, beginning in August 1918. This camp also shared with
ships of the sea the characteristic of a fairly stable population—
no troops having been transferred out of it between April and
October 1918. Those who had had the mild flu in the spring did
not get the virulent kind in the fall. Somewhat the same thing
was observed in the civilian populations. The third wave of flu, in
January and February 1919, appeared mainly to be checking off
the cities it had missed the previous fall. So, while first- and sec-
ond-wave flu were different in severity, one did seem to immunize against the other; the second wave likewise immunized
against the third.

Another thing was noted, particularly in retrospect. Whereas
Pfeiffer's bacillus was found in only about 10 to 20 per cent of flu
patients during the first wave, it showed up among the sick in
great abundance in the second wave in the fall. Then it was
commonly reported in 70 to 100 per cent of cases with influenza-
pneumonia.

This is suggestive of something; one hardly knows what, especially when he is aware that there is a bewildering variety of
germs in the nose, throat, and lungs at all times. It was another
dozen years before any virus hunter could offer a possible answer.

✳ 18 ✳

SHOPE AND HIS SHOATS

Learned doctors pontificate: "The cause of the 1918–19 pandemic is still unknown." This is technically true, and makes the uttering person sound authoritative indeed. Inasmuch as the cause of "Spanish flu" could not be established then, it never can be definitely known. The trouble with the statement is that it ignores one of the greatest medical detective stories and nicest pieces of biological deduction in history.

The one man who has come closest to explaining the pandemic is Dr. Richard E. Shope of the Rockefeller Institute for Medical Research. Dr. Shope is sometimes overlooked in discussions of human influenza. For example, Rivers's *Viral and Rickettsial Infections of Man,* Second Edition, is considered definitive. But its chapter on "Influenza" by Dr. Frank L. Horsfall, Jr., a fellow Rockefeller medical scientist, contains no mention of Shope.[1]

Perhaps one reason for omitting Dr. Shope is that he's an animal pathologist—one of the world's most famous. He is well known, for example, as the Iowa-born rabbit hunter who discovered "Shope rabbit papilloma," a virus disease causing warts and cancer in rabbits. It's true that he is not a clinical researcher

[1] But he is frequently mentioned in the influenza chapter by Thomas Francis in the Third Edition (1959).

working with human patients. It is also true that his choice of experimental subjects was not based on their capacity to endear themselves to us.

Shope was the first man to isolate an influenza virus, the first to disclose the possibility of immunizing against flu, and the first to offer a convincing—albeit somewhat controversial—explanation of what happened in 1918. The trouble is, he did it with *pigs*.

Everybody agrees that Shope's swine discoveries are brilliant —a great piece of detective work—but when he extends his reasoning from pigs to humans he finds some conservative scientists resistant. Some of his theories sound a little wild, even though he carefully labels his speculations as speculations. Yet as new information and more experience accumulate, the scales appear to tip more in his favor.

Shope doesn't claim to be the world's greatest authority on pandemic flu. On the other hand, he does claim—with a grin—to have the world's greatest collection of pig figurines. You see them around his laboratory at the Rockefeller Institute for Medical Research in New York, and his apartment across the street, on York Avenue, and at his five-acre farm near Kingston, New Jersey—in bronze, gold leaf, china, clay, wood, monel metal. Perhaps the most attractive one is a Balinese pig with multiple mammary glands reminiscent of the figure's cultural as well as zoological origins.

As for live, parasite-free, unvaccinated pigs, Shope buys from one to two hundred of them a year in suckling size from a Long Island farmer, at twenty-five dollars each. He keeps them, for his experiments, on the roof and in the basement of the Institute's Theobald Smith Building. He calls himself a born "meat hunter," and confesses that during some periods since 1928, when he first turned his attention to the pig, his family has been very nearly raised on laboratory pork. When a pig has given its lungs to science in the name of influenza, it still remains a first-rate delicacy, roasted. This is one advantage in working with pigs instead of guinea pigs or white mice.

A tall, amiable man with a long face, eagle-beak nose, gray hair thinning in front, a twinkle in his eye, and frequently a dead five-cent cigar or a twisted cheroot in one corner of his mouth, Shope, at the age of fifty-seven, is the personification of the unfettered career investigator. His friend Dr. Wendell Stanley observes that he is "the best example of a virus hunter I know."

Shope is a physician. His father and father-in-law were both practicing physicians. But his own clinical experience was largely confined to taking over their individual practices during summer vacations. Paradoxically, Shope turned his back on medicine to become distinguished in the veterinary world. In this role, you find him always busy—and always relaxed. Conferring with a visitor, for example, he may wear a long, faded, tan cotton coat with a few bloodstains on the hem in front. He sits with his feet on his desk and his chair tipped back against a G.E. refrigerator (containing swine-flu virus samples in the deep-freeze unit, and blood-test tubes and his secretary's nail polish in the lower compartment). His laboratory is bare and uninteresting, except for its magnificent views. From one side you can see the famous Memorial Cancer Center and Sloan-Kettering Institute, from a second side, the huge New York-Cornell Medical Center; seated at his desk, he has only to turn his head to the left to watch the tugboats going by on the East River on the third side.

Shope—a declared Republican and a Mason—was born on Christmas Day 1901 in Des Moines, where his father, Charles, was a general practitioner. This happy coincidence enables the children (a daughter and three sons) to dispose of Dad once a year with one big present. Shope remembers that his mother, however, was always careful to give him two big presents on Christmas.

The 1918 pandemic found Shope, then sixteen and already a high-school graduate, resistant both to the disease and to becoming a practitioner like his father. Wishing to study forestry, he went to Iowa State College in Ames to register. The office was closed, so he hopped a freight train and headed for Iowa City. There he enrolled at the State University of Iowa in its two-year pre-medical course. To get in, he had to join the Student Army Training Corps, known locally as the Saturday Afternoon Tea Club.

He went on to the College of Medicine, also in Iowa City, now

resigned to following in his father's steps. When he was a sopho-
more medical student, however, his curiosity got caught on the
hook of scientific research. It was simple enough. He was taking a
course under Dr. Oscar H. Plant, professor of pharmacology. Un-
wittingly, the twenty-year-old youth found himself in a kind of
parthenogenesis, or self-fertilization, of the research mind. The
student's and the professor's colloquy went about like this:

Q. Why don't dogs get tuberculosis?
A. I don't know.
Q. How do I find out?
A. You work in the laboratory.
Q. How do I get into the laboratory to work?
A. I'll fix you up with some space.

Dr. Plant found Shope a little money for dogs and a bench on
the top floor of the animal house, where the cockroaches, by eating the glue in the bindings of his books, possibly did more to destroy knowledge than Shope did to advance it. He tinkered with
the role of cholesterol in tuberculosis, because dog blood is high in
this fatty substance, and then went on to become an $800-a-year
lab assistant.

Shope stayed on for a year with an unusually attractive $2,500
salary after obtaining his M.D. degree in 1924. But Plant was a
friend of Dr. Paul A. Lewis, a pathologist at the Rockefeller Institute's animal-pathology laboratory in Princeton, and Lewis was
looking for an assistant. Plant recommended Shope, who soon was
making a regular $2,000 a year. So the Iowa College of Medicine,
whose primary purpose is to train doctors to attend Iowans, produced a poor but proud veterinary researcher for the Rockefeller
Institute and the state of New Jersey. Except for a three-year
hitch in the Navy and another three-year absence to do pharmaceutical research after the Princeton laboratory closed in 1949,
Shope has been with the Institute ever since 1925. He is also con-
sultant to the New Jersey State Conservation Department, which
sends Shope "everything with fur, feathers, or fins, when it dies."
Shope has turned up various "wonderful diseases," as he calls
them, in the wild and domesticated animal population of that
state.

For his first three years in Princeton, Shope studied tuberculosis and cholesterol, lived on $166 a month, supplemented the larder by hunting blackbirds, had a first son, and explained to these Easterners where he was from. When asked, he would say "*Eye*-a-wuh," as good Iowans do. Some looked puzzled and asked: "Do you mean Ohio?" He would explain, and they would say: "Oh! From Eye-*oh*-ah." It was almost more than a self-respecting Middle Westerner could bear.

In 1928 Paul Lewis sent him back to Iowa to investigate an epidemic of hog cholera, a virus disease. Dr. Charles Murray, professor of veterinary bacteriology at Iowa State, asked him: "Why don't you look into something we don't know anything about—hog flu?"

Murray described the disease and, as Shope recalls: "It sounded like a dead ringer for human influenza." Reading back issues of the *Journal of the American Veterinary Medical Association*, he found a most curious story. Hog flu appeared for the first time anywhere in the world in August 1918, in western Illinois. It caused serious losses at the National Swine Breeders' Show at Cedar Rapids, September 30–October 5, 1918. The pigs were mainly from the Middle West. Many were sent home, sick. Soon the disease had spread through five or six states. Millions of pigs became sick and thousands died. The big pandemic seemed to parallel that of the human pandemic for the first fall and winter. Whereas the virulent human flu then disappeared, never to return, hog flu continues to come back each fall and winter, infecting pigs that haven't previously had it.

The first to recognize "hog flu" and give it that name was a veterinarian named Dr. J. S. Koen, a Department of Agriculture hog-cholera inspector stationed in Iowa. Later Shope found it desirable to dignify hog flu as "swine influenza." Dr. Koen arrived at his judgment while the 1918 pandemic was still on, thereby bringing the wrath of farmers down on his head; they feared he would ruin the market for pork. Koen stood up to them, however. He insisted it was a new disease, hitherto unheard of, identical both in symptoms of sickness and in fatal lung damage with the human pandemic flu. In 1919 he said:

"I believe I have as much to support this diagnosis in pigs as the physicians have to support a similar diagnosis in man. The similarity . . . among people and . . . among pigs was so close, the reports so frequent that an outbreak in the family would be followed immediately by an outbreak among the hogs, and vice versa, as to present a most striking coincidence. . . . It looked like 'flu,' and it presented the identical symptoms of 'flu' and, until proved it was not 'flu,' I shall stand by that diagnosis."

To prove his point, of course, it was necessary to find the cause. Shope, listening to Dr. Murray, saw that if he could find the cause of hog flu he might have the answer to human flu, too.

It took him three years to uncover the swine-flu virus, and another five years to show its probable relationship to the human-flu virus. It took still another five years to explain how hog flu had happened to survive. Today most influenza experts would agree with him that the swine virus is probably a direct descendant of the virus that killed millions of people in 1918 and 1919.

Murray told Shope that if he wanted to experiment with transmitting hog flu he would have to export the disease out of Iowa to find a susceptible pig, for nearly one hundred per cent of the young pigs in that state had the disease by their first winter and, if they survived, as most did, they were thereafter immune to it. Shope arranged for Dr. Fred J. Crow of Iowa City to wire him when an epidemic started. Back in Princeton, Shope found Lewis enthusiastic for this new investigation; thus, when the telegram came in the fall of 1928, Shope was quickly on his way.

"I found sick pigs all over the place," is the way he put it.

He autopsied two that had died, put their lungs in thermos jugs, and shipped them to New Jersey via airmail, advising the pilots not to set the jugs near the exhaust pipe. Within a few days he received a telegram from Lewis: "I have a take. Looks like P. bacillus. Get smears of normal pig noses and come on home." This was easy, and Shope was soon on the train, carrying a bucket containing ice and some more infected pig lungs, in addition to his smears. He tipped the porter to put the bucket in the dining-car icebox.

Shope found that Lewis had cultured Pfeiffer's bacillus from the first two specimens. This was the same microbe that Richard Pfeiffer linked with influenza in the 1889–92 pandemic, and that again became implicated in the second wave of the 1918–19 pandemic—all in humans. Lewis had looked at the bacteria under the microscope, and was able to transmit the disease from pig to pig, via their snouts. The animals came down with an obvious flu. The scientists named their germ *Hemophilus influenzae suis,* to identify it with swine, though it appeared to be identical with Pfeiffer's bacillus, or plain *Hemophilus influenzae.*

Lewis told Shope to write a paper confirming this organism as the cause of influenza in swine—as soon as he had run a few more experiments to bolster up their evidence.

"Our joy was short-lived," Shope remembers. In further experiments, following the same pure-culture procedure Lewis used, he found himself unable to transmit hog flu or anything else. In 1929, during the next annual Iowa hog-flu epidemic, Shope obtained more specimens and got no further with these.

"We were," wrote Shope, "at this stage of the game, in almost the identical predicament . . . that investigators of human influenza had been at the close of the 1919 pandemic regarding the Pfeiffer bacillus. We had an organism . . . regularly present in the disease . . . but . . . it failed to produce the disease."

Yet he noticed that if he took crude lung suspensions or bronchial secretions from infected pigs, he *could* transmit the disease to susceptible Princeton pigs.

Lewis went off to Brazil to study yellow fever, and to die of it. Shope, working alone, turned to the question of a virus. They had tried a bacteria-free filtrate once in 1928, and it had failed. Again he filtered the bacteria out of his pathogenic bronchial juices and tried the filtrate on his pigs. In seven of ten cases it produced a disease—but not the hog flu that he knew. The new disease was much milder. The pig merely lost his appetite and coughed a little; he didn't become feverish and roll over and lie there as if he were about to die.

Shope, at the age of thirty, had isolated an influenza virus of some sort. But this virus by itself did not explain hog flu, a more severe disease than what he now saw in his hogs, any more than pure Pfeiffer's bacillus did. This was puzzling, and it would be some time before he found the explanation.

He published his findings on this new "filtrate disease," as he called it, in 1931. The next year, he tied the virus a little more tightly into his story by showing that pigs convalescent from the mild filtrate disease were immune to the severe hog flu. They did not become immune when inoculated with the bacteria alone, but they did so when injected with the filtrate-disease virus alone. Thus, to Shope must go the credit for producing the first successful vaccine against an influenza—in pigs.

However, this did not solve the question of regular hog flu as differentiated from filtrate disease. Hog flu had made its debut at the time the human race was suffering mightily from "Spanish influenza." If they were related, why was it that hog flu had continued to produce annual epidemics in the Midwest, whereas pandemic human flu had disappeared, giving way to the classic mild type?

Hog flu shows up for no more than three months of each year and disappears the other nine months. When it comes, it seems to explode all over the hog-flu region almost simultaneously, rather than spread from place to place. No susceptible pig escapes. Whole herds come down with it.

Human influenza is supposed to spread by person-to-person contact, along routes of travel and in crowds. Hogs live in crowds, but do not travel except on their one-way trip to market. How was it possible that flu could suddenly break out in every pigpen in the country?

Shope guessed that maybe the virus hid out someplace—perhaps in an intermediate host. He got the idea from the farmers. They had the notion that hog cholera, another virus disease, had something to do with angleworms. The pigs root them up and eat them. Shope's tests in 1941 proved that angleworms didn't lead to cholera. But he did implicate another worm in influenza— the lungworm. It lays eggs in the pig's lungs.

It makes a fantastic tale, but he was able to deduce that the lungworm was the hog-flu virus's home away from home. In the kind of laboratory and field studies that researchers describe as a "pretty piece of work," he established that the virus is a hitch-hiking, four-cycle parasite of a parasite. Not to make it sound more complicated than it is, let us summarize what he observed:

The lungs of swine are commonly infested with this parasite

known as lungworm. The worm lays its eggs at the bottom end of the finer tubes in the lungs. The hog coughs and, in so doing, swallows the eggs—they "reach the outer world in feces," explains Shope. Angleworms, burrowing through the soil, frequently eat the eggs. Within the angleworm, the eggs hatch and larvae develop.

The pig, a great rooter, eats the angleworms containing lungworm larvae. From the pig's stomach, the larvae pass into the blood stream and lymphatic drainage system and reach the lungs, where they grow into lungworms and lay eggs, and— This is where we came in.

It is also where the flu virus comes in—into the eggs.

The lungworm's whole cycle from hog to angleworm and back may take a month or several years. Shope found that the flu virus bravely digs in and rides it out, from hogs to eggs to ground to angleworms to larvae to next year's hogs. In effect, Nature sows the seeds of hog flu and harvests an epidemic.

To make the whole thing even more puzzling and complicated, Shope found that the virus becomes "masked"—a "masked marvel," to use Thomas Francis's phrase. While passing through the lungworm, it cannot be detected in any regular way, conceivably because it has thrown off its protein coat and pooled its nucleic-acid resources with those of its egg host. But it makes its reappearance, surely enough, when the pig becomes sick with flu. This may occur when the infected hog is exposed to some unusual stress—such as cold, damp weather, Shope found.

But how about hog flu as such?

In laboratory experiments, all that was necessary for Shope to produce a fatal or near-fatal flu instead of mild filtrate disease in a Princeton pig that had eaten Midwestern angleworms was to inject it with two or three doses of Pfeiffer's bacillus! Also, normal Iowa pigs, visiting Princeton, took sick in November when provoked in this manner.

Pfeiffer's bacillus is something you can find in normal hogs or humans at least ten per cent of the time, sometimes more. Ordinarily, it is harmless, but, according to Shope, in combination with the flu virus and cold weather the Pfeiffer bug becomes a holy terror.

And this, he speculates, was the cause of the high mortality in the 1918 human pandemic—an otherwise fairly mild virus working together with an otherwise fairly harmless bacterium to injure the lungs beyond their ability to function. The action is called *synergism*—a working together.

As Shope admits, there are some hardheaded influenza experts who don't go along with him when he jumps from hogs to humans. "You'd be surprised," he says, "how hard it is to get it out of your mind that one organism and one organism alone causes one specific disease."

That is the germ theory of disease, of course. A specific infection has a specific causative agent. Shope insists that the agent may be a partnership.

In any event, "in all probability, the swine virus was at one time, probably during the 1918 pandemic, a human pathogen," he says, meaning a cause of human and not merely hog flu.

The epidemiologists accept this virus part of his theory, we will see, a good deal more readily than they do the suggestion of synergistic action of the virus and the bacterium in human beings. There is no evidence for it in humans. The only way to test it, assuming the virus has not changed since it went underground, via pigs, in 1918, would be to expose susceptible human volunteers to a combination of swine-flu virus and Pfeiffer's bacillus. But it's not likely anyone will try to reproduce experimentally the virulent 1918 flu according to the Shope formula.

This pathogenic Pandora's box might contain another pandemic.

* 19 *

FRANCIS
AND HIS DOCTRINE
OF ORIGINAL SIN

EPIDEMIOLOGISTS—the public-health doctors who concern themselves with the nature of epidemics—lived in a sort of subclinical dread that someday a pandemic of virulent influenza would strike again. Their inability to find and control the factors that caused influenza to turn killer in 1918 contributed to their uneasiness. A leading flu fighter, Macfarlane Burnet, put the issue plainly: "I should define the essential objective of influenza virus research as the understanding of the conditions responsible for pandemic influenza of the 1918 type—and the establishment of the conditions necessary to prevent its reappearance."

Their latent fear approached the threshold of open anxiety in 1941. The 1918 pandemic had coincided with the First World War. Now here was a Second World War.

Each training camp becomes a crossroad not only for the nation's men but also for their home-grown germs. Green, susceptible recruits take in each other's bacterial and viral wash until each has had a few fevers and has built up new immunities. Then the troops go overseas for further, global mixing of microbiological life. This could be an outline for an epidemiologist's nightmare.

There appeared to be a real danger that pandemic flu might emerge as the worst of the Army's many acute respiratory diseases. But the situation was not quite as hopeless from the standpoint of disease prevention as it had seemed prior to Shope's isolation of an influenza virus from Iowa pig lungs.

In the middle 1930's, influenza became one of the most active and competitive fields of virus research, with discoveries coming so rapidly in the leading research centers of the United States, Great Britain, and Australia that it often was difficult for the researchers themselves to decide—or sometimes to acknowledge—who was first with one significant finding or another. Only one other field of modern research in a virus disease of humans seems to have produced quite so much rivalry, interest, and general activity, and that is poliomyelitis.

The epidemiologist singled out to lead the United States Army's attack on influenza was Dr. Thomas Francis, Jr. He is professor of epidemiology, and head of that department, in the University of Michigan School of Public Health, in Ann Arbor. The Armed Forces Epidemiological Board, headed by Dr. Francis G. Blake, his old teacher at Yale, chose Dr. Francis to be chairman of its Commission on Influenza. This put him in position to become the developer of the first influenza vaccine for mass use, with the help of Dr. Jonas E. Salk and others. It was a great honor to be so elected, but no great favor. As Francis has remarked, "the results are limited and the path is devious" in flu research.

Furthermore, one tough job leads to another. Because Francis had acquired a great deal of experience in the field-testing of flu vaccine, the National Foundation for Infantile Paralysis recruited him to direct the 1954 field trials and pass judgment on the Salk polio vaccine.

As author of the famous Francis Report on the Salk vaccine in 1955, Francis came much into the public eye and, in the turmoil surrounding the vaccine, became much more involved in public controversy than most scientists.

Allen Shoenfield of the Detroit *News* described Francis as a man "who might pass for a prosperous small-town banker with an exceptionally good tailor." Physically, he is a middle-sized, blue-eyed man with a clipped mustache, horn-rimmed glasses, a florid complexion, and sandy hair. He usually has about forty things to think about, in addition to the matter at hand. In fact, he has that number of persons working for him, in the University's modern School of Public Health building, where he presides as the nation's best-known epidemiologist and one of the world's foremost authorities on influenza.

For all of this, he is not an easy man to peg. Some reporters in 1954 and 1955 found him courteous but cold and distant; others, warm and frank; sophisticated; naïve; a hard-driving taskmaster, or "really a good guy under an emotionless exterior."

Dr. Francis—his friends call him Tommy or T.F.—has a reputation in virological circles for tough-mindedness, possibly because he is strongly oriented toward the control of disease, rather than toward its academic contemplation, and rather impersonally insists on directing the attention of his team to the yardage between it and the goal posts.

His close associates say that he never forgets anything, and "worries facts like a dog until he gets the answer he needs out of them." As one of them remarked, "You'd better be sure of your facts before you take them to him."

To all critics, scientific and journalistic, Francis usually manages to find a pointed rejoinder. To idealistic colleagues he quoted James Thurber during the polio-vaccine controversy: "If a woman wishes to go unarmed in paradise, she should be sure that's where she is." "There are times," added Francis tartly, "when critical experiments must be undertaken. . . . I dread the time when the scientist must have concurrence of all his colleagues and competitors." However, in reflecting upon the critical polio experiments of 1954 and the public sensation they produced, he confided: "I have become a little sensitive that some people seem to think the Francis Report is the only thing I ever did."

Francis, like one of his competitors in virology, Wendell Stanley, is Hoosier by birth—an event occurring in Gas City, Indiana, in 1900. His father was a Methodist clergyman who left the cloth for a few years to try his hand rolling steel and tinplate and re-

nas E. Salk, the world's best-known living medical scientist, "reads" test-tube cultures of viruses grown in living cells.

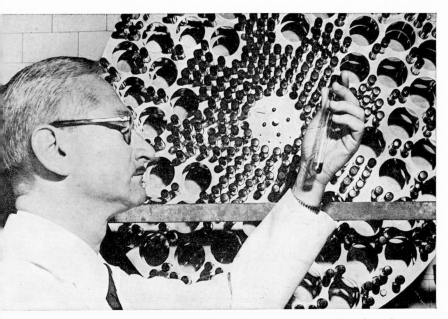

lbert B. Sabin, the leading critic of the Salk vaccine, inspecting a roller-tube culture, re-moved from a drum that revolves and stirs virus cultures during incubation.

PLATE 7

Hilary Koprowski. He was first to attenuate a polio virus and test it in a live-virus vaccine, taken by mouth rather than hypodermic needle.

Seymour S. Cohen, who discovered that the bacteriophage virus sheds its protein coat as it squirts its nucleic-acid core into a bacterium.

Salvador E. Luria, a leading investigator of the strange viruses that infect bacteria, can explain how a virus may cause cancer —in theory. (He is shown with Laura Sawyer, a research assistant.)

PLATE 8

fining oil in Indiana, and then returned to the clergy in Pennsylvania. Young Francis was raised in New Castle, Pennsylvania, in an atmosphere of service to the community. Quite probably, this background helped shape his destiny in public-health work. As a boy, Francis was impressed by the family doctor, Dr. William A. Womer, who let Tommy ride around on house calls via horse and buggy, and come into his office laboratory to watch microscopic examinations, urinalyses, and such. When Francis went to Allegheny College in Meadville, Pennsylvania, he thought he would become a chemist. Some time after serving in the Student Army Training Corps and working on the hospital detail during the 1918 pandemic, he decided to become a physician.

Upon graduation, he went to the Yale University Medical School (where for the first time he had influenza himself, four years after the pandemic). There, under the influence of Professor Blake, he became interested in respiratory diseases. After obtaining his M.D. degree in 1925, he stayed on at Yale as intern, resident, and then instructor. In 1928 he went to the Hospital of the Rockefeller Institute, and later into the Foundation's International Health Division, in charge of flu research. In his ten years in these illustrious surroundings he did some of his most important influenza research. He got interested in viruses while looking for the cause of the mild illness that commonly precedes lobar pneumonia.

Suddenly the whole question of influenza, an enigma since 1918, came alive. In 1933, two years after Shope discovered the swine virus, there came a report from the National Institute for Medical Research at Hampstead, London, of the discovery of a human-influenza virus. This established human flu as "a true virus disease," and generally confirmed Shope. But now pigs had to take a back seat.

The discoverers were Drs. Wilson Smith, Christopher H. Andrewes, and the late Sir Patrick P. Laidlaw.

London had a flu epidemic in 1933. Smith, Andrewes, and Laidlaw, working together, went on the assumption that it was caused by a filterable virus, and looked for one. They took throat washings from sixty-four flu patients, filtered the stuff, tried to culture it, and sought to transmit it to various animals. They had no luck at first.

Toward the epidemic's end, they tried to infect two ferrets with throat washings from one of the last available patients. A ferret is a domesticated relative of the weasel, sometimes used in hunting rabbits. The scientists swabbed filtered throat washings up the ferrets' noses. "Both animals became obviously ill on the third day," they reported in *Lancet*. The ferrets sneezed, yawned, ran a fever, and had a splendid nasal catarrh.

A flu virus had been recovered from humans at last.

Influenza can be readily passed from human to ferret nose, and ferret to ferret nose, the three scientists showed. But the animals had to be kept in strict isolation from infected humans and from each other. Otherwise, the animals might develop unintended, unnoticed infections of flu and become immune to experimental exposure.

As a matter of fact, the first virus isolated was lost. Nobody knew what became of it, but the disappearance of an agent of infection is a common occurrence in a laboratory. There simply comes a time when it no longer can be passed from one animal to another. Perhaps the virus dies out, becomes too weak to cause infection, or is neutralized by unsuspected antibodies. Immunology is filled with these little mysteries.

To make matters worse, the flu epidemic ended, so there were no more patients to furnish throat washings. Fortunately for science, Smith came down with the flu, quite probably having picked it up from one of the ferrets. His throat washings contained the virus. This was the first human virus strain to be preserved. The washings were dried and refrigerated. The virus now took its place beside the swine strain under the designation of "WS"—for Wilson Smith. It has been passed on "in perpetuity" to other laboratory hosts hundreds of times.

The British wrote to Shope and obtained some of his Iowa-grown virus to compare with theirs. They first thought that it produced a disease in ferrets "indistinguishable" from that of human origin. Later they detected some differences between the hog- and human-flu viruses. For one thing, hog flu hit a ferret much harder.

Now the hunt was really on. During 1934 and 1935 one development trod on the heels of the next. The British team and Francis, too, succeeded in passing the flu virus from ferrets to mice. After a few nose-to-nose passages in mice, the virus became for them a severe, often fatal disease. So now ferrets were left behind and mice took their place as the laboratory animals.

But Wilson Smith found he could cultivate his WS virus in hatching eggs, using Goodpasture's chick-embryo technique. And Francis and his Rockefeller associate, Dr. Thomas P. Magill, now of the State University of New York College of Medicine, in Brooklyn, induced a flu virus to grow in tissue cultures of chick embryos, adapting the Maitland technique to their own needs. As a matter of fact, they were able to pass the virus from one tissue culture to another seven hundred times without losing its power to sicken mice.

It fell to Francis to turn up two new strains of flu virus. In 1934 there was an influenza epidemic in Puerto Rico. He arranged to have some throat washings from human patients sent to him in New York. On the first try he got the virus going in ferrets, and within a year transferred it to his chick tissue cultures. One strain of this Puerto Rican export became PR8, the source of the first flu vaccine and a fixture of virus research ever since.

Francis isolated still another flu-virus strain in Philadelphia, and the British team uncovered two more.

These were exciting times. Shope in Princeton, Francis and Magill in New York, Smith, Andrewes, and Laidlaw in England, and Burnet in Australia mailed one another dried human sputum, ferret nose swabbings, dried mouse lungs, and, with immense good will, wrote long letters about what they were finding.

Laidlaw furnished an example of English scientists' frequent talent for writing good English in a lively manner without the verbal inhibitions and terminological twists that sometimes make a stiff mud of American scientific writing. He saw no reason to restrain himself when he and his colleagues tried to confirm their first findings: ". . . Our hopes were disappointed," he wrote in *Lancet* and then, after meeting with success: "We breathed again."

"We were naturally thrilled when we learned of Francis's success with an epidemic in another part of the world . . . ," wrote Laidlaw. "Imagine with what impatience we awaited news of the result of his tests to determine whether the Porto Rico strain was really identical with our strain. . . ."

Impatience was rewarded. The PR8 *was* identical with the WS, as far as Francis could find. The same was true of the Philadelphia strain. It looked as if everything might line up nicely—that the same virus caused flu whether it came from Puerto Rico, Philadelphia, or London.

The only thing out of step was Shope's "porcine strain," as the British called it. It was more virulent. Yet the swine virus bore some relationship to the WS and PR8 human-flu viruses.

The British found that the swine virus sometimes immunized ferrets against human flu (WS)—in other words, produced a cross-immunity. What they did was take some immune serum—from a ferret that had recovered from swine-flu infection—and mix it with nasal washings from a ferret sick with WS flu. They then put the mixture up the nose of a third, susceptible ferret. It did not get flu. Swine-flu antibodies, in other words, neutralized a human-flu virus.

Francis and Shope in 1938 found that the same thing happened in tests with the PR8 virus. Mice infected with PR8 flu proved to be immune to the swine virus. The opposite also was true. Mice first infected with swine virus were immune to PR8 virus.

Such cross-immunity is possible, we now know, if the antigens of viruses—the substances that incite the formation of antibodies —are closely enough related. In that case, the antigens produce specific antibodies that protect us against two or more viruses that are almost but not quite the same. But there is another possibility: through exposure to a large variety of related antigens we may develop non-specific antibodies that give a certain amount of overlapping protection against distinctly different types of viruses.

Dr. Keith E. Jensen (now at the Public Health Service laboratory in Montgomery, Alabama), while working with Francis in Ann Arbor, counted eighteen different antigens for Type A flu viruses alone. Each requires a different antibody. An antibody is known to be a protein molecule; there are hundreds of thousands of different protein molecules, so the answer to the question of specificity and non-specificity is far from being in the yes-no category.

Laidlaw was among the first to speculate on the swine virus as the cause of the 1918 flu pandemic. He held it "highly probable" that a combination of the swine strain and Pfeiffer's bacillus made the 1918 flu so potent. Laidlaw said in sum: ". . . The virus of swine influenza is really the virus of the great pandemic of 1918 adapted to the pig."

He based this intriguing observation on a 1935 study made by him and his two colleagues. They studied the presence of antibodies to the WS-flu strain in London residents of different ages. They found that most adults had some WS antibodies, and that a good portion of children under nine had them. In short, this virus infection had a wide and cumulative distribution according to age group.

They also looked for antibodies to the "porcine strain." None could be found in children under nine—that is, born after 1926—but there was an increasing percentage with hog-flu antibodies among teen-agers who were babies during or immediately after World War I. Among those over twenty—that is, born before 1915—more persons had antibodies to swine than to WS virus!

What a stumper that was! Andrewes, Laidlaw, and Smith said that the overlap in the WS and Shope strains was not enough for WS flu to "account for the occurrence of antibodies to swine influenza in human sera." They really appeared to be "immunologically distinct."

"It is unlikely," they agreed, "that the Londoners whose sera we examined acquired an infection from pigs, especially since swine influenza has not yet been recognized in England."

In brief, Laidlaw felt sure, hog flu must have originated in humans. It was a wonderful way to start an argument. Shope agreed with Laidlaw, of course; but Francis, Andrewes, and Burnet had them outnumbered; they did not accept the theory at the outset.

Francis, Magill, and Shope now got busy in New York and Princeton and did some more investigation. For one thing, they found that a hog *could* catch human flu (PR8), but PR8 infection alone or in combination with Pfeiffer's bacillus didn't behave like swine-flu virus. It was just barely infectious in hogs.

In 1936 the three Rockefeller men studied the flu antibodies of 137 persons of different ages. About half were immune to the PR8-flu virus; almost all the rest had a partial immunity. But swine flu presented quite a different picture. A high proportion of the adults had antibodies against the hog virus, but this was seldom true in children under the age of twelve—that is, born after 1924. In fact, only one child, six years old, was immune to swine flu.

Here was something other than purely circumstantial evidence. Until now the only link between swine and 1918 human pandemic flu had been that hog flu had appeared for the first time during the pandemic. Now both the British and American studies showed swine-flu antibodies generally present in the blood of adults in two parts of the world—one wholly free of flu in hogs—whereas in children born after the middle 1920's the antibodies were almost wholly absent.

"The presence in human sera of antibodies neutralizing swine influenza virus," said Shope, "is believed to indicate a previous immunizing exposure to, or infection with, an influenza virus of the 1918 type."

And, following this line of reasoning, one might surmise that the 1918 virus had virtually disappeared as a human problem some time between 1924 and 1926—at least in or about New York and London. Like some new star, briefly flaring into brilliance and then dying into obscurity again, this strange influenza had swept the civilized world and then, it seemed, taken refuge in the pig when man somehow gained the power to resist it—or, more probably, when the virus lost its virulence.

But Francis prefers to keep a tight rein on his imagination. For some years afterwards he believed that the swine-virus antibodies found in people of World War I vintage were the result of a broad spectrum of non-specific antibodies in their blood stimulated by repeated exposures to a variety of related virus strains; each antibody might have been caused by a specific antigen, to be sure, but a great conglomeration of antibodies, experiments have shown, can offer some general protection against antigens that themselves are strangers to the host.

There it seemed the argument might rest, inasmuch as it has not been possible to isolate a specific antibody, much less take it apart and compare its composition with that of another. The only test for its presence is with the antigen that produces the antibody, via the neutralization test.

Francis restated this viewpoint in 1953, and then within the year modified his thinking. What changed his mind was a remarkable study conducted by two men of his department, Drs. Fred M. Davenport and Albert V. Hennessey.

Serum is the clear plasma of the blood minus the clotting factor. Gamma globulin is the part of plasma which contains the antibodies. Davenport and Hennessey collected all the surplus serum and gamma globulin they could get their hands on, pooling it by age groups, from zero to sixty-five and over. From the University of Michigan Hospital came twenty-six pools representing 1,250 blood donors in the fall of 1952. From the Massachusetts Department of Public Health laboratories came lots of gamma globulin from 350 adult donors between 1943 and 1951.

They tested all these vital juices for antibodies. Now, of course, they had more strains of flu virus than swine, WS, and PR8 to think about. These are all of the same general type—A. In addition, they had to test for Type B, discovered by Francis in 1940; a new A-prime, uncovered in 1947; and the newer Types C and D.

But they now had a simpler way than the virus-serum neutralization technique to test for viruses and antibodies, a new way discovered by Dr. George K. Hirst, director of New York City's Public Health Research Institute.

In 1941, Hirst, then thirty-two, was busy growing flu viruses in hen's eggs at the Rockefeller Institute laboratories when he noticed something. Some chick blood had become mixed with the viruses and spilled into the dish beneath one egg. This was a common accident, but he noticed that the viruses were causing the red blood cells to clump!

This phenomenon is known as hemagglutination. Virologists have been celebrating Hirst's discovery ever since. Nearly a score of viruses, including mumps and smallpox, produce this reaction. What happens is that the viruses stick the blood cells together.

With the Hirst test, it is possible to make a spot check for the presence of viruses, and to estimate their number. Furthermore, one can make a hemagglutination-inhibition test instead of the regular neutralization test. For example, the laboratory worker can mix some human serum being tested for flu antibodies with the swine virus in a test tube, shake it well, add some O-type red blood cells, shake it again, and take a reading an hour later. If antibodies are present in the serum, they inhibit the virus and prevent the red cells from clumping. If they're not, the virus clumps the blood cells in normal fashion.

To determine the antibody level, or strength, the test can be made with serial dilutions in a whole rack of test tubes, with a machine to shake them. This constitutes a great saving on mice, money, and time.

What Davenport and Hennessey confirmed in their tests led to Francis's later observation that "you can tell how old a man is by his antibodies and conversely, what strains of virus were dominant when he was a youth."

For example, take the one strain of A-prime flu virus that first came to notice in 1947. They found antibodies to it at a maximum level in children under twelve, but low or even undetectable in persons over twenty. In contrast, children under eleven had no antibodies to the 1934 Type A virus (PR8). Persons in their twenties had a great deal of PR8 antibody; in the older age groups the amount declined some, but remained moderately strong right up to sixty.

And here was something for that romantic fellow Shope. Persons under the age of twenty-nine—that is, those born after 1923 —showed no swine-flu antibodies whatsoever. Older people, on the other hand, had plenty of swine-flu antibodies. The peak was in the age group between thirty-five and thirty-eight—persons under five years of age at the time of the 1918 pandemic.

Types B and C, as another contrast, showed a much more general distribution through all age groups after the first few years of life. Everybody seemed to have high immunity against C virus. It is known as a virus in search of a disease, because it so rarely expresses itself in clinical symptoms. Our antibodies do not give it a chance.

These stirring findings led Francis to state a new immunological concept or, as he likes to call it, the "doctrine of original antigenic sin." In brief, it's that the antibodies found in a person's blood tend mainly to reflect the strains of virus that infected him when he was a child. The first viruses that hit him determine a person's antibody pattern. This pattern "dominates his response to influenza throughout his life." Subsequent infections by other strains broaden his resistance, but it is unlikely that his resistance to these will be as strong.

Thus, what Francis hopes for in his new immunological concept is to convert the original sin of the first infection into a lifetime virtue. How? By vaccinating to lay down a foundation of antibodies in early childhood which will provide a sort of universal resistance to whatever comes along later in life.

Meanwhile Francis not only conceded but called attention to how clearly marked the swine-flu antibody pattern has become with the passage of time since 1918. The antibody is definitely present in persons now in their forties and definitely absent in all those born since the mid-twenties.

The new evidence, said Francis, "strongly supports the concept that a strain of virus similar antigenically to swine influenza virus was the prevalent one in 1918—but also that it was not a completely new strain at that time. . . ."

These were sweet words for Richard Shope. They prove that, much as humans may turn up their noses, they can learn something from pigs.

All the evidence adds up to the conclusion that the swine virus is a direct descendant of the virulent agent of 1918 influenza—a virus that for some reason lost its hold on man and joined the biological underground. This deduction does not, of course, explain why the 1918 virus, working in combination with Pfeiffer's bacillus or without it, was so virulent, or destructive of lung tissue, as the studies of Ernest Goodpasture and other pathologists showed. Ask Francis what causes virulence and he will tell you: "I don't know." Jensen adds: "This brings us to the brink of our knowledge."

But what about Francis's job of finding an influenza vaccine for the Army? While the flu fighters were following the antigen-antibody chain from one link to another, they were just as industriously looking for a vaccine.

The search began in 1935 as soon as they had the WS and PR8 strains of virus, and it increased in tempo as they noted that these viruses could be induced to grow in chick embryos, both within the eggshell and when transferred to test tubes. Just about everybody in influenza research tried his hand at making a flu vaccine between 1935 and 1940. Some, such as Francis and Magill, first sought an attenuated live virus that would produce antibodies but not flu in humans. Others—Smith, Andrewes, and Laidlaw, for instance—killed the virus with formaldehyde and found that the virus, even though dead and no longer able to multiply, would stimulate some antibody production when injected under the skin. They used infected mouse lungs as a source of their virus.

Popularity of the hatching egg as a culture medium for flu viruses waited other developments, soon to come. One was Burnet's working out of the details of growing the flu virus in the chick embryo. Even with this advance, however, the influenza-vaccine picture remained thoroughly confused. Indeed, efforts to clarify it only seemed to confound the virus hunters further. Some immunity could be produced by injecting fluids containing either live or killed virus. This much was certain, from many experiments. Yet it appeared that the degree of immunity might depend on the size of the dose of vaccine, just as sometimes it seemed that a large challenge dose of virus following vaccination overpowered antibody protection.

Sometimes a "flu shot" simply did not work. Or, when it did work, the protection did not last more than a few months, even though antibodies were still present. This could be because some vaccine doses were potent and others weak, or because the strains of virus in the vaccine were not the same as those causing the epidemic of flu at hand.

Here was another problem: it was difficult to run off a field trial that would show anything definite, one way or another. Some tests showed the vaccines to be forty- or fifty-per-cent effective in reducing the incidence of flu during an epidemic; others showed no difference between vaccinated and control groups; and still others found more flu in the vaccinated persons than in the controls.

With a vaccine that obviously yielded only a temporary immunity at best, it was important to vaccinate at a time when peak immunity would coincide with the peak of an epidemic. Nobody found a way to do that, because flu epidemics, while they usually come in the fall or late winter, are not wholly predictable. Many times the flu fighters prepared for one that never appeared.

"At this stage, then," Francis observed, "there was little consistent evidence from field trials that subcutaneous vaccination was effective in protection against influenza in epidemic times. . . ."

Nevertheless, in 1941 we were going to war, and there were those who remembered their feeling of helplessness during the 1918 catastrophe.

The Armed Forces Epidemiological Board asked Francis to see if he could not develop a concentrated, multi-strain, killed-virus vaccine against influenza. It rather expected, from the periodic character of the disease, that an epidemic of Influenza A might hit during the winter of 1942–3. Such an epidemic could constitute a grave setback in military training. Francis suggested that what he could produce might be only a temporary expedient. The Board said it would settle for that.

The epidemic did not materialize that winter, but the vaccine did. The Commission engineered a vaccine containing Francis's 1934 A-type strain from Puerto Rico, a newer Type A strain recently isolated—just in case there had been any immunological changes in the virus—and the 1940 B-type flu virus. At the Commission's direction, the pharmaceutical companies cultivated the viruses in eggs, concentrated them, killed them with formaldehyde, and suspended them in salt water.

They now used a sort of biochemical pin-cushion method of concentrating the viruses—an adaptation of the Hirst hemagglutination test, in which flu viruses cause red blood cells to clump. The viruses, grown in chick embryos, stick to blood cells, and hence can be removed from the egg protein fluid and finally washed out of the blood cells, in high concentrations. Later, Wendell Stanley, then operating a vaccine-research center for the Armed Forces at the Rockefeller Institute laboratory in Princeton, added another method of flu-virus purification, using the ultracentrifuge to separate virus and proteins.

Francis meticulously arranged the test conditions so that this time there could be no question whether the vaccine succeeded or failed. As a matter of fact, the matched control system he imposed became a model for future epidemiological studies, including one half of the 1954 Salk vaccine field trials. The basic scheme was to give the vaccine, the real thing, and a placebo, or dummy injection, to alternate students in the Army Specialized Training Program without letting the volunteer, the physician who gave the injection, or, for that matter, the members of the research team know which was which until all observations were complete and the data ready for analysis. Thus, the coldly objective scientist could eliminate all possibility for psychological bias on the part of a human guinea pig or the doctor diagnosing his subsequent illnesses, either of whom might conceivably be susceptible to suggestion.

Some eight thousand received injections in the late fall of 1942.

But where was the epidemic of Influenza A? The experts waited all winter for it. As Francis said, rather tersely: "It did not occur." But they did find that their vaccine stimulated excellent antibody levels and that in a four-month period these fell off only about one-third. The question mark was bigger and more tantalizing than ever.

Would the vaccine prevent flu?

In October and November 1943, Francis and his fellow Commission members went after the answer again. They gave a vaccine containing PR8 and still another new strain of Type A virus to 6,263 men in the Army Specialized Training Program at nine different colleges, inoculating still another 6,211 with a placebo. This time the vaccine barely had time to take effect before influenza began to appear—and it was a Type A epidemic. There were outbreaks in various parts of the country all winter.

The vaccine worked!

Those who received it had a 2-per-cent rate of hospitalization for influenza, against a 7-per-cent rate in the comparison group. The reduction in flu thus was about 70 per cent. In two of the nine locations, flu broke out at about the same time vaccination was going on, enabling the researchers to analyze the incidence of flu in the vaccinated and unvaccinated during the time the vaccinated were developing antibodies. At first there was no difference in the attack rate in the two groups, but after six to seven days, as the vaccine produced antibodies, the flu rate for the vaccinated dropped sharply while that for the control group continued to rise.

In 1945 the Commission had a good opportunity to test its B-type vaccine against epidemics of Influenza B in Ann Arbor and in New Haven, where George Hirst was doing a study. The reductions in flu incidence were truly spectacular—about 89 per cent at the University of Michigan and 96 per cent at Yale.

As a consequence, the Army in 1945 decided to vaccinate every man with Type A and B vaccine manufactured for it by the pharmaceutical companies. Eight million men were vaccinated.

But influenza vaccine produces results of a boom-or-bust sort, unlike anything ever seen with smallpox and yellow-fever vaccines, where the viruses behave in a stable, dependable manner. There was no new epidemic until 1947, a year in which 1,238,-000 American troops had vaccine against Influenza A and B. This time the vaccine was completely ineffective.

Now, in another one of the fine field trials of the Francis type, with 10,328 vaccinated and 7,615 unvaccinated, the flu epidemic struck rather late—in March. The incidence among those vaccinated was 7.19 per cent; in the control group, 8.09 per cent. What a disappointment that was.

The cause of the failure was soon revealed. This epidemic was due to a new strain of Type A not affected by the vaccine-produced antibodies that were abundantly present. The Influenza Commission called this new acquaintance A-prime.

Obviously, it would be necessary to make a new vaccine incorporating A-prime as well as the others if flu vaccine was to amount to anything. Now, we imagine, even the tireless Francis must have suddenly felt rather tired—almost as if he were coming down with the flu himself.

Would it ever be possible to produce an effective vaccine? That was not quite the right question. The Commission on Influenza had shown it was possible, but would it be possible to keep up with—let alone stay ahead of—new strains of virus as they kept showing up? Whether the vaccine produced antibodies or not was hardly important if they were good only against yesterday's flu.

The appearance of A-prime underscored what the flu fighters had had an inkling of long before in the case of the swine and WS viruses and became much more aware of when Francis turned up Type B. Strain variation is a characteristic of influenza viruses.

Virologists are still far from completely agreed about the nature of these variations. Burnet and Stanley, for instance, plainly label the different strains as mutations, or evolutionary changes in the hereditary characteristics of the virus. Stanley ran into the problem with the many strains of tobacco-mosaic virus which turned up while he was proving that his TMV crystals were specific agents of infection. What mutation means, generally speaking, is a change in the arrangement of genes in the chromosomes of the living cell's nucleus—more broadly speaking, a change in the chemical composition of nucleic acid, such as is found at the core of viruses.

Epidemiologists like Francis, however, shy sway from this view and speak of "antigenic variation," on the ground that they prefer not to commit themselves in genetic matters. But this is like explaining a change in the weather as a "meteorological variation." Something causes this "reshuffling within the same universe," as Francis phrases it, but he maintains that nobody quite knows what.

But he does know that new or different strains of flu virus turn up and slip by old antibodies. As early as 1942 his Commission sought to cope with this problem by setting up a series of Strain Study Centers, under the direction of Dr. Magill, to keep a constant eye out for new flu viruses.

In 1948 the World Health Organization extended this idea. WHO established a World Influenza Center at the National Institute of Medical Research in London, under the direction of Dr. Andrewes, one of the team that discovered the first human-flu virus. American Army and Public Health Service laboratories agreed to co-operate.

The plan was to establish a world-wide network of laboratory "listening-posts." When influenza broke out in any part of the world and could not be identified from the antigen and antibody "fingerprints" on file for all known types, virus samples could be flown to London for expert study. If a new strain turned up, it could be identified and incorporated in a new vaccine that might be useful in heading off epidemics until another mutant appeared.

The question was, when would another big epidemic hit?

The answer came in April 1957.

LAST GREAT PLAGUE,
1957 MODEL

Asian influenza first appeared, as far as it can be traced, somewhere along the road between two towns in the province of Kwei-
chow, in southwestern China, in February 1957. Chinese refugees
carried the disease into Hong Kong, where 250,000 persons, ten
per cent of the population, came down with it.

The New York Times and its far-flung foreign correspondents
were well ahead of American epidemiologists on this epidemic.
Dr. Maurice R. Hilleman, then chief of respiratory-disease research at the Walter Reed Army Medical Center, in Washington, said that he first learned of it from the *Times* issue of April
17, 1957. He could see from the ten-per-cent attack rate that
"something unusual was afoot."

The next day Hilleman cabled the Army's 406th Medical General Laboratory in Zama, Japan, to investigate and recover the
virus. The Laboratory dispatched a medical officer to Hong Kong
to investigate.

Thanks to the *Times* and his own initiative, Hilleman became
the first man to proclaim the Asian flu as a new strain of Type A.
The first two samples of throat washings and patient serums

reached him by courier on May 13. The 406th had obtained one specimen from a Navy man who had caught the disease in Hong Kong and come down with it while aboard ship en route to Japan. Hilleman cultivated this virus and shared its progeny with the Public Health Service, the Commission on Influenza, and other laboratories in the WHO network. Some of its offspring went to the pharmaceutical laboratories for vaccine production. It was called A-Japan–305–57, meaning it was laboratory specimen No. 305 of a Type A virus isolated in Japan in 1957.

Soon throat washings and patient serums (all sealed, of course) were flying out of the Far East in all directions. Richard Shope's son Captain Robert Shope, a medical officer stationed in Malaya, flew to Singapore, obtained samples from the flu epidemic there, and sent them to Andrewes in London. The virus was a new one to everybody.

Well, almost new. It appeared that nobody had antibodies to Asian-A until a Dutch doctor found some in the blood of Netherlands residents in their seventies and eighties, dating it, according to the Francis doctrine, with the pandemic of 1889–92. Presently a few American oldsters in Pennsylvania and Massachusetts turned up Asian-A antibodies, too! Someone recalled that the 1889 flu had been called Siberian fever, placing it on the same continent with the new one from southwestern China.

Asian flu proved to be highly infectious, though mild. From southwestern China it rolled rapidly in all directions, reaching even Moscow.

The first place it was reported in the United States was at the naval station in Newport, Rhode Island, in early June. But California was its chief port of entry and principal take-off point in this country. A California girl carried it to a church camp in Grinnell, Iowa, and a California Scout carried it to a Boy Scout jamboree in Valley Forge, Pennsylvania.

Arriving in the off-season for flu, it didn't spread fast in the United States during the summer. There were only small sporadic outbreaks, but there were good indications that the virus was being well seeded throughout the country from these various crossroads of person-to-person contact.

Both military and civilian health leaders quickly took stock of the situation. Contemplating its own long experience, the Commission on Influenza recommended that the military services purchase and administer as quickly as possible an extra-potent vaccine containing the Asian virus only and then follow it up two months later with a booster injection of a multi-valent vaccine of weaker strength but containing additional Asian virus plus equal amounts of the Shope swine, human Type A, Type A-prime, and B strains. This, according to the Francis doctrine, would produce maximum antibody protection in an all-round manner.

Surgeon General Leroy E. Burney of the Public Health Service meanwhile warned the public that it could expect a big epidemic—perhaps a pandemic—in the fall. He called in the six manufacturers licensed to make flu vaccine and asked them to put on a crash program—to make a single-strain Asian-flu vaccine and make it fast. As all knew, pandemic influenza had a history of hitting hard with the first coming of cold weather and then striking again later in the winter. For the first time, Burney said, it seemed possible to anticipate an epidemic of influenza and prepare for it.

It appeared that the Public Health Service was determined not to be caught unawares during a public-health crisis, as it had been during the 1955 polio-vaccine mess. Consequently, the American press and its readers in 1957 were the beneficiaries of one of the most complete explanations to patients in medical history.

The Public Health Service did a first-rate job. It alerted the medical professions, organized the experts, formed committees, called conferences, issued statements, and published pamphlets. It issued a glossary of terms relating to influenza, defining those elusive substances, antigens and antibodies. It even defined *surgeon general* as "the head of the Public Health Service." This was correct as far as PHS went, and overlooked only the chief medical officers of the Army, Air Force, and Navy. Each is a surgeon general.

The manufacturers produced, but they ran into a lot of trouble trying to make this strange virus grow abundantly in chick embryos. They were able to make the single-strain vaccine, but it was only about forty per cent as potent as Francis and his experts said it should be. It was a great deal better than nothing, however.

The pharmaceutical laboratories received their first Asian-A on May 22 and had the first 500,000 doses of the new vaccine ready for release on August 12. They promised 60,000,000 cubic centimeters—15,000 gallons of vaccine—by February. They delivered 50,000,000 cubic centimeters by December, when demand for the vaccine dwindled.

Burney's prediction was accurate. In late September the virus took wing, like a misguided missile.

The National Health Survey estimated that 11,933,000 persons were sick in bed with acute upper-respiratory diseases for one or more days during the week of October 13–19. That was the high point. It was an incredible number. The situation didn't get back to anywhere near normal until December. At that time the cumulative total of cases was around 100,000,000, with well over 300,000,000 days in bed. Not all this was Asian flu. It included everything in the respiratory-infection line. Burney estimated that 20,000,000 of these cases, or one in five, were Asian flu.

Again, flu was a somewhat nebulous thing, just one more fever that you treat without specific cure by going to bed, taking some aspirin, and going on a liquid diet. Nobody can offer you anything "better"—unless you are susceptible to advertising. Probably a hundred or a thousand substances will kill the flu virus on contact, but nobody knows how to keep a germicide in contact with all the viruses in your nose and throat, or in the cells of your mucous membranes.

People went to bed in droves. But there was nothing dramatic about it—except in the statistics on employee absences kept by such enterprises as the Metropolitan Life Insurance Company. Metropolitan Life noted that the number of its employees throughout the country who stayed home sick for eight days or more during the last quarter of 1957 was 247 per thousand, or about one in four. This was eighty-five per cent higher than the corresponding period in 1956.

In New York, right at the time in mid-October when Asian flu was at its nationwide peak, the *Times* carried an article headlined IS IT A REAL EPIDEMIC? The article alluded to anonymous authorities who conceded that school absenteeism was running as high as thirty per cent, but who claimed that not one of these cases had been determined to be Asian flu. These unnamed "authorities" were plain silly—and so was the *Times* for listening to them. The claim ignored the fact that doctors rarely go to the trouble of diagnosing any flu except by epidemic and clinical signs, unless for research purposes. The disease is commonly over with before doctors can get a report back from the laboratory. It was an epidemic all right—a world-wide pandemic.

Statistically, the death rate remained low—but not as low as most people probably thought. Figures for the entire country were not available, but from the data the National Office of Vital Statistics did have, we can now roughly estimate that nearly 23,-000 persons died of influenza and/or pneumonia in a four-month period. The normal expectation was that some 12,000 would have died without the epidemic, so the Asian flu might be blamed for 10,000 or 11,000 deaths. While the 23,000 amounted to only about one twentieth of the 1918 toll in the corresponding months, it could not be said that Asian flu was exactly a harmless complaint, or that public-health people were needlessly alarmed.

Neither can we picture the mass vaccination program as a great triumph in disease prevention. Nevertheless, Surgeon General Burney's estimate of the situation in December 1957 was reasonable: "The rapid production and distribution of the vaccine over the past two months has unquestionably reduced the impact of the epidemic. Many millions of persons, we can be certain, did not contract Asian flu because of the protection of the vaccine."

Several groups ran evaluation studies of the vaccine. A study by the National Institute of Allergy and Infectious Diseases gave a fair indication of the results. Thirty-two Maryland convict volunteers were vaccinated. Two weeks later a challenge dose of live Asian-flu virus was put up their noses to test their immunity. Fourteen, or 44 per cent, got flu. Twenty-three unvaccinated volunteers also were exposed to the virus; eighteen, or 78 per cent, got the flu. Thus, a rather weak vaccine, given on a one-shot basis, reduced the chances of infection upon direct exposure by close to 45 per cent.

Meanwhile the Commission on Influenza conducted four field studies in much the same manner as it had done in 1942, 1943, 1945, and 1947, with the co-operation of member groups. More than ten thousand persons received vaccine and about eight thousand acted as controls. Asian-A vaccine of rather variable strength, from weak to strong, reduced the incidence of the disease by about one half to two thirds. The vaccine provided "an important degree of protection," but the antibody response was "suboptimal," the Commission reported.

No serious untoward effects were noted in the evaluation studies, but from five to ten per cent of those vaccinated felt mildly indisposed. With the stronger vaccine, there were some sore arms and transitory fevers.

The flu experts watched the Asian virus for signs of the 1918 virulence, but there was no sharp increase in its fatal effects. There was virtually no sign of Pfeiffer's bacillus, though some did die of a staphylococcus pneumonia following Asian flu.

The experts especially watched for signs of the notorious W-curve in the death rate. Ordinarily the graph of winter pneumonia losses, when figured according to age, takes the form of a U or a V, being high among infants, low among young adults, and high again in old age. But in 1918 it took the form of a W, the death rate hitting three high points—among infants, young adults, and the aged. There was no W in the Asian-A pandemic, and the U remained rather flat.

A second wave came in Japan while the first wave was still striking the United States. There was a second American wave in early 1958, but it was only about half as bad as the October one. The influenza-pneumonia death rate remained high, however. Francis said: "Speculators may place bets on two waves, three waves, or home permanents. But the evidence is against further marked change in severity of a virus which has already been passed so many times in susceptibles."

As previously mentioned, Davenport, who succeeded his boss as chairman of the Army's Commission on Influenza in good time to catch the brunt of the preparedness work, looks upon influenza as the "last great plague of mankind."

It is exceedingly doubtful if we have seen the last of the last great plague as yet. The virus appears to be too artful a dodger to be knocked out permanently by any vaccine presently available. Davenport emphasizes that small children bear the burden of influenza. Thus, for any immunity against influenza to be of great value, it should first be of use in children.

But here's the rub: the Public Health Service warned that "children generally have had somewhat more severe reactions to influenza vaccine than adults," and thus left the matter of flu shots for any particular child to the advice of the child's physician.

The need for a combination of high potency and low toxicity was a problem still to be solved. Said Davenport: "It is our belief that eventually we will obtain all of the antigens of the influenza A and B families and that they can be incorporated in a polyvalent vaccine."

This would be a sort of family-size package including antigens to stimulate Grandma's antibodies as well as Junior's. The ideal time for its first administration is clear: in infancy, the formative years, when the original antigenic sins are committed.

As we have seen, the Asian-flu pandemic provided fresh support for the doctrine that as the twig is bent so grows the tree, immunologically as well as other ways. Some old people with no apparent antibodies to Asian A began, oddly enough, to make antibodies to that strain when vaccinated with straight A vaccine (PR8).

In other words, our antibody system has "memory," as Francis contends. It tends to fight what it remembers best, the old enemies rather than the new. This response is called "anamnestic," referring to the faculty of memory.

Two things are obvious. Influenza is produced by a thoroughly unstable virus, and the disease has fascinated many first-class scientists. Let us see if we can sum up some of its characteristics and maybe even explain them a little.

1. Flu confuses people. A dozen nose, throat, bronchial, and lung infections present more or less the same symptoms as flu— even incipient polio. Unlike more respectable childhood diseases, you can have it more than once.

2. Flu doesn't scare people. We are accustomed, sometimes

grateful, to take to our beds periodically with sore throats, coughs, chest colds, and "la grippe." Nor does it excite family doctors. It only overworks them. Anyway, there is nothing much they can do about it unless it turns to pneumonia.

3. Flu kills in combination with something else, for the most part—childhood vulnerability, pregnancy, a chronic condition such as heart disease, or the debilities of old age. When it murders people in their beds, it often has a bacterial accomplice.

4. All the viruses in the Influenza A family behave like gypsies. They come to town and pitch camp, cause a big epidemic and then smaller epidemics that keep coming back for a few years, and finally steal away, to be replaced eventually by a new group with different characteristics.

Nobody knows where the new acquaintance comes from—or where it goes. There is some reason to suspect that different virus strains may lie "seeded" and "sleeping" in the population, the earth, or some intermediate host, and then, because of circumstances we do not understand and cannot control, rise up and go on the prowl. The riser-upper may behave like a tiger or a tabby cat, but it's quick on its feet and moves fast when fully awakened.

Whether the flu virus has the unleopard-like ability to change its spots, as many virus chemists and geneticists believe, is still a question. Most think it goes through true mutations, a new strain arising as an old one disappears, with something chemically changed or added. But there is also an inkling that the new strain may actually be an old, dormant strain that has suddenly come to life.

5. Above all, the flu virus is versatile, with a strong capacity for self-preservation—as good, quite possibly, as that of man himself. As Richard Shope once pointed out, a virus, as a parasite dependent on a living host cell, is up against it—whichever way it jumps. If a virus kills its host, it may die with him. If the host recovers, the virus gets slugged by the antibodies produced. But the nebulous flu virus appears to have found a way around this dilemma and incorporated certain escape-artist mechanisms in its make-up.

PART FOUR:

SECOND
BIG
BREAK-THROUGH
IN VACCINES

THE VIRUS THAT

DESTROYS

PEACE OF MIND

THE VIRUSES that cause paralytic poliomyelitis are old enough, as man's parasites go. They presumably have populated the earth for thousands of years. Yet they have struck him—particularly his children—far harder in the twentieth century than at any other time in history. In fact, polio might be called the disease of modern living. The higher our health standards, the less natural resistance and the more polio we seem to have had—prior to the Salk vaccine, at any rate. This is contrary to our experience with epidemic diseases caused by bacteria; these have tended to recede as living conditions improved, even without a vaccine.

One of the most amazing things about poliomyelitis is that no epidemic of it was noted until seventy-one years ago. Large epidemics of other virus diseases, such as smallpox, yellow fever, influenza, and measles, are recorded much farther back in history. Then, in 1887, Stockholm had an outbreak. Forty-four cases were reported.

The first United States epidemic of any size occurred in Otter Creek, Vermont, in 1894. There were 119 cases. Other local epidemics followed, but not repeatedly in any given place. The first big American epidemic—huge for polio—occurred in 1916. That summer, polio killed 6,000 and paralyzed 27,000. We've had bigger polio years in total reported cases, but nothing equaling 1916 in the rate of death and paralysis. The epidemic hit hardest in New York City, paralyzing about 9,000—2,000 fatally. There was literally panic in the streets as thousands of families fled, or tried to flee, seeking refuge on farms, in suburban towns and summer resorts. Guards posted along the highways turned back many New Yorkers at gun point in an effort to quarantine the city and keep the epidemic from spreading elsewhere.

Before this modern era, family doctors occasionally saw "infantile paralysis" in babies, but rarely more than one or two cases in one place or at one time. They sometimes diagnosed it as "teething paralysis" or "summer complaint." The infection started just about like any other—with fever, a sick feeling, headache, nausea. Stiffness or pain in the neck and back, the first signs of paralysis, came only after the first stage had passed, the fever disappearing and then returning in a more severe form. Only then would come the torturing muscle pains of acute poliomyelitis.

Doctors did not regard the disease as especially communicable, and not at all in the class of measles, chickenpox, mumps, or the other usual childhood diseases. Such bacterial diseases as scarlet fever, diphtheria, typhoid fever, pneumonia, and, worst of all, tuberculosis were far more menacing, to children as well as adults.

Pathologically speaking, poliomyelitis is an inflammation of the spinal cord and brain. "Polio" means *gray;* "myel" means *marrow.* When motor cells in the gray marrow of the spine are damaged, the muscles that they control cannot move. An unused muscle withers.

At the top of the spinal cord, where it enters the brain, is a cone of nerve tissue called the spinal bulb, medulla oblongata, or brain stem. This bulb controls breathing. When polio virus damages it, the result is bulbar poliomyelitis, paralysis of the chest muscles, and often death.

On the other hand, the virus can invade the spinal cord—and

also the brain—and *not* produce paralysis. And sometimes the paralysis is only temporary. These outcomes in paralytic polio are actually more frequent than permanent crippling.

One of polio's peculiarities is that, while the virus will infect the brain itself, it doesn't do any great damage there. The motor-nerve impairment may make a polio child a somewhat slow learner, but there doesn't appear to be any deficiency in intellect or personality owing to brain injury.

Polio researchers have come to understand the nature of the virus only in the last ten years or so. Today the virus does not sound nearly so terrifying as the paralysis it produces. A great many of us have been infected with one or another, sometimes all, of the three varieties of polio virus without ever knowing it. At least, the virus infects our intestines, in the same manner as the viruses of "intestinal flu" or some gastrointestinal upsets.

In fact, the polio virus's most frequent habitat the world over (as far as we now know) is the gastrointestinal tract, or alimentary canal, rather than the nerves. It invades the cells in the throat or the intestinal walls. As a consequence, many of us become naturally immune to any polio that might reach and injure our spinal cords.

Polio viruses can be found in both primitive and civilized countries with never a sign of an epidemic. A good microbiologist can isolate polio viruses in the summer excretions of a healthy population almost at will, unless that population is a particularly isolated one, such as an Eskimo village. An outbreak of poliomyelitis depends, it appears, on the number of susceptible persons available, plus the chance of exposure.

Some scientists trace paralytic polio as a disease of civilization to the rise of the water closet (flush toilets first were called water closets because ordinary closets often were converted to toilets and lavatories). Whereas sewers—and we might also add water heaters, bathtubs, and abundant soap—have washed away many of the pathogenic, or disease-causing, microbes that beset us, cleanliness lays us open to paralytic polio for one simple reason.

Under less sanitary conditions, babies are exposed, either directly or indirectly, to one another's filth to such an extent that they are almost universally contaminated with polio virus and, of course, whatever else is to be had. Evidence indicates that polio in small babies is mainly a mild, passing infection. They have so-called "inapparent infections," produce antibodies, and become immune—save for a few who die or the rare infant who survives as a cripple. (In the old days such deaths tended to get lost from sight in a generally high infant-mortality rate, and the same is true in more primitive countries today.) Specific resistance acquired in babyhood tends to blend with a general increase in resistance to disease as people grow older, with the result that almost all who survive infancy escape polio for life. This is why old-time doctors saw polio only as infantile paralysis.

Now, however, we try to keep our babies isolated and antiseptically clean. But the cleaner we keep our babies, the more we prolong their susceptibility. The more we prolong their susceptibility, the more polio we see in older children and young adults—at a time when the disease strikes much harder and the paralyzing effects are much more severe.

Both the civilizing effect and the age shift are clear in the studies of Dr. John R. Paul, Yale University professor of preventive medicine. Paul, a small, quiet, restrained physician, is an elder statesman of polio research, recognized as a leading authority on how the disease spreads.

In his field studies he has found immunity to poliomyelitis to vary from close to none in nearly all children of two Eskimo villages to almost solid immunity from the age of five upwards in Arabs. Said he: "When poliovirus does penetrate into Arctic areas and is given the opportunity to attack these highly susceptible 'virgin' populations, we witness a severe epidemic involving not only children but parents and grandparents as well." In contrast, "there would be little need today to vaccinate children in North Africa or the Middle East, unless one restricted the priority group to the youngest children . . . of seven months to three or four years.[1]

"In the United States," Paul summarized, "There are all gradations of susceptibility and immunity. Not only do the poliomye-

[1] John R. Paul: "Indications for Vaccination Against Poliomyelitis," *The Journal of the American Medical Association*, December 29, 1956.

litis incidence rates vary geographically between northeastern, north central and southern areas . . . but the age distribution of acute paralytic cases within these regions also differs somewhat. Differences in the latter may exist between white and nonwhite populations. In some areas, such as the Latin-American population of . . . southern Texas, there is a situation almost like North Africa. . . . In others, which represent some of our 'best areas,' it is almost frighteningly like the Arctic. . . .

"There are gradations within the same city. A population living in the poorest urban area acquires infection and gains its immunity to poliomyelitis . . . in infancy; an urban or suburban population living in or near the same city, but in better quarters, acquires infection and gains its immunity later in life. . . .

"One of the disturbing features about the age incidence of paralytic poliomyelitis in this country today is the increasing frequency of adult cases, often in young parents. Young parents run the extra risk of being infected by their children, who may pick up the virus perhaps in a nursery school, and . . . expose . . . particularly their mothers, to a heavier dosage of virus than the latter ordinarily would receive. . . ."

Natural immunity to one or more types of polio ranges from as high as eighty-five per cent in the lower to as low as fifteen per cent in the higher American socioeconomic groups. In the pre-Salk vaccine era, polio authorities estimated the cost of lifelong freedom from polio for the population as a whole was one case of paralytic polio for every 100 to 200 persons harmlessly infected with the virus. But that one victim became more and more visible publicly.

In the 1916 epidemic the most susceptible age group was one to five. In recent years the peak danger age shifted to the five-to-nine group. Following mass vaccination, however, children under five again became the group suffering the most polio.

The number of reported cases in the United States began a sharp climb in 1946, when there were more than 25,000, including both paralytic and non-paralytic, and reached a peak of nearly 58,000 cases in 1952. Somewhat more than half of these were paralytic; 3,300 died.

Public-health crusaders feared that poliomyelitis was becoming a major problem. Until these repeated epidemics in the post-war years, some had been quick to point out that there were many larger disease problems receiving far less attention than polio—mental illness, to take one of many examples. This is still true. Heart disease, cancer, and accidents are still the great killers and cripplers—of children as well as adults. In total sickness, influenza, measles, and the common cold are far more frequent health problems than polio. As a matter of fact, if one studies the communicable-disease reports of his own state, he is apt to find that in mere frequency dog bites top all other public-health troubles.

But polio is different. It is necessary to appreciate its differences to understand why it has become the most studied and most talked-about virus disease.

The epidemics usually come during the summer vacation, suddenly striking children when they are generally most active. They become individually vulnerable during periods of temporarily lowered resistance resulting from fatigue, injury, or minor infections, it appears.

The disease strikes somewhere just often enough so that most of us know of someone who was healthy and happy and then acutely ill, with the outcome in doubt. Later he reappeared, dragging himself on crutches and in braces, or pushing about in a wheelchair, permanently paralyzed in some part of his body. Or he was reported to be clinging to life in an "iron lung" that does the work of paralyzed chest muscles. There are three hundred thousand of these visible cripples in the United States.

Parents have said, with utter realism, that they would much rather see their child dead than remaining a lifelong cripple, a physical and economic burden to himself and to his relatives. Crippling polio is expensive. The victim is a tremendous liability. He makes family life more difficult.

That's the cruel, hard fact of the matter.

But the sentimental side is just as strong.

The idea of a crippled child of any kind gets people all stirred up. And, by and large, polio survivors seem to be a courageous, determined people who evoke pity or admiration. They don't hide themselves away—so it seems. They make heroic efforts to

be self-sufficient. They go on to college and become president of
the United States—or, at any rate, parents themselves. With any
kind of help, many make a winning fight.

To the story of polio we must add another dimension not common to scientific research—the National Foundation for Infantile Paralysis. This organization—in 1958 it dropped "for Infantile Paralysis"—has been tremendously effective in pre-empting
public attention in behalf of polio victims. The Foundation has
raised approximately a half-billion dollars by voluntary subscrip-
tion and, very intelligently, assigned about eight per cent of this
to support of research conducted by some of our best-trained scientists. Whereas the Federal government and other foundations
played a major role in financing research against other diseases,
the N.F.I.P. paid almost all of the bill for polio research in the last
twenty years.

The world's most famous polio victim and four-time President
of the United States, Franklin D. Roosevelt, established the National Foundation for Infantile Paralysis in 1938, following the
remarkable success of his birthday balls in raising money for
the Warm Springs Foundation, a polio rehabilitation center in
Georgia.

Dr. Paul de Kruif, author of *Microbe Hunters,* apparently gave
Roosevelt the idea for a national foundation that would not simply aid polio cripples, the foundation's first objective, but also
finance a basic research program to prevent or cure the disease.
Many doctors personally responsible for sick patients regarded
De Kruif, an ex-bacteriologist, as a popular medical writer who
too often went overboard. His often reported "golden promise of
cure" in one disease or another was many times well ahead of the
doctors—and of reality. Conscientious physicians well know, from
long experience, that promising new leads in medical research
usually wind up as false hopes.

De Kruif took charge of the Foundation's research-grant program for the first three years. Roosevelt assigned the administrative, publicity, and fund-raising activities to his good friend and
law partner Basil O'Connor. O'Connor, for some years also president of the American National Red Cross, has remained as the
non-salaried president and executive head of the National Foun-

dation ever since. Meantime, he became senior partner in the law firm of O'Connor and Farber. O'Connor is a genius at organization, and also a "hard-bitten attorney," in the words of Chief Justice Earl Warren of the United States Supreme Court. Certainly he has been hard-driving.

Both writer and attorney are accustomed to working with pointed words "for the record," in full public view. This fact is of some significance in our scientific story, for the National Foundation has not been a quiet organization, or accustomed to hide any new light under a bushel. On the other hand, the attorney and the writer did not long see eye to eye on methods of achieving their common objective. De Kruif was interested in research into the relationship between infectious disease and the body's nutritional state. The one connection between paralytic polio and nutrition seems to be that the disease attacks the well-fed more often than those with deficient diets—deficiency in vitamin B_1, for instance. As another science writer remarked, "Starving one's child, however, is hardly to be recommended as a polio preventive." De Kruif and his scientific committee resigned from the National Foundation in 1941 without a public statement, leaving O'Connor in command.

An Irish Catholic, originally from Taunton, Massachusetts, Dartmouth- and Harvard-trained, O'Connor has been variously characterized in pleasant and opprobrious terms. One N.F.I.P. local chapter chairman described him as a "very high type fellow, sincere and dynamic and smart as hell." [2] Most people stand in awe of O'Connor.

He is a medium-sized man in his late sixties, with a florid face, a look of perpetual concern, and, often, a white carnation in the lapel of his dark suit. His face is a familiar one in health circles inasmuch as his Foundation prominently displays oil paintings and candid photos of him. O'Connor conducts his affairs in a grand manner. For instance, when he is in New York, he stays in a penthouse at the Waldorf Astoria.

O'Connor has worked alertly, aggressively, for the conquest of poliomyelitis. In 1941 he publicly committed the Foundation to the complete eradication of this disease, but World War II con-

[2] David L. Sills: *The Volunteers* (Glencoe, Ill.: The Free Press; 1957).

stituted a substantial interruption in polio research. The death of
President Roosevelt on April 12, 1945, and the end of the war
that summer lent the force of sentiment and renewed opportunity to O'Connor's ambition. He would conduct a conquest of polio in the memory of one of our greatest and most popular presidents.

The March of Dimes and later the Mothers' March on Polio,
in which a vast volunteer group worked under strong central
leadership, were fabulously successful year after year. Whatever
the Foundation needs, "we will get it," O'Connor testified before
a Senate committee. "The public always gives us what they think
is right."

As modern personal hygiene and public sanitation increased
our susceptibility to the virus, so modern publicity methods sen-
sitized us to a state of public anxiety over who and how many
polio might paralyze. This general concern, backed by money,
translated itself into a sense of pressure upon virologists to *do
something* to prevent paralytic polio.

It was not, as some virus hunters have remarked, an ideal climate in which the scientist might pursue his ideas wherever they
might lead him, but no other climate was available. On the other
hand, O'Connor enjoyed wise scientific investment counsel. He
patronized the best scientific institutions. He spread polio-research money around broadly and generously, waiting the first
sign of a break-through. That would be the signal to pour vast
sums into applied research. First, new knowledge was needed.
But knowledge is hard to buy.

The research problem virologists faced in polio was a particularly knotty one. The idea of developing a vaccine against polio
was old; it goes back a half-century. The more the polio investigators learned prior to World War II, however, the less it appeared possible that the disease could be prevented by a vaccine.

The beginning difficulty in polio research was, as in the case of
yellow fever, the finding of suitable experimental animals, polio
having been thought to be wholly a disease of human beings.
(This view may require revision eventually, for recently specific
antibodies to one or more types of polio have been reported in

cows, suggesting that they have been infected with polio virus.)

Dr. Karl Landsteiner, while still in Austria, established the cause of polio in 1908 and, in so doing, introduced the first polio "guinea pig"—the monkey. (Later he came to the United States, to the Rockefeller Institute, and won the Nobel Prize for his discovery of the A, B, AB, and O blood types, thus introducing blood-matching and making safe transfusion practicable.) Landsteiner took bits of spinal cord from a Viennese urchin who had died of polio, suspended these in fluid, and injected it into the bodies of a monkey and a baboon. He produced fever and paralysis in both. He showed that the cause was a virus, by filtering clear fluid from infected cord and injecting it through a hole in the skull of a monkey; each time he did so, he produced polio.

This helped straighten out Simon Flexner, founder of the Rockefeller Institute, and Hideyo Noguchi, who had pursued a false scent—"Flexner's bacillus"—as the cause of polio. Flexner and Noguchi made an intriguing observation in 1913. They suspended pieces of rabbit kidney in fluid from a human victim of kidney disease and dropsy. They then infected this culture with spinal cord from a monkey with polio. They showed that the virus, when incubated and passed through a series of test-tube cultures of this mixture, would still infect monkeys with polio.

Their experiment was the earliest clue to the fact that the polio virus is not necessarily an addict of nerve tissues, contrary to what later pathologists and microbiologists firmly believed. Yet these pioneers bogged down in the crudities of their clever experiment. They lacked a way of showing that the virus had multiplied, as it probably did multiply, in their tissue cultures. They could not prove that the original virus hadn't been distributed throughout their test tubes simply by a series of dilutions of the infected fluid.

Others attempted to make a polio vaccine à la Pasteur. They ground infected spinal cords and brains of monkeys, weakened or killed the virus in one way or another, suspended the mixture in a fluid, and injected it in monkeys. The procedure seemed to produce some immunity, but the results were uncertain. As a matter of fact, they found that monkeys supposedly rendered immune by infection with live virus sometimes developed paralysis when virus was injected directly into their brains. These experimenters were left in the position of believing that, even though the monkey had some antibodies in the blood, these would not protect him from paralysis.

Pathologists knew from their post-mortem examinations of patients who died of polio that the virus did its damage by attacking the nerve cells of the spinal cord and brain. No sign of the virus could be found in the blood or other organs of the body. The idea took root that the polio virus was exclusively neurotropic—that is, would attack nerve cells only.

Drs. Albert B. Sabin and Peter K. Olitsky, working at the Rockefeller Institute in 1936, supplied further evidence for this theory. They induced polio viruses from monkeys to multiply in a tissue culture made of brain cells from a human embryo that had miscarried. At the same time, they were unable to cultivate the virus in other human tissues—lung, kidney, liver, or spleen. Their work was technically excellent, and the results were convincing. It was all in keeping with the Pasteurian theory of specificity: specific germs cause specific diseases and attack specific cells. The polio virus attacked nerve cells—period.

In 1939 Dr. Charles Armstrong of the United States Public Health Service found a second and a third experimental animal. Armstrong infected the brains of cotton rats and then white mice with the Lansing strain of polio. This he had isolated from the spinal cord and brain of an eighteen-year-old lad who died of polio in Lansing, Michigan. His work added still further evidence of polio as a "nerve virus."

Meanwhile, both Paul and Sabin developed a different slant. They isolated the virus from the alimentary canal, at entrance and exit, and especially in human feces. But they had no proof that it grew in the intestine, or that it passed from there through the blood stream to reach the spinal cord. On the contrary, new evidence indicated that the virus entered the nervous system through the nerve ends in the nose. This surely seemed the case in monkey experiments. Most authorities believed that somehow the virus by-passed the blood stream in reaching the spinal cord—probably making its way along various nerve pathways, as the rabies virus does. Even if one could set up an antibody barrier in the blood, the virus could go around it. Or so it appeared.

It was evident that polio did produce immunity somehow, but the antibodies did not behave in a predictable manner. That was the biggest problem. A vaccine is worthless if it does not produce antibodies, and the antibodies are of little value if they do not block the disease. An attenuated live virus, such as Max Theiler found to combat yellow fever, presented a great danger because of the annoying "fact" that the virus grew only in nerve tissue. Pasteur's anti-rabies vaccine, made from rabbit brains, produces an allergic encephalitis, or inflammation of the brain, in one of every thousand persons who receive it (or one in ten thousand— the estimates vary).

Doctors give the Pasteur treatment only to persons believed to have been bitten by a rabid animal. Vaccination against polio can hardly be regarded as a similar emergency, except possibly during an epidemic. If polio epidemics constituted a greater danger than they do, then a risk of doing occasional harm with the vaccine might be rationalized from a public-health viewpoint.

The requirement in polio, however, is to immunize a great many people who never would have it, to prevent the disease in the relatively few who would be paralyzed by it. It would be foolhardy to try either a virus that was not completely killed or one that, though properly attenuated, was suspended in nerve cells that might set up a brain allergy.

The outlook for a polio vaccine appeared poor indeed. If only the laboratory workers could get the virus to grow someplace else —then it might be easier to get at the immunity problem.

ENDERS:
POLIO RESEARCH'S DEBT
TO MUMPS

WE HAVE already mentioned Horace Walpole's fairy tale about the three princes of Serendip who, in their travels, always came across unexpected things. This capacity for good fortune, Walpole ascribed to their keen powers of observation when chance favored them with something worth observing. In one of the most pleasant tales of the virus hunt, the three princes come alive in the persons of Drs. John F. Enders, Thomas H. Weller, and Frederick C. Robbins. They refuted the school of thought holding: "Polio virus will grow only in nerve tissue. There's nothing you can do about it."

Each since has gone his separate way, but following World War II their paths converged in Enders's laboratory at Children's Hospital in Back Bay, Boston. During their association they achieved these three things:

A reliable method of cultivating viruses in test tubes, thus introducing the modern tissue-culture era of virus discovery, both old viruses and new;

The second big break-through in methods of producing viruses for vaccines, an advance comparable to the Goodpasture discovery of the way to grow viruses in hen's eggs;

The immediate means for a non-neurotropic polio vaccine.

Their later comments about their discovery were charmingly casual:

"It was all very simple," said Robbins.

"A fortuitous circumstance," reflected Weller.

"I guess we were foolish," remarked Enders, somewhat cryptically.

This is strange talk for men who broke the polio-vaccine bottleneck. Nonetheless, it is typical of John Enders, who has sometimes behaved as if he were surprised that the break-through occurred in his laboratory. Occasionally he seems on the verge of apologizing, but refrains; this would embarrass all the people who have honored him with prizes—Mrs. Albert Lasker, for example, and the Nobel people, who gave the three of them the 1954 Nobel Prize in physiology and medicine. More important, he wouldn't want the faculty that has given him intellectual comfort and shelter for thirty-odd years to be ashamed of him! A man must live up to Harvard Medical School, commonly regarded as the world's greatest. Yet when a *Life* writer asked Enders how the three happened to make the discovery, all Enders said was: "I've wondered about that a good many times."

Somewhere in this uninspired comment may be a clue to why it *was* Enders, Weller, and Robbins. It might be the statement of a shy, simple man not able to find words for his creativity. In fact, this is the popular view of Enders at Harvard Medical School—modest and humble. Still, it could have been the remark merely of a man who preferred a good Boston magazine, such as the *Atlantic Monthly*. Some few who have worked with Enders regard him as a man of calm determination, canny and almost cussedly independent. He himself protests that he is not as humble as some people make him out.

The close observer surmises that actually John Enders uses vagueness as a foil. A scholar of language and literature as well as professor of bacteriology and immunology and director of a virus-research laboratory, he is perfectly literate and articulate when he chooses to be. But he sees nothing to be gained by talking about himself.

This is one of at least three reasons why Enders, now sixty-two—he was fifty-one at the time of the discovery—easily qualifies as the most respected virologist in the United States today. He impresses his colleagues because he doesn't try to impress anyone. In this Age of the Hard Sell, what could be more impressive? Secondly, as Dr. John Gordon, Harvard professor of epidemiology, pointed out, "The man has a green thumb for growing viruses." Enders's laboratory made its lucky strike in polio as part of a whole series of advances in virus culture. Thirdly, to his fellow scientists Enders epitomizes the ideal scientific investigator. Dr. René J. Dubos commented: "He has a genius for stating his ideas simply, a genius for not being fooled by empty words— like the word *genius.*" One would expect Enders to be careful not to let imagination or hope outrun his facts.

Enders's laboratory is in the Jimmy Fund Building of Children's Hospital, one of the family of hospitals grouped around the Medical School on the Longwood Quadrangle. There he presides over a staff of ten or a dozen who occupy about half of the second floor in this modest-sized but modern-looking seven-story building built through Variety Club subscriptions in the memory of a little boy who died of leukemia. The polio break-through was made, however, in an old red-brick annex where Enders had a laboratory consisting of three or four rooms and a closet or two. Everybody was "all in together." But his equipment was excellent, and so was the talent of his little staff.

More recently he has expanded some. In 1957, the year after the medical faculty thought to promote him to full professor, Enders inherited the study of Dr. S. Burt Wolbach, for many years a leading Harvard pathologist, who had died. Enders had not asked for better quarters, but Dr. Sidney Farber, professor of pathology at Children's, insisted that Enders have Wolbach's study. After all, a Nobel Prize should entitle a man to some consideration.

Now Enders occupies a nicely appointed, book-lined room, and sits in a comfortable, leather armchair at a gold-striped black study table with captain's chairs to match. There are attractive pictures of sailing-ships and distinguished professors on the walls, including one of the great Hans Zinsser—"He was my master," Enders remarks with simple reverence. Under the windows are a black-topped workbench and the customary microscope. At one end is a sink; by it may be found a saucepan and a Bunsen burner, for heating water; in it are a jar of instant coffee and blue-and-white china cups and saucers. Not an early riser but literally a ten-o'clock scholar, Enders customarily arrives on this scene about midmorning and works until six or seven if need be.

This "green thumb" tissue culturist may be lacking in showmanship. He may be the despair of the Medical School's news director, who couldn't get a copy of Enders's paper when he went off to New York to report to fellow virologists that he had an attenuated virus ready for a measles vaccine (see Chapter 28). But there is no lack of color in the man.

Associates are prone to think of him in words such as "Lincolnesque" and "Churchillian," though he's not as homely or intrinsically sad in appearance as Lincoln and not at all cocky or flamboyant like Churchill. Enders has a large, oval face and square-set jaw, large, blunt nose, large ears, and a hairline that recedes to the crown of his head, where it makes its stand in a horseshoe of wispy, dark but fading hair. In attire, Enders favors bow ties, tweed suits, and a buttoned vest to carry his gold watch and heavy chain and, presumably, to guard him against any chill New England draft.

He is prone to sit much like Churchill, in an old man's slump, with his head slightly bowed and his collar loose about his neck. His gray-eyed gaze, as much over as through his glasses, is uncomfortably direct and alert, as if he were asking himself: "What does *this* fellow have up his sleeve?" But there is a twinkle in his eye, and a grin on his lips. He obviously loves to talk with, rather than to, people, and is quick to compliment a person on a sensible thought.

His leisurely quality, as his polio experiments showed, is a creative asset. It takes time to think, and, if one is too heavily committed and pressed for time, one may not obey the impulse to do something different. Besides, creative thought cannot be hurried.

There are several elements in Enders's character which have exercised selective influence in bringing him and his green thumb to the center of the virus-research stage. This aversion to being pushed is one such element. He gave expression to it early in 1958. Sorely pressed to finish his latest measles report and write chapters on virus culture and mumps for a new textbook, he turned to the blackboard and easel his staff had given him as a birthday present and wrote in a firm hand: "He that endures to the end is saved."

Because he is of mixed Dutch and German descent and also an immunologist, he might just as easily have written there the motto attributed to the German who developed the earliest theory of immunity, Paul Ehrlich: *"Geld, Geduld, Geschick und Gluck"*—"Money, patience, fate, and luck."

Some account for Enders and his lack of urge to "go places" by the fact that he is a Connecticut Yankee—he was born in West Hartford, on February 10, 1897, the son of John Ostrom and Harriet Goulden Enders. His mother is still alive and in Hartford. His father died in the spring of 1958. "Why should I go anyplace when I'm already where I want to be?" the native New Englander is supposed to ask himself.

Others believe Enders's stability is derived from the kind of security to be found in banks. His father was president and later board chairman of the Hartford National Bank and his grandfather, president of the Aetna Life Insurance Company. His brother, Ostrom, is now president of the bank. Their father left the family an estate valued at $19,000,000.

Thus, a wise choice of parents freed John Enders of a hidden hunger that gnaws at many a good professorial mind at Harvard, as well as elsewhere. "I think it is a good thing," replied Enders when asked his attitude toward money. His financial independence possibly accounts for his unambitious pace, and also may explain why it took him twenty-seven years to rise from a lowly assistant to a full professor. He didn't need a raise.

In his one known venture into business, Enders was a failure. After World War I service as a flying instructor and graduation from Yale University in 1920, he became a real-estate agent. His firm conviction that people ought to know whether they wanted a house and not have to be sold hastened his decision to enroll in the Harvard School of Arts and Science, with a generous allowance from his father and the determination to become an English teacher.

After four years of English literature and research in the Celtic and Teutonic languages, he found the prospect dull, particularly after he went to live with several medical students in a Brookline boardinghouse, near the Medical School. Illustrating a fascinating circumstantiality about much of his life, this minor happenstance proved a turning-point. Among his fellow boarders was Hugh Ward, an Australian, who was a Rhodes scholar and an oarsman, as Enders had been at Yale. Enders accompanied the Aussie to the laboratory in the Department of Bacteriology and watched him change the media in bacterial cultures.

There Enders met Dr. Hans Zinsser, then professor of bacteriology and immunology. Commonly, we wave a man's teachers aside as pretty dull stuff, but if one looks back in the life of any outstanding scientist, one almost invariably finds an outstanding teacher who inspired him. Zinsser was one of medical science's most inspiring teachers. Max Theiler, discoverer of the yellow-fever vaccine, picked up a little book by Zinsser in London and was moved to turn his back on clinical medicine and go into research. Just so, Zinsser—a man with a profile like John Barrymore's but less rakish—opened Enders's eyes with "his usual powers of seduction."

Enders, already with A.B. and M.A. degrees and on the verge of completing a Ph.D. in English, decided to take a Ph.D. in bacteriology and immunology (he is not an M. D.). He then spent fifteen years with Zinsser, receiving his first appointment to the faculty when he was thirty-two. These were fabulous years for Enders. Zinsser's staff lunched with him in the laboratory, sitting at his feet, so to speak, while he conversed on science, music, poetry, art, medicine, professors—he knew them all. It may have been in the shadow of this brilliant man that Enders acquired his much-manifested sense of his own unimportance.

Enders became interested in viruses, their victims and vaccines, in the late 1930's. Rather quickly he scored a minor triumph in behalf of cats, while working with Dr. William McD. Hammon (who later, at the University of Pittsburgh, introduced gamma globulin, the antibody portion of blood, as a temporary protection against polio). Enders and Hammon became interested in a serious, usually fatal disease of kittens variously known as panleucopenia, cat distemper, or enteritis. The disease inflames the intestines. They found it was due to a virus that infected the bone marrow and reduced the protection afforded by white blood cells, themselves a part of the body's system for fighting disease. Enders and Hammon made a vaccine first from the spleen and lymph nodes of dead kittens and then from the blood of vaccinated cats. It worked well, and is now a standard item of veterinary medicine.

Enders next turned to the problem of getting ultra-microscopic organisms to multiply in tissue cultures. With Zinsser, he hoped to find a method of mass-producing the cause of typhus fever, and then to make a vaccine. The cause is a rickettsiae, an organism related to viruses but larger. However, as mentioned before, discovery of the widely used chick-embryo vaccine against typhus fell to Herald R. Cox of Lederle Laboratories.

These were beginnings for Enders, who was turning forty and was quite uncelebrated. Yet he had taken four short, essential steps toward events to come. First, he had been washed in the radiance of the imaginative, enthusiastic Zinsser. Therefore, he had been cured of the academic commonplace, for Zinsser was red-blooded and inclined to hoot at academic snobbery, dogmatism, and affectation of any kind.

Second, Enders had turned his attention to viruses and, third, to the problem of cultivating them in the test tube. Fourth, he developed a liking for working in what some fresh collegian might call a biologists' bull session.

Though he doesn't comment on this aspect—it would mean calling undue attention to himself—it is apparent that Enders derives a deep satisfaction from the friendships of the laboratory, the comradery of ideas, and the social act of two, three, or more people thinking out loud, working together, and trying this or that. The purpose is serious, as much so as the purpose of a highway construction crew, but in the case of fundamental research the crew is not sure where the road will come out.

For example, with Weller, then a senior medical student, and others, Enders sharpened his tissue-culture wits on an old friend of the microbiologist, the cowpox virus. The cowpox virus will do practically anything you want it to do in the laboratory, and grow almost anywhere—in rabbits, chick embryos, or various tissue cultures. One idea that came out of these experiments stuck in Enders's mind and later became important—continuous culture. Alexis Carrel, the high priest of the science of keeping tissues alive outside of the body, long before had shown that one could grow bits of tissue in a test tube for years if one could keep it free of bacterial infection. Now, with the cowpox virus in a culture of chick-embryo tissue, Enders saw it was possible to keep *both* the tissue culture and the virus in the culture alive and in continuous cultivation for months. In other words, while the chick cells grew and multiplied, so did the virus particles in them.

Enders also experimented with influenza and measles. However, he was somewhat at loose ends at the beginning of World War II. Zinsser had died not long before, rather suddenly. Enders, then still only an assistant professor, asked Dr. Frederick F. Russell, professor of preventive medicine, what he might do to contribute to the war effort. "Why don't you work on mumps?" suggested Russell. He explained that mumps had been a bad problem among the young men coming into the World War I training-camps, and might be again.

Enders might have tried his mind and hand at other wartime virus worries, such as the control of influenza, typhus, or yellow fever, but Thomas Francis, Herald Cox, Max Theiler, and others were making good progress in these fields. The idea was to find a problem that was being neglected. As it happened, mumps caused little trouble in World War II. But if Russell had not steered Enders into mumps, it's doubtful that he would have presided at the polio break-through.

We might imagine that Enders, being a New Englander, was drawn to the mumps virus because it is so stable and fixed in its habits. The disease is ancient, having been accurately described by Hippocrates, centuries before Christ. It is well known for two characteristics, one common, the other not so common.

Mumps causes an enlargement of the salivary gland under the

point of the jaw on either side. Occasionally it produces a painful enlargement of the testicles; this can lead to sterility. The male fear of this happening is an exaggerated one, however. Mumps orchitis, as this manifestation is called, occurs in about one of every five cases, but loss of virility is rare. The virus almost never destroys all of one gland, let alone both. Meningitis, or inflammation of the membrane covering the spinal cord and brain, is another, more important complication, varying from under one to about ten per cent in any given epidemic.

Mumps leaves its victims solidly immune against a second attack.

Goodpasture had isolated the mumps virus in 1934. "We started where he left off," recalled Enders. He had five collaborators in his wartime study of mumps, including Joseph Stokes, Jr., of the University of Pennsylvania. The group made good progress, developing both antibody and diagnostic tests and showing that it is possible to have an inapparent infection. For this reason many persons are immune without recollection of having had the disease.

The Stokes-Enders group developed a killed-virus mumps vaccine made of an extract from infected monkey glands and showed that it was at least temporarily effective both in monkeys and in human volunteers. It is still available, but there is little demand for it. Later they attenuated the virus by growing it in eggs. Since then Drs. Werner and Gertrude Henle of the University of Pennslyvania have experimented with an attenuated live-virus mumps vaccine, and the Russians are using a similar vaccine in children.

Enders had to use monkeys as his virus host because of a notable lack of success in growing the mumps virus in tissue cultures. This problem was in his mind immediately following the war, when in 1946 Children's Hospital invited him to establish a new Infectious Disease Research Laboratory.

This was a big change for John Enders, ending some seventeen years as an active teacher in the Medical School's Department of Bacteriology and Immunology. Except for the training of young doctors working as his assistants and the writing of textbooks, he was now free of teaching responsibilities and able to devote more time to virus hunting.

True, he had not come too far up the faculty ladder for a man of forty-nine. He had been promoted to associate professor in 1942, about the time it was definite that he would not succeed Zinsser as chairman of the Department. Gossip about the Longwood Quadrangle is in conflict as to whether Enders passed up an offer of the chairmanship, or was passed over by the faculty committee that attends to such appointments. Either way, it was an example of excellent judgment. Chairmen of departments seldom find time between committee meetings to make discoveries that win Nobel Prizes.

Now to Enders's small but new laboratory in the old annex of the Jimmy Fund Building came the other two princes of Serendip, Tom Weller and Fred Robbins, who had been classmates and roommates in Medical School (Harvard, 1940).

A casting director could hardly have done better in his selection of the actors in the special bit of drama to come. Fred Robbins came back from service as an Army bacteriologist in the Mediterranean. He wanted training as a research pediatrician, and obtained it on a National Research Council fellowship paid for by the National Foundation for Infantile Paralysis. He came from a rich intellectual background. His father is William J. Robbins, plant physiologist and director of the New York Botanical Gardens. In 1948, the year of the polio tissue-culture discovery, Robbins married Alice Northrop, daughter of Rockefeller Institute's John Northrop, who shared the 1946 Nobel Prize in chemistry with James Sumner and Wendell Stanley. By 1954 the son-in-law was able to match prizes with his father-in-law.

Robbins, thirty years old at the time he joined Enders, is a big, handsome, friendly, full-faced brunet of the type a behavioral scientist would call outgoing. He is an Alabamian by birth.

A year older than Robbins, Tom Weller is a small, blond, spunky man who is at times daringly outspoken and at other times notably reticent. Weller was born and raised in an academic environment, the son of the late Dr. Carl V. Weller, head professor of pathology at the University of Michigan, in Ann Arbor. He likewise had been an Army bacteriologist during the war—in Puerto Rico. In 1947 he became assistant director of the new laboratory.

This was the team.

By the merest chance their research was supported by the National Foundation at the climactic moment. The Foundation had given the Harvard Department of Bacteriology $200,000 for a five-year "study of viruses," not specifying polio or any other kind. The Department parceled out some of the money to Enders, Weller, and Robbins.

Not one of them had any experience or working interest in the polio field at the time. In fact, Robbins had cheerfully stated that he wanted to work with Enders—on any virus except polio. As it happened, he set out to find a virus cause of infant epidemic diarrhea, a disease that from time to time devastates hospital nurseries. Weller wanted to investigate the virus of chickenpox. But he and Enders also resumed the mumps-virus study.

In early 1948 Weller and Enders found a way to make the mumps virus grow in a tissue culture. They used a sort of "ragout" of chick-embryo fragments mixed with ox blood and other ingredients.

The success of their method depended on one factor of the utmost importance in opening the modern era of test-tube cultivation of viruses. It was typical of Enders but was in complete contrast to the dynamic hustle of subsequent polio research. As Enders said, "We waited."

By this he meant that they took a leaf from their pre-war experiments with continuous tissue cultures. Unlike others, who were in the habit of transplanting their viruses from one subculture to another every three or four days to escape an overgrowth of bacteria, they changed the medium—that is, the vital juices surrounding the tissue—after this lapse of time, but kept the tissue itself growing a week or two weeks and, eventually, for as long as thirty to forty days.

Now the mumps virus flourished and multiplied. The virus could be easily detected because the tissue-culture fluid caused red blood cells to clump—technically, a positive Hirst hemagglutination test. Curiously enough, they used no ultra-modern tissue-culture technique, but rather one of the oldest—cells suspended in the nutritive fluid in a flask and incubated at 96.8 to 98.6 degrees—the technique introduced by Hugh and Mary

Maitland of Great Britain in 1928. This was the same Maitland method that yielded Max Theiler's 17D yellow-fever virus.

Science now saw that slow, continuous incubation was necessary to cultivate some viruses *in vitro,* meaning in glass tubes. But a second major step was necessary for the polio breakthrough. This was to eliminate the bacterial contamination that had plagued Alexis Carrel and a score of other pioneer tissue culturists. Others had used the wonder drug penicillin to sterilize tissue cultures of unwanted bacteria not long before Enders, Weller, and Robbins began working together. It now occurred to them to try penicillin plus another antibiotic, streptomycin, for the first time in the cultivation of viruses.

For his attempt to grow the chickenpox virus, Weller chose human embryo—bits of various tissues obtained from babies stillborn or dying after premature birth at Boston Lying-In Hospital, across the street. He set up a series of culture flasks, containing embryonic skin and muscle plus the two wonder drugs, in March 1948. Quite by chance, he had some culture flasks left over. Now came the "fortuitous circumstance." Rather than throw the unused cultures away, he put some polio virus in them.

For some years Enders had had a tube of polio virus—the Lansing strain, preserved in frozen mouse brain—in his deep-freeze storage cabinet. Dr. Sidney Kramer of the Michigan Department of Health had sent it to him. Weller, like Robbins, had reacted in a refractory manner to all the emphasis on polio research. But what could be more natural, since the polio virus *was* at hand and the Laboratory *was* working under a National Foundation grant, to dab a little of the Lansing strain into some of the culture tubes?

Enders had still another impulse. Robbins meanwhile had been getting ready for his first diarrhea-virus experiments. He chose mouse intestine as the most likely tissue to start with, but was still looking for a source of virus.

Robbins recalled events as follows:

"Tom was . . . trying out human embryonic tissues. I had undertaken to try cultures of mouse intestine, but I wasn't doing very well. I tried mumps virus on it, but I couldn't prove to the chief that I had anything. I wanted to work on something else. He

said, 'I've been wondering about polio virus growing in the intestine. Why don't you try it?' "

Enders confirmed Robbins: "It was in the back of my mind
that, if so much polio virus could be found in the gastrointestinal
tract, then it must grow someplace besides nervous tissue."

Robbins fancied his chief's whim, because intestinal tissue certainly seemed a logical place for polio virus to grow. It was well
known that the virus could commonly be found in the intestine,
in the absence of epidemics or paralysis. Robbins continued:
"Tom inoculated his cultures of human muscle and skin first. I
tried the virus in mouse intestine. But it was no go. But Tom's
cultures worked the first time."

The stereotype for these moments of discovery calls for a flash
of lightning, a thunderclap, earthquake, or special moonbeam
through the clouds—something so dramatic that it indelibly
etches itself in the minds of the protagonists and finally in history. This is not the way things happen to John Enders. About
all we can say is that the time, place, and people were right for
virus research to take another gigantic step forward.

They had to wait, of course. The polio virus multiplied in cultures eight to twenty days old. How did they determine this?
First, by injecting the culture fluid into the brains of live mice
and watching them develop paralysis. This by itself tells you
nothing more than that the virus has survived the experiment
and is still present in the injected fluid. Whether the virus has
multiplied can be determined by inoculating a series of mice with
greater and greater dilutions of the infected fluid. This is called
titration, from the French word *titer*, meaning "standard." The
titer is the greatest dilution—containing the fewest virus particles—that will still induce an infection.

If a given dilution of a fluid specimen infects the test animal
beyond the established end point of dilution for previous specimens, then the virus in it must have multiplied. Weller and Robbins were able to titer, or dilute, their cultures 1,000,000,000,000,-
000,000 times and still produce paralytic polio in their test mice.
The results were irregular at first, and Enders didn't believe
them. "We had to prove it three times over before Dr. Enders
would accept the fact," said Robbins. "Our titer kept dropping

off." By this he meant that in some series of dilutions the end point of infectivity arrived too soon to prove multiplication of the virus.

Enders was more convinced when they noticed something else. The fluid in the flasks containing the polio tissue culture didn't turn yellow as fast as that in the normal tissue cultures used for comparison. The reason is this: Phenol red dye is used to detect acid in a tissue culture; the acid shows that it is growing. As it grows, the red turns to orange and the orange to yellow. But the growth of virus in the culture will inhibit tissue growth, slow down acid production, and hence prevent the change in color.

Transplanting bits of the infected tissue to glass slides, incubating it further, and examining the cells under the microscope, they saw something else: some of the human cells were dying. This definitely must be due to the presence of live virus.

The Enders team now recalled the report of Dr. Chung Hua Huang, a Chinese microbiologist, now in Peiping. Huang, while working in the bacteriology laboratory at the Columbia University College of Physicians and Surgeons in 1942, had done a brilliant piece of research. Working with the virus that causes western equine encephalitis—a so-called horse sleeping sickness that sometimes spread to humans—Huang saw two things in his chick-embryo tissue-culture tubes: (1) a normal tissue culture transplanted to a glass slide continues to grow out around its edges, but if multiplying virus are present, this outgrowth stops; (2) in the presence of live virus, the tissue culture's acid production diminishes.

Thus, in making an original discovery of their own—that polio virus does not require nerve tissue, but will grow in other tissues as well—the three scientists also confirmed Huang's observations. And, like him, they saw the significance of what they had done. They now had dependable indicators of virus multiplication in the tissue culture itself, and no longer had to depend on tests on mice or monkeys to determine whether the virus grew in the culture. It was as if they had signed an Emancipation Proclamation for virus growers. Goodpasture had observed viruses producing disease in the tissues of an unhatched chick. Now they had seen signs of virus disease in the cells themselves. Enders coined the word "cytopathogenic" to describe this production of disease in cells.

To do what Huang did, but do it with polio virus—that was news!

First, however, they felt the need of a good deal more work. Mumps, chickenpox, and diarrhea were forgotten. They worked all summer and fall on one detail after another.

They kept the Lansing strain of polio growing for 224 days in a series of thirteen cultures of skin and muscle, replacing the nutrient fluid every four to seven days and transplanting the virus to fresh tissue every eight to twenty days. Fluids from each culture killed mice, and also produced paralysis in monkeys in seven to ten days after they were exposed.

The team branched out into other tissues, begging bits of this and that from Boston Lying-In and Children's hospitals. For example, they obtained human embryonic brain and showed that the polio virus grew there, as Sabin and Olitsky had done before them. They tried human intestine, and the virus grew there, too. This was a source of some relief to Robbins, who'd had bad luck with his mouse intestine.

It was the first evidence that viruses could reproduce in the walls of the intestinal tract. The great importance of the antibiotic drugs in keeping tissue cultures free of bacteria was evident here. The intestines are always contaminated with bacteria. Now it was possible, as Robbins demonstrated, to take this tissue straight from the source, without any attempt to wash or sterilize it, and to use it as a host for virus culture—simply by adding penicillin and streptomycin to kill the bacteria. As we already know, the drugs have no effect on the viruses.

Weller went further. Embryonic tissue, from the fetal stage of life, has special characteristics for rapid growth, as do cancer cells. What would the virus do in a culture that was neither of nervous nor of fetal origin—in other words, mature human skin or muscle?

The tissue that came to mind was foreskin, which was readily available, due to circumcisions. Weller obtained foreskin excised from boys four to eleven years of age.

If you were a baseball fan like Max Theiler, you might say the scientific hit-and-run signal was on. The Lansing strain grew vigorously in foreskin, in a series of five cultures extended over eighty-eight days! Polio virus seemed to grow anywhere.

The next question was a natural one.

Would a culture of the Lansing virus respond in an orthodox manner to a neutralization test with immune serum? The scientists obtained serum from monkeys that had recovered from the Lansing-type polio—Isabel M. Mountain at Johns Hopkins sent it to them. They found it possible to stop virus multiplication with this immune serum—simply by putting some into a polio tissue culture. In short, Lansing-type antibodies affected the Lansing-type virus just the way one would expect.

The next question was also a good one. Was there something special about the growth characteristics of this Lansing strain, or would other types of polio virus do as well in their tissue cultures? They obtained viruses of the two other major types. These grew, too.

In their first experiments Enders, Weller, and Robbins had used the Maitland method, suspending their tissue fragments in flasks containing three cubic centimeters of balanced salt solution and ox-serum filtrate. Now they looked for a better mass-production method and, for the time being, settled on the roller tube. The roller tube is placed in a rotating drum, or rack, with dozens of others, and slowly turned throughout the period of incubation. In this way the tissue is alternately bathed in vital juices and exposed to air in the sealed tube.

This was believed to promote growth, but Enders's laboratory and others since have turned to a simpler method. Using the enzyme trypsin, they break down their tissues into individual cells. Trypsin, one of the pancreatic juices that decomposes proteins, digests the intracellular cement binding the cells together into tissues; it doesn't harm the cells themselves. These cells, together with the virus, are placed in a slant tube—an ordinary, stoppered test tube laid in a racket at a slight angle above the horizontal. The tubes are racked in long rows in an incubation room and kept at body temperature for the desired length of time.

In the case of polio, it is possible to get a good "harvest" of virus within a day or two after "seeding"—tissue culturists use these words in the same manner as do farmers. As it turned out, the polio virus is not as slow-growing as it first appeared. It was merely that, for the scientists to make the discovery in the tissue-culture system they used, prolonged incubation was needed to disclose in unmistakable fashion what was happening.

This was what a combination of the antibiotics and slow-growing mumps virus did for polio research. A man in a hurry could not have made the discovery. He had to be somewhat in a hurry as long as bacterial contamination threatened his cultures. With that threat out of the way, it was possible to try continuous culture with the mumps virus and wait for virus multiplication to show up. It then became possible to reveal the reproductive potentialities of polio virus.

Thus, in this at first casual and then intensified effort, our three modern princes of Serendip got polio-virus culture out of its impasse just forty years after Landsteiner had discovered the virus causing the disease.

The first sign of their break-through came in March, but prudent scientists hoard evidence against the prospect of a long, hard winter of criticism that may follow a new claim. No criticism befell these well-met scientists, however. Their observations were soon confirmed.

Science published their first report on January 28, 1949: "Cultivation of Lansing Strain of Poliomyelitis Virus in Cultures of Various Human Embryonic Tissues." What a load of significance there was in that word "various"!

In conclusion, they wrote: "These phenomena are of interest from two general points of view. First, they leave no doubt that poliomyelitis virus *in vitro* can multiply in cells other than those of the nervous system and can cause profound injury of such cells. Secondly, they provide criteria by which the presence of the virus can be recognized *in vitro.*"

These two facts opened up a new world of experimental and clinical possibilities, all adding up to one grand idea: it was now possible to work with both the virus and the disease in a test tube, without a test animal and without further need or concern for brain or spinal-cord tissue as a special habitat. They established polio as an enteric (intestinal) virus.

As Dr. Sven Gard of the Nobel committee later remarked in presenting them with the Prize in Stockholm, "These discoveries incited a restless activity in the virus laboratories the world over. The tissue culture technic was rapidly made one of the standard methods of medical virus research. . . ." Indeed, the advance was as important to virology as Robert Koch's first culturing of bacteria on agar plates was to bacteriology. Certainly as a tool of disease prevention, there is nothing in virology to equal it except Goodpasture's fertile hen's egg. These—the chick-embryo technique and tissue culture—are the two great weapons in carrying out our first dictum of vaccine making: "To cook rabbit, first catch the rabbit."

Now the excitement began, and Basil O'Connor went into orbit as administrator of a $15,000,000 National Foundation program to get a polio vaccine into American children.

In the rush to apply the Harvard discovery, and in the excitement greeting the hopeful news that a good vaccine was now on its way, just how Enders, Weller, and Robbins came to make their discovery was quite lost from view in America.

This did not bother John Enders. Well aware of all the polio researchers involved in this advance of knowledge, he did his kindly best to give credit to others. For example, there was the lecture he gave at the National Institutes of Health in Bethesda just three weeks before he, Weller, and Robbins went to Sweden in December 1954 to take their places with Ernest Hemingway and Linus Pauling among the Nobel laureates of that year. Enders gave Huang full credit for being the first to observe dependable indicators of virus multiplication in the tissue culture itself, and hence "render the tissue-culture system independent of the experimental animal."

It was as if Enders were gently rebuking the turn of fate that honored him and neglected Huang. In his Nobel lecture, however, he was too considerate of his hosts to dwell on this oversight —or, for that matter, to so much as hint that he thought Goodpasture also deserved the Prize. Instead, he talked of "fishing in troubled waters."

In biology, he said, principle and theory are not as fixed as they appear to be in physics, chemistry, and other exact sciences. Therefore, the random experiment—just to stir things up and see what happens—is frequently desirable. This was his explanation of their discovery.

To some haughty scholars, the Enders "green thumb" approach might appear undignified, if not downright embarrassing. He seemed to sense this, and, like any good prince of Serendip— Pasteur, Fleming (who discovered penicillin), or Theiler—he was humble about it. Being the self-effacing type, he told a visitor at the end of a four-hour interview. "The only thing I am finally sure of in biology is individual variation."

One other rather revealing incident involved the two younger princes, who since have moved quickly up the academic ladder. (In 1952 Robbins accepted an appointment as full professor of pediatrics at Western Reserve University in Cleveland. In 1954, shortly before they received the Nobel Prize, Weller became full professor of tropical public health in the Harvard School of Public Health.)

Weller and Robbins perceived that they had the means to produce a vaccine. Enders agreed, but counseled against going into the vaccine-testing business. "Our laboratory," he said, "is not set up for vaccine production."

In reality, John Enders himself wasn't set up for it. It might have meant an end of the kind of life he loved, perhaps frustrated him in his pursuit of the measles virus. We do not know all that was in Enders's mind at the time, but it may be that he thought of all the sore trials that had pursued the vaccine makers —Jenner, Pasteur, Sawyer.

In retrospect Robbins and Weller have thanked their serendipitous stars for the wisdom of Enders, who, even though the two young men had the energy and enthusiasm, influenced them to resist the temptation to become immortals like Jenner. He saved them more headaches and heartaches than we can imagine—until we turn to the story of Salk and his vaccine.

SALK, THE POLIO
VIRUS KILLER

THE SALK polio vaccine, described by Basil O'Connor as a "planned miracle," is typically a product of contemporary living. Here the Man in the Long White Coat, who pores over his ideas and bits of recondite data, hoping to add something of interest to the sum of knowledge, has found himself working shoulder to shoulder with the promoters and organizers—The Man in the Gray Flannel Suit and The Organization Man—who want to put useful knowledge across with the utmost impact. Best man in this marriage of science and modern communications is Dr. Jonas Edward Salk, a quiet, serious-minded, warm-hearted young man, the most publicized virus hunter of all.

Salk was born on October 28, 1914, the eldest son of Daniel and Dora Salk, in the Manhattan equivalent of a log cabin—a tenement flat at Madison Avenue and 106th Street. "Biographical Notes for Magazine Writers on Dr. Jonas E. Salk," a November 5, 1953, release of the National Foundation for Infantile Paralysis, described Daniel as a manufacturer. *The New York Times* amplified this fact to say that the father, since retired, worked in the garment district as "a designer of women's neckwear and blouses."

It appears fair to state that by any standards, those of the small town as much as New York's, Jonas was raised in rather modest circumstances. But he was not culturally underprivileged; the Salks are a self-respecting Orthodox Jewish family. For many offspring of the lower middle class, this environment would constitute a distinct privilege.

On the other hand, one can scarcely spend the first twenty-eight years of one's life in New York City, as Salk did, without learning to adjust to human pressures. Here millions of people live, like anonymous mice or aggressive moles, in the long shadows of high buildings and the dark, noisy rush of subways. In the elevator shafts rising upwards as well as the tunnels underground, one finds little sun and much crowding for a place in it.

The Salks gave the oldest of their sons a good Jewish name, Jonas. Scholars hold the word to be a corruption of "Jonah," who was a Hebrew prophet. The name has at least two meanings; a few have tried to read prophecy about Salk into it. One meaning is "dove"—allegorically, the chosen instrument of God. The second designates one who brings ill luck—the Old Testament story held that Jonah disobeyed his God and brought down a tempest on the ship in which he sought to flee; Jonah saved the situation by jumping overboard, whereupon the whale swallowed him. It is doubtful if Salk's given name influenced him in any way, but the fact that his surname contained only four letters did make some difference in his fame, as we shall see.

The Salk sons were blessed with good minds and were encouraged to use them. The traditional Jewish family, often in contrast to the Anglo-Saxon family of equivalent status, tends to respect the higher education and authority of the learned professions. A good education for its children is a serious objective. Jonas's brother Herman became a doctor of veterinary medicine; the third son, Lee, a doctor of clinical psychology.

But the eldest did best. An opinion survey in 1958 pronounced Jonas Salk to be one of the two best-known living American scientists (Robert Oppenheimer was the other). Another survey ranked him with Albert Schweitzer as one of the two greatest medical heroes of our time.

In the many interviews that Salk felt it his duty to give during the period of the vaccine's development, he said little of interest about his boyhood. He held it more becoming of a scientist to direct attention to the vaccine rather than to himself. In this effort he was singularly unsuccessful, as he once conceded when he plaintively inquired: "Why do they want to know what I have for breakfast?"

Fairly early in life Jonas Salk chose to pursue the humble path of the laboratory worker. Such a career may bring intellectual pleasure, peace of mind, scholarly comradeship, and perhaps some satisfying sense of sacrificing the things that other people consider important, but it offers a statistically high probability of complete obscurity.

As a shy, slender, dark-haired boy, Salk was serious-minded and bookish. One relative recalled: "Even as a kid, when Jonas said something, you could put it in the bank." At home, in the Bronx, where his family moved to a four-room apartment, Jonas kept his things picked up.

His greatest desire as a boy, according to these sources, was to read everything he could get his hands on. He placed his schoolwork first, and won high grades. To describe him, his teachers used pedagogic words of approval—neat, precise, industrious.

His love of learning won Salk a place in Townsend Harris Hall, then a high school for special honor students. He graduated before he was sixteen.

The New York City public-school system could not claim directly to have inspired Salk to develop the polio vaccine. He received not a single science course before college, none being available at Townsend Harris. He excelled in the classics. To this day, he can quote Emerson, Thoreau, Roger Bacon, and Lincoln, and carry on a literate conversation with the poet Robert Frost (as he has done on television).

As a matter of fact, Salk thought of becoming an attorney when he entered the City College of New York (because it was free). In his first year there Salk took science courses "out of curiosity." Thereafter, he could not get enough of them. He obtained his Bachelor of Science degree in 1934, while he was still nineteen.

Now, having also done some spare-time and summer-vacation work as a laboratory technician, he was sure of what he wanted to be—a medical scientist. When he applied for admission to the New York University College of Medicine, he said as much. The doctor interviewing him suggested that there wasn't much money in research. "There is more in life than money," Salk replied.

Eventually he spoke of science as "a way of life," and when the time came, he listed himself in *Who's Who in America* as "physician, scientist."

Salk's passion for research came to the attention of his professors, who noticed that the eager student, only twenty and a good two or three years younger than most of his classmates, spent considerable time at the laboratory bench. One of them suggested that Salk drop out of medical school at the end of his first year and take a one-year fellowship in chemistry, to lay a good research groundwork. Returning to medical school in 1936, Salk was successful in obtaining one fellowship or scholarship after another to meet the cost of his medical education.

He could not help being aware of the exciting advances in virus research. Here at N.Y.U. was a young assistant professor of bacteriology, Dr. Maurice Brodie, who had a new vaccine against polio. There was much talk in the medical school about Brodie's vaccine—also about one introduced by Dr. John Kolmer of Temple University in Philadelphia, who already had the Kolmer blood test for syphilis to his credit.

A medical student's humanitarian hopes could not help vibrating, like violin strings under the bow, to the microbiological events of the 1930's. One did not have to depend on laboratory conversation or wait for the medical journals to learn about the Brodie and Kolmer vaccines. The story was in the newspapers then, as the story of the Salk vaccine was twenty years later— even the tragic outcome. This was the beginning of a controversy over the comparative superiority of live- and killed-virus polio vaccines which still continues.

Kolmer had been experimenting with ways of taming the polio virus for three years or more, as had Brodie, then in his late twenties. The latter made headlines first. In July 1934, Dr. William H. Park, director of the City Health Department research laboratory, announced that he and two other City doctors had tried a new polio vaccine on themselves. Later it turned out that Brodie, Park's assistant in charge of infantile-paralysis research, and two girl technicians also had taken part in the experiment.

The vaccine was injected in two large doses of five cubic centimeters. "There is no danger," commented Park, a well-known figure in bacteriology. The source of the virus was the ground-up spinal cord and spinal bulb, or brain stem, of polio-paralyzed monkeys. Brodie had tried to develop a vaccine with live polio virus, but this had "proved dangerous," he asserted.

He killed the virus with the standard strong antiseptic, formaldehyde, also known as formalin. The idea, he said, was "to expose the virus to formalin for the minimum amount of time needed to kill it," without destroying its capacity to produce antibodies. These, he said, appeared in the blood of ninety per cent of his monkeys.

Kolmer, then forty-eight, was research director of the Institute of Cutaneous Research in Philadelphia. He met the challenge of the Park-Brodie publicity and announced two days later that he soon would have an attenuated live-virus vaccine ready for human testing. He and his assistant, Miss Anna M. Rule, had tried the vaccine on themselves as well as on monkeys.

Kolmer sharply disagreed with Brodie's statement that a killed virus provided protection. "All attempts to vaccinate monkeys with a completely killed . . . vaccine have heretofore failed," he said. Kolmer said that his live virus had been rendered harmless for humans by repeated passages through monkeys. He further devitalized his virus solution, made from spinal cords of infected monkeys, with two different chemicals that did not kill it. This made it, he presumed, quite similar to Pasteur's rabies vaccine, a virus first adapted to rabbits and then partially inactivated. For children, Kolmer recommended half-centimeter doses given in a series of three, at weekly intervals.

It became something of a race to see whether Brodie or Kolmer would be first to try his vaccines on humans other than himself and his colleagues. Meantime, warnings were heard—among others was one from Dr. W. Lloyd Aycock of Harvard University. The vaccination of all children against infantile paralysis was too hazardous, said Aycock. He explained that the need was for methods of finding and vaccinating susceptible children only, adding: "Nature does a better job of immunizing than we could hope to do artificially. . . . To vaccinate everybody when less than one in 1,000 needs to be protected would not seem justifiable in the absence of a guarantee of safety. There is as yet no guarantee."

It is not clear from their published reports whether Kolmer or Brodie was first to vaccinate children, but they began about the time Salk was starting in medical school. Kolmer, sometime in the fall, inoculated twenty-five persons from eight months to fifteen years old, including his two teen-age sons. In November, Park announced that twenty-five children had been vaccinated with the Park-Brodie vaccine six weeks before and now had been tested and found immune. In December 1934 this number increased to three hundred. Kolmer had increased his total to fifty. No ill effects were reported with either vaccine.

Polio was epidemic in several parts of the country during the next year. The situation was right for mass testing of vaccines, or so it seemed. By the fall of 1935 some ten thousand children had received the Brodie vaccine and twelve thousand the Kolmer, in field tests made in a variety of places, from North Carolina to California. By now, however, both of these brave virus hunters were on the defensive.

A dramatic dispute among bacteriologists and public-health officers arose at two meetings of the American Public Health Association. The burning question was whether certain cases of paralytic polio that had appeared in vaccinated children were the result of the vaccine or owing to mere coincidence—that is, owing to an overlap of the period in which a natural case of polio was incubating and the period in which the vaccine was building protective antibodies. There is an immunologist's no-man's-land here, when it is too late to prevent polio but not proper to pronounce the vaccine a failure if polio occurs. To blame the vaccine as the cause of the disease in this period requires some detective work.

Dr. James P. Leake, a respected Public Health Service officer, discussed several suspicious cases and recommended that use of both Brodie and Kolmer vaccines be discontinued. Dr. Thomas

M. Rivers, then of the Rockefeller Institute, now vice-president of medical affairs for the National Foundation, said that he doubted the safety of the Kolmer vaccine, but that the Brodie vaccine probably was safe.

Both vaccine makers stood their ground. The showdown came in November, in St. Louis, where both Brodie and Kolmer reported their results. Kolmer pronounced his vaccine "safe for the immunization of human beings." He explored ten cases of polio that had developed following the first or second injections, including five deaths.

Were these due to the vaccine or to coincidence? "In at least some of these," he said, "it is a reasonable assumption that the vaccine was not responsible for the attacks, and in no instance has poliomyelitis developed after the full three doses. . . ."

Brodie did not entertain any possibility of danger in his vaccine, but conceded that there was still a question about how much immunity it conferred on the vaccinated.

In the discussion it became apparent why a scientist who values his reputation must submit his data, his interpretations, and his conclusions to the contemplation, confirmation, refutation, or indifferent shrugs of his colleagues. It may be hard on his ego, but he has to do it. This jury of his peers protects not only the individual himself but also science and the public from human fallibility.

It fell to Rivers to cast the largest stone. He said that the Kolmer vaccine had been tested at the Rockefeller Institute and had not protected the Institute's monkeys. Occasionally a large dose had paralyzed a monkey. He said that there was no experimental evidence to support the contention that the monkey-passage virus was less virulent in man. The chemicals Kolmer used killed some viruses, but did not affect others. Kolmer had reported that no polio occurred among the many children who had received the third injection. This, Rivers maintained, could be due not to the vaccine but to the possibility that these children were the ones with natural resistance in the first place. In any event, there was no adequate control group—no children left unvaccinated for comparison.

Dr. Leake rose and said to Dr. Kolmer: "I beg you to desist from the human use of this vaccine."

Rivers turned to the Brodie vaccine. Rockefeller Institute tests likewise had shown that this vaccine gave monkeys little or no protection. Others had tried a killed-virus polio vaccine years before, he said, but their results had been so discouraging that nobody had had the nerve to try it again—until now.

Amid some public shock, the 1935 vaccination program was laid to rest. Leake, in December, published in the *Journal of the American Medical Association* a list of twelve cases of paralytic polio associated with the two vaccines. There were six deaths. The list made grim reading. A boy, five, became paralyzed in his vaccinated arm six days after receiving a second dose and was dead three days later. A girl, twenty-one months old, likewise became paralyzed six days after a second dose; she died five days later. And so on.

Leake charged nine cases and five deaths against the Kolmer vaccine. Three other cases were blamed on the Brodie vaccine. One was a California youth of twenty who had received the vaccine at the urgent request of his parents, who believed he had been exposed to polio. But apparently it was the vaccine that killed him. Thus, Rivers to this extent was wrong—the Brodie vaccine was *unsafe* as well as ineffective.

It was obvious to Salk, as it was to everybody else who followed the story, that making a polio vaccine was not child's play, but dangerous business, both for the child and for the scientist who would save that child from polio. Salk became a student of the Brodie mistake, as his first published report on a polio vaccine in 1953 showed. It was plain that he did not intend to repeat it.

Long before 1953, of course, it was evident that both the Brodie and the Kolmer vaccines would have been destined to failure even if the first had been completely killed and the second truly attenuated, or non-virulent. Sir Macfarlane Burnet, the Australian virus hunter, who at one time or another appears to have thought of everything, in 1933 had reported indications of different types of polio virus, each probably producing its specific antibodies and therefore each requiring a separate vaccine.

In any event, these vaccines were made from a virus taken from spinal-cord and brain tissue. We saw how diligently Max Theiler worked to get away from his yellow-fever virus that was adapted to mouse brains. Even when he did so successfully, one chance variant in his tissue cultures caused a few encephalitis deaths in Brazil. In actual fact, the chance of an allergic reaction in the brain from a crude vaccine made from spinal-cord or brain cells is probably greater than that of getting paralytic polio without the vaccine.

In the beginning, when he had hope of emerging as a savior of mankind from polio, Brodie had said: "If we fail, why, another well-intentioned effort to cope with this disease has failed." It was worse than that. Park was an old man, with a full career behind him. Kolmer had a good reputation and was well established in Philadelphia, where he remained. But Brodie, born in Great Britain and trained in Canada, was young and now, it seemed, had no future. He left New York and took a job in Providence Hospital in Detroit, but he could hardly forget. In 1938, in *The Fight for Life*, Paul de Kruif—prone to jump on medical-miracle bandwagons too quickly, he confessed—charged Brodie with deceiving himself, Park, and De Kruif.

The Brodie episode ended in 1939. In April, Park died, at the age of seventy-six. Only a month later, curiously enough, Brodie, still in his early thirties, died in the hospital very suddenly. The story one hears today among virologists is that he committed suicide, but his death certificate does not support this: it gives the cause of death as coronary thrombosis. But we can say, figuratively, that this young scientist died of a broken heart.

Contemplating the grim outcome of good intentions, one health officer said at that St. Louis meeting in 1935: "We must know the past to appreciate the present and prepare for the future."

The future then was very much in the making in the person of Jonas Salk. In 1938, Dr. Thomas Francis became professor of bacteriology at N.Y.U. Salk, then a senior medical student, sought out the new professor in his laboratory and said: "I have some time to fill in—is there anything I can do?" Francis sized Salk up as "a good young man, interested, with ideas." He put the student to work on a study already under way—the inactivation of influenza virus with ultra-violet light. They found it possible to kill the virus without destroying its capacity to produce antibodies. Francis made Salk senior author of the published report, as a gesture of encouragement.

Following his graduation in 1939 as a doctor of medicine, Salk continued with Francis for nine months on another fellowship, before beginning a two-year internship at Mount Sinai Hospital in New York. He also married Donna Lindsay, a Smith College graduate and social worker.

Friends and relatives, noting that Jonas was sticking to the laboratory as usual, asked when he was going into practice now that he had both an M.D. and a wife to support? Why did he keep going after these $1,500- or $2,500-a-year fellowships?

"Why," replied Salk, "did Mozart compose music?"

It was now evident that Jonas Salk was a dedicated young man.

The University of Michigan summoned Francis to become chairman of the department of epidemiology in 1941. Salk went to Ann Arbor the following year, having obtained a National Research Council fellowship financed by the National Foundation for Infantile Paralysis. Thus Salk, without realizing it at the time, entered the O'Connor field of gravity.

Francis was an influenza authority and head of the Army's flu-prevention program. He already had made an experimental flu vaccine at the Rockefeller Institute, and was now experimenting with formaldehyde inactivation of the virus.

Salk joined in the flu studies, receiving a draft deferment because of the essential nature of his work. In 1943 he teamed with Francis in the field-testing of a vaccine against influenza Types A and B. This was the first convincing human demonstration of the potency of a killed virus in producing antibodies. The big question remaining was how to improve on the temporary duration of the vaccine's effectiveness.

This kind of thinking—that you can kill a virus and still get immunizing good out of it—served to differentiate Salk and his teacher, Francis, from the live-virus school of thought. The latter is inclined to stick by the attenuation approach to virus vaccines, pointing to the tried-and-true smallpox vaccine and Theiler's 17D yellow-fever vaccine. But those were the *only* truly attenuated-virus vaccines that we had. Francis was not impressed. He called his colleagues' argument a "two-case generalization."

Out of such controversies come scientific progress. It is essential to our understanding of what is to follow to appreciate, however, that some of our great heroes in virology—John Enders, for example—had no real confidence in the killed-virus approach from the beginning, whatever the merits of a fresh viewpoint. The live- virus advocates, reasoning from what was known rather than what might remain to be learned from new experience, believed that the way to produce a solid immunity against any infectious disease is by natural infection with a mild, non-injurious dose of that disease. This requires a tame, modified virus that, unlike the killed one, will multiply after it is put in the body, creating more viruses and thus thoroughly conditioning the mechanism of the blood which produces antibodies against the disease. When the killed virus is used, as these critics see it, antibodies are produced only against the virus particles injected at the time. The individual does not have an infection from a killed virus.

True, perfectly good killed-bacteria vaccines have been made, but here the "antigenic mass" of microbial material—the total jolt to the antibody mechanism—can be made much larger than in the case of a virus. Furthermore, no one expects more than temporary immunity, for six months or a year or two. This is worth while, and can be maintained by repeated inoculations of individuals who will be exposed to highly infectious and lethal diseases that strike large numbers of the population. Polio does not fall into this category. In fact, natural immunity is so widespread that many virologists do not consider a temporary protection against polio worth while. Susceptibility might return; quite possibly a false sense of security would remain.

But there was no longer any question that a killed-virus flu vaccine would produce antibodies. The problem now was to achieve lasting immunity, if possible. This, Francis and his followers hoped might be done through a series of properly spaced injections that would produce reinforcement, or a booster effect. Also, to stretch out the effect of one, two, or three doses might prove helpful. Hence, the Francis group turned to experiments with "adjuvants," or aids, to prolong the provocative effect of the virus antigen on the antibodies.

The best adjuvant seemed to be mineral oil. The vaccine maker simply substitutes oil for water as the fluid suspension for his virus. When injected, the oil vaccine forms a deposit under the skin or in the muscle—wherever it is placed—and then only gradually releases the virus into the blood stream. Thus, antibody stimulation is continued over a much longer period.

In his five years at the University of Michigan, Salk finished his graduate training and achieved academic status as an assistant professor of epidemiology. Meanwhile, Dr. Max A. Lauffer, professor of biophysics at the University of Pittsburgh School of Medicine, found the opportunity to expand his virus-research program, and began looking for the right man to head such a program as associate professor. Francis recommended Salk, then thirty-three, and Salk accepted the job.

As it turned out, he did something quite different from the basic research Lauffer had in mind. When Salk went to Pittsburgh in 1947, he contemplated no work in polio research, still in its neurotropic Dark Age. But in the next five years, events in this field moved with spectacular swiftness. As Salk explained to John Troan, then of the Pittsburgh *Press:* "Everybody else was fooling around with the polio thing, so I thought I'd play around with it, too, to gain some experience."

Fundamentally, the development of a successful polio vaccine became possible as the result of four discoveries, each of breakthrough significance:

1. We already know of the Enders-Weller-Robbins success in breaking the neurotropic bottleneck and getting polio viruses to grow in ordinary tissues. Subsequently, the Connaught Laboratory at the University of Toronto worked out mass-production methods of cultivating the virus, settling upon monkey kidneys as the best medium for fast multiplication, and this laboratory became the chief supplier of virus for the Salk vaccine.

2. In 1949 the great polio-research team at Johns Hopkins University in Baltimore—Drs. David Bodian, Howard A. Howe, and Isabel Morgan Mountain (she is now at Columbia Univer-

sity)—showed why Brodie and Kolmer had encountered inconsistencies in the immunizing effects of vaccine containing only one strain of virus. Led by Bodian, they found that there are three distinct types of polio virus, each producing specific antibodies of its own.

3. In 1952 Bodian and a tall, handsome lady virologist from Yale, Dorothy Horstmann, working independently, added an important piece of information indicating that antibodies against polio could protect against paralysis. Bodian and Dr. Horstmann showed that polio was not first and last a disease of nerves, as so many had thought, but only last. It enters the blood stream at one point or another in the alimentary canal, probably the throat, and then produces a general systemic infection of the blood. These scientists were the first ones to detect the virus in the blood streams of their monkeys and chimpanzees, during an incubation stage called "viremia." This precedes the appearance of paralytic polio, which, if it comes, strikes anywhere from five to thirty-one days after infection. Hence, they concluded, antibodies in the blood almost certainly would present a barrier to outside infection and ward off subsequent invasion of the spinal cord and brain.

4. Dr. Mountain, nee Morgan, meanwhile had made a polio vaccine by killing the virus with formaldehyde and had showed that it produced specific antibodies and no ill effects in monkeys. Then, in early 1952, Howe made a triple-type, killed-virus polio vaccine that seemed promising when tried on six Baltimore children. Thus, the Johns Hopkinsites recovered old ground in the light of new knowledge. Howe concluded that much more work remained to be done. It was the scientific understatement of the year. A few brilliant experiments can tell the microbiologist what path to pursue, but they don't provide him with much idea of what the path is like. He learns the path and its possible pitfalls only by taking it—to the end.

Salk chose to be the man who would follow the path to the end.

Although the Bodian group's experiments had shown that there were three distinct immunologic groups of polio virus, the question remained: Is that all? Until it was answered, no one could possibly make a vaccine without running the risk of repeating the mistake of Brodie and Kolmer.

Answering this question would take a large laboratory—in fact, several large laboratories to divide the work—plus thousands of monkeys, gallons of immune serum, dozens of technicians to do all the tedious animal injections, titrations, and autopsies, and two or three years of time at least.

In fact, the National Foundation and four university laboratories (Pittsburgh, Kansas, Southern California, and Utah) needed three years to do the job after Basil O'Connor, with his usual vigor for tackling "the impossible," said: "Do it." It cost the Foundation $1,370,000, plus thirty thousand monkeys from India and the Philippines. (This was the beginning of the monkey kingdom's massive sacrifice to save humanity from polio. Ever since, polio research has killed monkeys at the rate of tens of thousands per year.)

Now Salk met O'Connor, and their great and well-advertised polio-vaccine adventure began. The Foundation invited Salk to become a member of its Committee on Typing and take part in the sorting of one hundred different known polio-virus strains, or samples. In five years the Foundation granted Salk $1,250,000 for his part in the typing plus the development of a method of preventing paralytic polio.

On the Committee, Salk sat with some great virus hunters. Among them:

Francis, his teacher who had isolated the Mahoney (Type I) strain;

Armstrong, who had found the Lansing (Type II) strain;

Dr. John F. Kessel, of Los Angeles, who had uncovered the Leon (Type III) polio virus;

Bodian, originally a product of the University of Chicago and one of the best basic scientists polio research has known;

Aycock, who had foreseen the danger in the Kolmer and Park-Brodie vaccines;

Sabin, a brilliant worker who had seen many ideas about polio's transmission and route of bodily invasion come and go;

Dr. Louis P. Gebhardt. We should mentally check the name of

this bacteriologist from the University of Utah. In 1955 Gebhardt became the first to detect live virus in the Salk vaccine made by the Cutter Laboratories.

In Pittsburgh, the Municipal Hospital for Contagious Diseases was falling into disuse as the result of the advent of antibiotics, which made it possible to treat patients with infectious bacterial diseases more quickly and effectively at home or in isolation rooms of general hospitals (this passing of the old contagious-disease hospitals is a general trend). Salk persuaded the administrative authorities to give him a dozen rooms on three floors for his National Foundation-financed laboratory and monkey house. Eventually he had a staff of fifty persons working for him. The hospital is a modern yellow-brick building on a steep hill not far from the University's famous skyscraper building, known as the "Cathedral of Learning." Salk found the tempo to his liking. The School of Medicine, like the University and the Steel City itself, are accustomed to building big. Here the boy from Madison Avenue and 106th Street found his métier. Later the old Contagious Diseases hospital would be renamed Jonas Salk Hall.

The Typing Committee finished its work by the end of 1951 and now became an Immunization Committee. It had confirmed Bodian: there were just three types of polio virus. A number of scientists applied for National Foundation grants for the development of a polio vaccine, Salk and Sabin among them; any competent man could have money for this purpose. Basil O'Connor had dedicated himself to the conquest of polio.

Salk, by now research professor of bacteriology and director of the Virus Research Laboratory at the University of Pittsburgh, now was in an excellent position to make a vaccine himself. He had the big laboratory and staff, and the experience of working with the viruses and their immune serums in the typing program. The basic knowledge was at hand and he could now—as O'Connor later told a Congressional investigating committee—"put the ingredients together."

At once Salk faced Brodie's dilemma. It was a sort of having-your-cake-and-eating-it-too proposition. He had to be sure to kill the virus, so that it would not kill or paralyze children. Yet he had to preserve its capacity to stimulate polio antibodies when injected into the body.

This is not easy to do, particularly when one has to work with three types of virus at once. During the typing program Salk had some trouble getting the Brunhilde strain of Type I—Brunhilde was one of Howe's chimps—to produce good antibodies in his monkeys. In fact, he had to resort to a trick he had learned in working with influenza vaccine: he suspended the virus in mineral oil.

But the Brunhilde strain did not strike him as a good bet for a human polio vaccine. Type I would be the most important virus in the vaccine—this type is responsible for the vast majority of paralytic polio—and it must be a potent antibody producer. So he turned to the most potent of them all, the Mahoney strain, isolated by Francis in a family in Akron, Ohio. Three Mahoney children had the virus in their intestines, but did not get polio. However, the Klines next door lost three of their five children to this dangerous strain, following tonsillectomies in all five. In selecting this type, Salk boldly committed himself to fighting fire with fire, and counted on being able to kill the virus without any exceptions whatsoever.

For his Type II he chose the MEF-1, isolated by American Middle East Forces bacteriologists in Cairo, Egypt, in 1942, from an adult with bulbar polio. For Type III he took the Saukett strain isolated by his own laboratory in 1950 from a little boy with paralytic polio.

The crucial issue was safety, as Salk conceded when he subsequently said in a radio broadcast: "It was necessary to undo the fear created" by the 1935 vaccine tragedy. In his 1952 experiments Salk killed the virus by exposing the infected tissue-culture fluid to formaldehyde in the ratio of 250 fluid to one formaldehyde at a temperature of melting ice (33 to 34 degrees Farenheit) for a period of seven, ten, or thirteen days, terminating exposure after tests on the brains of live monkeys and in tissue cultures revealed no further virulence.

This process became known as "cooking," though actually no heat was involved. Salk amplified the figure of speech as follows in explaining his development of the vaccine to *Life* writer Robert Coughlan:

"The method is very much like the one a housewife uses when she wants to prepare a new dessert, say a cake. She starts with an idea and certain ingredients and then experiments, a little more of this and a little less of that, and keeps changing things until finally she has a good recipe. In the process, she will have deduced certain universal laws which govern such things. From there, she can go on to make further improvements during the years."[1]

This is an accurate description of the evolution of the Salk vaccine, which underwent a series of important modifications before, during, and after the 1954 field trials. For example, in the early experiments Salk soon discovered that it was sufficient to cook the virus culture fluid in a ratio of 4,000 to one of formaldehyde at a temperature of 97 to 99 degrees Fahrenheit (body temperature, in other words).

Also, he developed the theory that his method of virus inactivation provided a "margin of safety"—a built-in safety factor, as some described it. This, he believed, was a guarantee against another disaster. Few claims, we should note at once, ultimately have been subjected to more critical scientific scrutiny.

Salk's "margin of safety" dealt with the problem that live virus particles might survive in a mixture of tissue-culture fluid and formaldehyde beyond the capacity of his tests to detect them. Here he would be at the mercy of the inexactness of his science. He needed some way of being sure that, given a uniform consistency of his materials and thorough mixing so that the antiseptic reached every virus particle, any undetected, unmeasurable infectivity was eliminated.

Happily, he noted that when he plotted the "cooking" process on graph paper printed with a semi-logarithmic scale, and connected the points, the formaldehyde reduced the virus population in a straight line for as far as he could test the action. Therefore, if he extended the exposure period sufficiently, the curve—in statistics it is possible to have a "curve" that is a straight line—would cross the zero base line. Exit the last live virus particle!

[1] Robert Coughlan: "Science Moves In on Viruses," *Life*, June 22, 1955.

If he started with 1,000,000 live-virus units, for instance, he calculated that after twelve hours of "cooking" only 100,000 survived. After twenty-four hours there were only 10,000, and after
forty-eight hours, only 1,000. By the end of three days, when he
came to the limit of the measurable, he figured that only one of
the original 1,000,000 virus units was left. If he continued the
process to six days, the chance of a live virus particle surviving
was one in a trillion. So he carried on the "cooking" still another
three days, concluding: "The material treated for a total of nine
days or longer should, theoretically, be free of any demonstrable
virus—even if all of the fluid being converted into vaccine were
tested in tissue culture or even in man."

Such a scientific assumption arising out of, but extending beyond, evidence is commonly called "neat" or "pretty"—if it
works!

It would take a brave microbiologist to say that, because his
tests could not detect the presence of a virus particle, none was
present. And Salk did not say so, actually. Rather, he said that
he had observed a phenomenon that gave him cause for absolute
confidence in the safety of his vaccine. He remarked about this
to the press: "There is no question of 'how safe is it?' It is safe, and
it can't be safer than safe."

Certainly his own experience bore him out. He vaccinated more
than twelve thousand children and adults prior to the mass field
trial of 1954 without a sign of a slip-up. When asked if it hadn't
taken personal daring to move his vaccine from monkey to man,
he stoutly replied: "I have the courage of my convictions. I
couldn't do it unless I was more critical of myself than others are
of me. It is courage based on confidence, not daring, and it's confidence based on experience."

The next question involved the antibodies. Killed virus produced antibodies in monkeys. But how would it behave in humans? Every microbiologist knows that monkeys, mice, and men
do not always behave the same way, in their susceptibility and
resistance to disease. Salk pondered the move from animals to
humans for some time. He had many discussions about it with
his staff collaborators—Byron L. Bennett, L. James Lewis, Elsie
N. Ward, and Julius S. Youngner. How should it be done? The

measurement of antibodies is as crude a science as the detection of infectious organisms in test animals. The immunologist cannot see, count, or weigh antibodies. He cannot say: "Here is one polio antibody, and there are two."

The virus worker, as explained before, determines the presence of antibodies in an animal or human being by a neutralization test based on the fact that antibodies destroy germs of the kind that produced them in the first place. The worker exposes the subject's blood serum to a standard dose of the infectious agent, and injects the mixture into an animal or a fresh tissue culture. He dilutes the serum and repeats the process until he finds the titer, or end point of neutralization, carrying the procedure through a standard series of dilutions—4, 8, 16, 32, 64, 128, 256, 512, for example. At some point the serum antibodies will cease to inactivate the virus dose and the test animal or culture will become infected. That will be the antibody titer for the serum tested. This varies not only from one disease to the next, but, with the same disease, from one patient to the next.

A high antibody level in polio may be 64 or 128—rarely, it may run up to 4,096 and that is wonderful. But, however pretty the mathematics, no amount of calculation alters the fact that the numbers are relative and not absolute.

Who would be the first humans to be tested?

We might suppose that Salk would find some human volunteers without antibodies to polio, vaccinate them, and then demonstrate that they had developed antibodies. It would be almost unthinkable that the polio researcher would begin by injecting his vaccine and later inject a challenge dose of live virus to test immunity, as Jenner did with smallpox.

Salk resorted to an old trick in immunology. He used children who had already had polio and therefore were presumably immune to one type or another, but in whom he could measure any antibody increases due to his vaccine. In the spring of 1952 he went to the D. T. Watson Home for Crippled Children in Leetsdale, Pennsylvania, with his proposal, and won ready approval from the staff, the parents, and the patients themselves. The first task was to test his subjects for polio antibodies, to give him a basis for comparison. The vast majority—in fact, sixty out of seventy-nine—had antibodies for Type I, the most common polio.

Salk cooked his polio virus in formaldehyde for ten to thirteen days. He suspended part of the vaccine in water and the rest in oil. The children would receive injections for each of the three types in their forearms, and a second round six weeks later.

On June 30 he went to Watson Home and, for the first time, administered his vaccine to human beings.

"When you inoculate children with a polio vaccine, you don't sleep well for two or three months," Salk reflected.

The results, on the other hand, were calculated to produce sound sleep. He tested the children's blood for antibodies before and after each dose and again five weeks after the second and last injection. Whether the virus was in water or oil, the antibody titers repeatedly bounced up to high levels following the first dose.

In no instance did a subject develop polio, even where there had been no detectable antibodies for a given type prior to vaccination. In such cases there were now antibodies at levels of 8 to 256. Where detectable antibodies were already present, presumably from the polio that crippled the child, these now rose to higher levels. For example, a customary titer of 4 for Type I before vaccination commonly shot up to 32, 64, or 128 and sometimes higher after vaccination.

Soon Salk extended his vaccine tests to persons with no history of poliomyelitis. These were sixty-three mentally retarded inmates of the Polk State School in Polk, Pennsylvania. They ranged in age from four to thirty, but represented an older age group on the whole because of the large number in their late teens and twenties. While none of the sixty-three was a polio victim, there had been a polio epidemic of six cases at the Polk School in the fall of 1951 and the test group showed a high level of natural immunity to one or more polio types.

These experiments, too, went off without mishap. One purpose was to see how the vaccine would work when the three types of killed virus were combined in one triple vaccine. It worked just fine.

Salk later indicated to reporters that he had experienced his biggest thrill three and a half months after giving the Watson Home children their first injection. At that time, in October, he tested the antibodies in their blood in comparison with their blood prior to vaccination. The paired tests were made in test-tube tissue cultures of monkey kidney cells mixed with the blood serum and doses of live virus many times greater than enough to kill a mouse and more than enough to overpower any weak antibodies that might be present, though not detected, in the pre-vaccination blood.

The children's antibodies three and a half months after the first injection were strong enough to neutralize the live virus, whereas their pre-vaccination blood would not do so. What Salk saw when he looked through his microscope at the kidney cells in his test tubes was this: Cells mixed with live virus and the post-vaccination blood continued to grow normally. The antibodies protected the cells. When pre-vaccination blood was used, the cells did not grow. The virus killed them. *"These comparisons serve to indicate that the antibody rise is real,"* he wrote in italics in his first report.

During the fall and early winter Salk labored over the compilation of his data and the writing and polishing of a lengthy report that was to command eighteen pages of closely packed type when it appeared in the *Journal of the American Medical Association* for March 28, 1953. In such periods of concentrated effort his family saw little of him; when they did, he could hardly be counted as there. But even in his preoccupation he was able to show a sense of humor. "Jonas, you aren't even listening," Mrs. Salk concluded one night. "Dear," he replied, "I'm giving you my undevoted attention."

Salk already conceived theoretical and practical implications that became clear to him as he went on ("it is clear" is one of his favorite phrases, as may be seen from his scientific reports, themselves models of clarity). For example, he perceived a possibility that to him later became a certainty: "It is possible, with non-infectious material, to approximate, and perhaps to exceed, the level of antibody produced by infection." This claim raised a lot of scientific eyebrows. Could it be that a dead-virus vaccine, in-

capable of causing virus multiplication in the body as the smallpox and yellow-fever vaccines do, would produce a higher level
of immunity against polio than polio itself?

In January 1953, Salk went to a closed meeting of the National
Foundation's Immunization Committee in New York and told his
colleagues what he had. "Because of the great importance of
safety factors in studies of this kind," he reported, "it must be remembered that considerable time is required for the preparation
and study of each new batch of experimental vaccine before human inoculations can be considered. It is this consideration, above
all else, that imposes a limitation in the speed with which this
work can be extended."

But the fact that he had a promising vaccine leaked out in Earl
Wilson's column: NEW POLIO VACCINE—BIG HOPES SEEN. A March
of Dimes campaign was in progress, and the National Foundation
people themselves found the news too good to keep. At a campaign kick-off dinner, with the press welcome, as always, they announced "tremendous progress." People are happy to contribute
money for medical research of any kind, particularly polio, but
the fund raiser and publicity man who comes back to them year
after year wants to give them something for their money besides
hope.

The headlines dismayed Salk, who had returned to Pittsburgh.
He went back to New York and told O'Connor that he thought
the claims for his vaccine ought to be toned down: "I'd better go
to the public myself and try to set the pitch in middle C instead
of high C." O'Connor readily agreed, and arranged for a press
conference, a radio broadcast, and a television film, all to be
timed in anticipation of the A.M.A.'s publication of the first report.

The national network program, at 10:45 p.m. on March 26, was
entitled "The Scientist Speaks for Himself." O'Connor, speaking
first, pictured the American people as active partners—indeed,
stockholders—in polio research.

Salk, with his high forehead, receding black hair, light horn-
rimmed glasses, bulldog jaw, and dark, conservative suit, looked
serious and dignified. He spoke competently, facilely, with a

quiet air of confidence and an occasional display of his underlying natural warmth, about his wish "to make clear the facts, so that they *not* be misunderstood nor misconstrued."

He lost the toning-down battle, nonetheless. Somehow his words only added to the excitement: "The results of these studies provide justification for optimism, and . . . may lead to the desired objective. But . . . there will be no vaccine for widespread use for the next polio season."

Young Dr. Jonas Salk—a real-life Dr. Kildare—was a great hit. The press liked him. Despite his restrained, sometimes guarded manner, he struck reporters as "a great guy," naturally frank and friendly—maybe a little naïve. Known for both cynicism and sentimentalism, they were drawn to Salk as they are not drawn to pompous, arrogant "stuffed shirts." They liked his habit of taking their questions seriously and making civil replies. They felt close to him, and soon were calling him "Jonas." Here, it appeared, was a good scientist who also was a good human being. "He could sell me the Brooklyn Bridge," one reporter was to comment in 1955 when there was a question among some virologists as to whether Salk had not, in fact, sold the bridge to the American public.

In May 1953, Salk, having prepared and tested some new batches of vaccine, decided to extend the experiments beyond his institutional groups to children and adults in the community who had not had polio and had not knowingly been exposed to it.

In his choice of his first candidates he followed the tradition set by Jenner and other physicians. He vaccinated himself, his wife, Donna, and his three sons: Peter, then nine, Darrell, six, and Jonathan, three. Jonathan was the youngest person to have received the vaccine.

The results were as Salk expected—uneventful—and he proceeded to vaccinate 474 school children and a few adults, mainly in the neighborhood of Leetsdale and Sewickley, a fashionable Pittsburgh suburb. Here, where soap and bathtubs were plentiful, natural immunity to polio would be at its lowest. Tests showed that sixty per cent of the children, aged three to eight, had no detectable antibody for any of the three polios. An additional thirty

per cent had immunity only to one type. Again, following vaccination, the antibodies soared—in the Salk family, too.

Meanwhile, too, O'Connor appointed a new Vaccine Advisory
Committee. Dr. Thomas M. Rivers, then director of the Rockefeller Institute, became its chairman. O'Connor wanted the
process of delivering the Salk polio vaccine to the American public speeded up, he told the committee. It met in May 1953 with
Salk and discussed the possibility of a mass field trial of his vaccine.

Salk still had some unanswered questions in his mind, such as
the best way to kill the virus with formaldehyde, the margin of
safety provided by different periods of "cooking," the comparative
merits of oil and water vaccines, and the number and timing of
doses to get the maximum build-up of antibodies.

The committee decided that, "if a suitable vaccine were available, the National Foundation should undertake a controlled
study to determine its effectiveness." It used the word "controlled"
in the scientific sense rather than the administrative sense of "directed," of course. Because of the low incidence of polio in the general population, a huge number of children would have to be vaccinated and then carefully observed throughout a polio season, in
close comparison with an unvaccinated group.

The following October Salk said he was about ready for a mass
trial. Speaking before a meeting of the American Academy of
Pediatrics in Miami, he was able "to say without equivocation"
that the antibodies produced in the 635 subjects thus far studied
were due to the killed virus in his vaccine. By now, too, he had
seen post-vaccination antibodies persist in his 1952 subjects for
one year.

"The most dramatic responses were observed in persons who, at
the time of injection, possess some antibody as a residual from an
earlier natural exposure," he said. As Salk saw it, he was on Nature's side and she on his, for his vaccine seemed to build on and
beyond whatever natural immunity existed.

He concluded his Miami report:

"The simple fact is . . . an experimental method for inducing
measurable amounts of antibody for the three known poliomyelitis

viruses, employing a killed-virus vaccine, is available, and it now becomes possible to determine whether or not—and to what extent—the incidence of naturally occurring paralysis may be influenced. . . .

"There have been no set-backs nor anything but revelations that shed more light on the course ahead. . . . We have not stumbled down a by-way but have selected a road, with many lanes, that seems long indeed. Our problem is to select not only the fast lane but the one that is safest and most certain."

THE FRANCIS REPORT

BASIL O'CONNOR took Salk's second report, in Miami, as a green light in the fast lane. In early November 1953, a month later, he announced that the vaccine would be tested in 500,000 to 1,000,-000 children, depending on how much vaccine was available. The children would be inoculated between January and June. Perhaps some lives might be saved in 1954.

The situation was this: in year after year of polio campaigns, a tremendous public demand had built up for something to stop polio. O'Connor understood his "polio public." It was impatient; it was irresistible. It had no time—and no ear for the "standstill school," as O'Connor labeled any counsel of caution.

An Associated Press dispatch from Pittsburgh pictured the enormous pressures on Salk: "Children would die the very next summer of polio. Children would be crippled. As a father of three small boys, as a human being, he was compelled to hurry. As a scientist, he was compelled to move slowly."

But there were many plaguing questions that bothered virologists. Salk felt he had eliminated the problem of vaccination abscesses by using a more refined grade of oil in his vaccine. In early 1953 he was very much pro-oil. But meanwhile the medical profession in general was discovering something else with penicillin shots that contained beeswax and peanut oil to make the effects more lasting. A deposit of foreign substance in the flesh, where it can remain as a chronic irritant, is a good way to build up an allergic reaction, or sensitivity, or possibly, in the case of an oil, to start an irritation leading to cancer. Salk quietly dropped mineral oil. He used vaccine in water in 1954 and thenceforth. Water worked fine.

Also, the safety question popped up again. On the same day that O'Connor announced the field-trial decision, Dr. Albert Milzer sounded a negative note from Michael Reese Hospital in Chicago. Milzer, who had been experimenting with a polio vaccine containing virus killed by ultra-violet light, reported that he had tried to kill the virus with formaldehyde, according to Salk's recipe. "For reasons not apparent to us, we were not successful," said Milzer. He turned up live virus in his monkey and tissue-culture tests. "We must avoid the tragic consequences that have accompanied poliomyelitis vaccine research in the past," he said.

Both Dr. Hart E. Van Riper, then the National Foundation's medical director, and Salk felt obliged to make public replies to Milzer. Van Riper said, in sum, that anyone who could not reproduce Salk's results had not followed his methods. This struck some observers as a curious statement, for it seemed to reverse the traditional scientific view that the burden of proof is on the claimant rather than the one testing the claim. "We can state flatly that no human being has been, or ever will, in any field trials, be inoculated with any material that has the remotest suspicion attached to it," said Salk.

Some scientists on the Immunization Committee—the old, reconstituted Typing Committee—shook their heads at such positiveness. Some felt that O'Connor's establishment of the new Rivers committee on vaccine by-passed them. They were not in agreement with O'Connor or Salk about it being time for a field trial. "What, then, is the next step?" asked Thomas Francis. Sabin, among others, considered the Mahoney strain dangerous—Salk had found it hardest to kill.

Other committee members didn't like the idea of all the critical experiments being done in one laboratory—Salk's. They wanted more time to confirm his claims. Several favored setting up a vaccine-evaluation program with a group of universities participating and sharing their findings with one another.

One evidence of the minority's dissatisfaction with the fast lane was the swift coming and going of Dr. Joseph A. Bell, a crack epidemiologist from the Public Health Service's National Institute of Infectious and Allergic Diseases. The Foundation had requested Dr. Bell to come up from Bethesda on loan. Bell did so, and drafted exacting standards for the field trials—for instance, the requirement that every bit of vaccine used be triple-tested for safety, by the manufacturer's laboratory, by Salk's laboratory, and by the P.H.S. Laboratory of Biologics Control.

The latter had the responsibility, under Federal law, for licensing commercial vaccines. The law does not require licensing of an experimental vaccine used on a voluntary basis without charge, but the participation of the Biologics Control people seemed a desirable way of preparing them for the future, inasmuch as they had no experience with polio vaccine.

O'Connor did not like Bell's plan. Bell resigned after a couple of months and returned to Bethesda. The press, apparently blinded by what the *New England Journal of Medicine* was to describe as "incandescent publicity," and, in any event, responsive to the melodramatic qualities of the polio story, ignored this conflict of the scientific and administrative approaches. Later, in 1955, *The Reporter* illuminated one aspect of it thus: "Basil O'Connor had given years of his life to the work. He was identified with the suffering and hope of polio victims. All his efforts were now bent on finding an effective vaccine while he still headed the organization." [1]

Public attention now centered on preparations for the field trial. Van Riper, of the Foundation staff, would have over-all supervision, with advice from a committee of health officers. This would be the biggest field-testing program in the history of preventive medicine.

Vaccination would be carried out in the schools by volunteer physicians under the supervision of local health officers. No child would receive the vaccine except at the written request of his parents.

[1] Lin Root: "The Polio Gamble," *The Reporter,* July 14, 1955.

The Eli Lilly and Parke, Davis companies were already co-operating with Salk in experimental vaccine production. O'Connor talked to ten companies. The vaccine would not be patented or Foundation-controlled, he assured them. Five [2] agreed to make experimental vaccine for the Foundation at cost. The program would cost the Foundation an estimated $7,500,000.

Vaccination would be limited to second-graders in two hundred counties selected because of their high average incidence of polio during the previous five years. The idea was to observe how much polio the vaccinated second-graders had during the 1954 polio season, and compare their experience with non-vaccinated first-graders and third-graders in the same areas. This struck O'Connor and the Rivers committee as the most feasible plan.

Epidemiologists who knew their medical statistics looked askance. This wasn't the way Bell had wanted to do it. One epidemiologist got in touch with Francis, then beginning a year's sabbatical leave from the University of Michigan, and asked if, in view of his experience in field-testing influenza vaccine, he wouldn't consider doing a carefully designed study independent of the Foundation's.

The question was not whether an evaluation conducted by an organization committed to the conquest of polio could be regarded as impartial and independent—though there was that question, too. Rather, as Francis himself indicated in his famous report of 1955, the experts would place a great deal more confidence in a comparison based on matched controls, or what is known as a double blind test.

This plan required preparation of doses of vaccine and of a placebo, or dummy, which would appear precisely the same and would be so labeled and numbered that they could not be told apart except by referring to code numbers whose meaning was kept secret from field workers. The vaccine and placebo (salt solution) would be given to alternate children, with neither the physician nor the child knowing which was which.

[2] Parke, Davis and Company, Detroit, Michigan; Eli Lilly Company, Indianapolis, Indiana; Wyeth Laboratories, Inc., Marietta, Pennsylvania; Pitman-Moore Company, Zionville, Indiana; and Cutter Laboratories, Berkeley, California. A sixth pharmaceutical laboratory, Sharp and Dohme, Philadelphia, Pennsylvania, eventually became a vaccine producer also.

O'Connor saw the use of placebos as a drawback, whatever the statistical merits, and so did some of the health officials on his advisory committee. This plan was vastly complicated in its details of operation. Furthermore, it meant denying half the children the real vaccine and its presumed benefits. It also meant leaving parents in ignorance as to whether their child had been given the real thing or not. It just didn't seem fair to deceive those who received the dummy shots.

The search for scientific truth, however, is not concerned with good public relations except as the search makes for greater public faith in the truth seekers. It was borrowing trouble to expose the study to the charge of bias. This bias could be of several kinds. In the first place, there are different attack rates among first-, second-, and third-graders; resistance increases with age. This, in itself, made valid comparison a hardship if all the vaccinated were in the second grade.

Secondly, such authorities on polio epidemiology as John Paul in New Haven and John Fox in New Orleans had shown that lower-class groups had more resistance than upper-class groups, so the first- and third-graders would have to be studied to see if they matched the second-graders in socioeconomic status. The vaccine would show better results in a more resistant group, naturally.

Furthermore, physicians in the study areas who examined sick second-graders during the polio season would know that these children had been vaccinated. This could introduce an unmeasurable mixture of biases. Some might assume that an ill-defined condition was not polio if the child had been vaccinated. Others might look for polio much more closely in vaccinated children. Indeed, the doctor might unknowingly be affected by his admiration (or lack of admiration) for the National Foundation. Polio without paralysis—and sometimes with—is difficult to diagnose; the diagnosis, in many instances, ultimately depends on individual medical judgment.

This is the kind of technical stuff a cold-blooded expert in field surveys would think of, but an angel of mercy or a fund raiser might not.

In late November, Dr. Francis of Ann Arbor—then touring the

European medical centers—returned to his hotel room in London to find the telephone ringing persistently. Dr. Hart E. Van Riper, the Foundation's medical director, was calling from New York. Van Riper came to the point: would Francis come back and take over the evaluation of the field trial? Mr. O'Connor had changed his mind. It would be better to have it done by an independent institution such as the University of Michigan.

Francis had been out of direct touch with the Foundation since the previous May, when the new Vaccine Advisory Committee had been set up and the Salk vaccine taken out of the hands of the Immunization Committee. He said that he would come back and discuss the proposal. He knew that Bell had come and gone. He knew there were arguments, and he sensed that pressure was building up. Compression creates heat. As he became keenly aware, eventually, a man's reputation as a scientist could be incinerated in such an atmosphere. He had faith in a killed-virus vaccine and felt that a field trial was in order, but he did not intend to compromise himself or his institution.

Francis was certain, from his flu-vaccine field trials, that vaccine-versus-placebo was the only sound approach. The annual incidence of polio is so low that even with a large test population the most sensitive instruments are needed to draw valid conclusions about persons who do or do not have the disease in a given year. But Basil O'Connor would have to be convinced.

Returning to the United States in early December, Francis talked to O'Connor and indicated his unhappiness with the plan to vaccinate second-graders only. They argued the question. Francis did obtain Van Riper's agreement that the man who directed the study would be permitted to design it. He spent several weeks talking to Federal and state epidemiologists, some of whom argued that the study would be worthless without matched controls. He had his showdown with O'Connor at a National Foundation staff meeting in January 1954.

Francis laid down a number of conditions. One was that the $900,000 to finance the evaluation be paid to his University and not to him directly. Another was that he and his staff would be the only recipients of data and the only source of the final report

—meanwhile all information would be kept secret. Thirdly, while O'Connor said he was committed to several states to vaccinate second-graders and use first- and third-graders as controls, Francis got him to agree that a second study should be done simultaneously on a matched-control basis, with placebos.

Though this behind-the-scenes conflict of strong men is not generally known, it is doubtless one source of Francis's reputation for tough-mindedness. He is one scientist who stood up to an administrator and made his point. To have done it with Basil O'Connor must be counted as something of a feat. People find it hard to tell O'Connor "no." He himself said, on another occasion, that nobody changed his mind for him. When he changed his mind, he said, he would do it himself.

In February the Foundation—still with no supply of vaccine in sight—announced that Francis had agreed to set up and direct a Poliomyelitis Vaccine Evaluation Center at the University of Michigan. In his first public statement Francis cleared the air somewhat by stating: "It is not known at present whether the vaccine to be used will be highly effective, moderately effective or ineffective in protection of human subjects against paralytic poliomyelitis."

Francis publicly demonstrated his awareness of the bias issue and disposed of it: "We will match our personal integrity and the integrity of the University of Michigan against anyone who might even suspect the possibility of bias."

He thereupon went about setting up his Evaluation Center in an old red-brick and fieldstone building, formerly the University Hospital maternity department, where Jonas Salk's two older sons had been born.

Before there was anything to evaluate, however, there were some hitches in the manufacture of the vaccine. At the end of January, O'Connor had announced postponement of the start of mass vaccinations from February to late March or early April because of delays. He mentioned the "usual production problems" associated with a new product.

Not until June 1955 did the American public get an insight into the nature of these delays. Said Dr. Leonard A. Scheele, then

Surgeon General of the Public Health Service, in his technical report to Mrs. Oveta Culp Hobby, then Secretary of Health, Education, and Welfare:

> In March 1954, soon after vaccine production for the field trial was started, live virus was detected by monkey and tissue culture tests in four out of six supposedly inactivated lots of vaccine. The staff of the Laboratory of Biologics Control became concerned about the feasibility of producing safe vaccine on a large scale.
>
> A series of meetings were held between the staff of the National Institutes of Health, the National Foundation for Infantile Paralysis, its Vaccine Advisory Committee, Dr. Jonas Salk, Dr. David Bodian, and the manufacturers. The group reviewed possible sources of the difficulty and established more stringent processing controls. They also established the requirement that a series of consecutive lots with negative tests must be produced by a manufacturer to demonstrate consistent performance before acceptance of his product.
>
> Dr. Salk also presented an analysis of trials, using vaccine prepared in his own laboratory, on 5,320 human volunteers which he had carried out between May 1953 and March 1954. . . .
>
> Before April 24, when the decision to start the large field trial was made, Dr. Salk had injected 7,507 children with vaccine prepared by the manufacturers. This small-scale test, regarded as a preliminary safety check on commercially-produced vaccine, caused no harmful effects.

One perplexity was that live virus would escape detection in safety tests by one laboratory and yet turn up when one of the other two laboratories tested the same batch. Lilly, Wyeth, and Parke, Davis had the best luck in ironing out their difficulties and settling down to consistent performance—with the exception of one instance of live virus turning up in one Lilly batch after a long series of safe ones. All five companies were able to make

some good vaccine, but the Foundation decided to rely on vaccine from Lilly and Parke, Davis for the field trial.

The public received news of the live-virus problem only from
Walter Winchell. Late in March, in a Sunday evening broadcast,
Winchell breathlessly flashed to Mr. and Mrs. America that "the
Salk vaccine may be a killer rather than a polio cure." A noted
bacteriologist, he revealed, had told him that the Federal laboratory in Bethesda had found "live—not dead—polio virus" in the
vaccine. According to later information, this noted bacteriologist
was Paul de Kruif. "There is absolutely nothing to be concerned
about," commented Salk. A few communities dropped out of the
field trial; otherwise, the alarm quickly subsided.

Certainly Salk's own experience was reassuring to him and to
everyone involved. With the vaccine he made himself, only one
reaction occurred among his first 4,000 children, aged six to nine.
This child, known to be allergic to penicillin, had a skin eruption
and itching, but others with known allergies had no trouble. In
Salk's hands the commercial vaccine did just about as well as his
own.

The ecclesiastical process of canonizing a saint, however, requires an official "promoter of the faith," or "devil's advocate," to
pick flaws in the evidence. Scientific inquiry and a free press assign this unpleasant task to anyone with the courage to speak up.
The leading public critic of the Salk vaccine seemed to be Dr.
Albert Bruce Sabin, professor of research pediatrics at the University of Cincinnati College of Medicine. White-haired, dark-
eyed, with a sharp nose, small, dark mustache, nubbin chin, and
general mien of Reynard the Fox, Sabin is a sociable man and
something of a gourmet; he also has a reputation in virological
circles for asking the sharpest questions, in unctuous, Oxonian
tones.

A Polish immigrant Jew, Sabin is like Salk in being a product
of the Bronx and New York University. While Salk was still in
medical school, Sabin, eight years older, was making a scholarly
name for himself at the Rockefeller Institute as the first to cultivate polio virus in a culture of brain tissues. Also like Salk, Sabin
was a National Foundation grantee. But the two men differed

strongly on one point: Sabin firmly believed in live-virus vaccines. In fact, he had developed a live, mouse-adapted virus for a vaccine against the dengue fever that attacked American soldiers in the South Pacific during World War II. In addition, at the time of the Salk vaccine development, Sabin was searching for non-virulent strains among the polio viruses he was growing in his monkey-kidney cultures at Children's Hospital Research Foundation in Cincinnati. He hoped to make a live-virus polio vaccine. While it was true that many virologists felt that Salk was getting more credit than he deserved, Sabin said that if there was jealousy, he was not conscious of it.

Sabin explained that he had questions that needed answers, honest doubts that he felt it his duty, both as a scientist and as a citizen, to raise. In March 1954, when Salk made another report on his vaccine at a New Orleans medical meeting, he sent Sabin a copy of his paper in advance. In it, Salk granted that his own "hypothesis is contrary to that held by many who are of the opinion that a live-virus vaccine is the ultimate to be desired. . . ."

On the same day Sabin made news by stating that there had been "undue haste." In the face of Salk's growing confidence that his vaccine would provide a lasting immunity, possibly even for a lifetime, Sabin said that a killed virus could provide only a temporary protection at best. This handicap, as he saw it, could pose a real problem. It is difficult, if not impossible, to get most people to have frequent vaccinations, year after year, unless such vaccinations are compulsory. Temporary protection against polio in childhood might only mean susceptibility in later life, when the risk of paralysis or death is greater. So Sabin said—repeatedly as time went on.

In contradiction of Sabin, the Public Health Service issued this statement: "We believe the judgment of the Vaccine Advisory Committee is sound and that the National Foundation is justified in proceeding."

The mass vaccinations began on April 26 with vaccine that had been triple-tested for safety and, as events showed, *was safe*. By the middle of May, 642,360 first-, second-, and third-graders had received their first "Salk shot" and a promise of a "Polio Pioneer" button as soon as they had their third injection. In all, 1,829,916 children, aged six to nine, took part in the study. Francis divided it into two parts:

Placebo areas. Here 209,229 first-, second-, and third-graders in eighty-four areas of eleven states received the real vaccine; 201,-229 received placebo injections; and 338,778 received neither. Those inoculated did not know whether the pinkish fluid in the hypodermic syringe was the real thing or not. All they knew was that they had been stuck in the arm with a sharp needle.

Observed areas. Here 231,902 second-graders in 127 areas of thirty-three states were vaccinated; 123,605 other second-graders plus 725,173 first- and third-graders acted as non-vaccinated controls.

It was a magnificent demonstration of voluntary co-operation and, as Francis put it, "public confidence in the scientific approach to problems." Some 20,000 physicians and health officers, 40,000 registered nurses, 14,000 school principals, and 50,000 teachers volunteered their services, as did 200,000 other citizens, all members of the National Foundation. Only 18,388 children dropped out before getting their Polio Pioneer buttons, leaving 422,743 who received three doses of the killed-virus vaccine.

Francis and his staff—about 132 at its peak—now had their work cut out for them. He took a year's leave of absence—not his sabbatical. Dr. Robert F. Korns, chief epidemiologist for the New York State Department of Health, took leave to serve as deputy director; Robert B. Voight was there on loan from the United States Census Bureau as chief of statistical operations, together with others from the Census Bureau and many from the Public Health Service. Twenty-eight state laboratories participated, plus state and local health officers.

The Poliomyelitis Vaccine Evaluation Center established an elaborate system to obtain reports of all polio cases and deaths in the test population. It requested that all fatal cases and all major illnesses of any kind be reported to the Center by telephone, emphasizing that any case occurring within four weeks after the last vaccine injection was to be given special attention, with a complete autopsy of the spinal cord and brain in event of death.

Francis did not intend to lose sight of the fact that in vaccinations, experimental or otherwise, accidents happen. Every case of fever, cold, rash, pain in the arms or legs, hay fever, asthma, poison ivy, or anything else was considered for its possible relationship to vaccination. There were 2,625 "minor reactions" and sixteen "major reactions" in the vaccinated group, but the rate did not differ appreciably from that of the placebo group.

In view of the polio incubation period—five days to five weeks —the occurrence of polio in a vaccinated child could be conceivably related to the vaccine only if it occurred between a few days and a month or so after an injection. Most polio occurs seven to fourteen days after exposure.

There were thirty-four cases of polio in vaccinated children during this period, defined as from May 1 to four weeks after complete vaccination. One died. This was Patricia Redick, eight, of Tulsa, Oklahoma. She had her first injection in late April. Not long afterwards she had her tonsils out. In May she received a second vaccine shot. She died two weeks later. The surgical trauma of tonsillectomy may permit the virus to enter the nervous system and so provoke paralysis. In this case, as in the others, there was no cause to suspect the vaccine. All were attributed to coincidental infection. In addition, there were four deaths not due to polio.

In the same period there were seven polio cases but no polio deaths among children receiving the harmless placebo, and eighty-eight cases and three polio deaths among the observed children who received no injection of any kind. In these two groups there were two additional deaths not due to polio.

In June it was apparent to insiders that the vaccinations had gone off smoothly, without slip-up or accident. The Evaluation Center continued to watch for deaths and illnesses throughout the study period ending in December 1954. There were 440 deaths in the entire study population of 1,800,000 non-vaccinated and vaccinated. The leading cause was accidents (thirty-five per cent), followed by cancer (twelve per cent). Even that famous has-been among leading killers, pneumonia (nine per cent), exceeded polio (five per cent).

By the end of the polio season—it was generally over in September—members of the Center staff believed that the vaccine was not only safe but also substantially effective in reducing the incidence of paralysis. This could be guessed merely by noting whether the bulk of the cases from the observed areas fell into the vaccinated or non-vaccinated column. This was merely an impression, of course. It required validation through confirmation of diagnosis and statistical analysis.

Francis had insisted that the findings must remain secret until he was ready to report them. O'Connor doubted that this would be possible. Francis also had said the evaluation would take about a year. O'Connor wanted it sooner.

All data was recorded on punch cards for machine tabulation as soon as it came in from the states. The code used for the placebo study was not "broken" until the end. Not until then could anyone tell whether a reported case of polio had received the vaccine or a placebo. Thus Francis carried out his intention to keep everybody, including himself, as much in the dark as possible until the process of validation was complete.

Two or three times the Center's assistant chief of statistical operations, Morton Boisen, came into the director's office with a work sheet in his hands and teased: "Want me to tell you something?" "Nope," Francis replied doggedly, still guarding against bias.

He felt himself to be playing the role of Caesar's wife and was a little uncomfortable about it. The best he could do was try to keep himself above suspicion. When his report was finally in, O'Connor would (and did) thank him for insisting on a placebo study conducted in a strictly orthodox, scientific manner.

In August, however, O'Connor conceivably would have given a great deal for a tame statistician who would tell him how the data was falling. As a matter of fact, the Foundation did, as some at Ann Arbor saw it, compromise the secrecy rule by canvassing the health officers in the more than two hundred test areas and ascertaining that the polio rates for these localities were forty per cent lower than might have been expected from previous years. This was open to interpretation, of course. It could simply signify a year of low incidence. On the other hand, maybe the vaccine was responsible. Francis protested this kibitzing, and refused to help O'Connor in a big decision he had to make.

The pharmaceutical companies were counting their costs and wondering where they would go next on vaccine production.

They had done a great deal of tooling up and hiring and training of personnel, who had gained considerable experience in making a tricky vaccine.

Should the companies plunge ahead in the expectation that the vaccine would prove effective and that there would be a big demand for it in 1955, or should they let all this talent go? If they did that, there wouldn't be much vaccine for the 1955 polio season.

They needed someone or something to persuade them to stay in the vaccine business. If the experimental vaccine was a success, then all future vaccine would have to be licensed by the Laboratory of Biologics Control. But the Laboratory could not promise to license any product that was still on trial. It would wait for the Francis Report and then act.

At about this time, Minister of Health and Welfare Paul J. J. Martin of Canada, fully informed of the progress in making and testing vaccine as reported to him by Dr. Robert D. Defries, director of the Connaught Laboratory in Toronto, planned a Canadian program. In the same alert, aggressive manner that characterized O'Connor's own actions, Martin, a politician and layman, made plans for vaccination in 1955, using Connaught-made vaccine paid for by the Canadian government. A half-million children would be vaccinated as an extension, in effect, of the 1954 field trials, in which Canada participated with the United States.

In the United States the situation was quite different. Polio had been almost exclusively a National Foundation program. Basil O'Connor had the initiative and Mrs. Hobby, Martin's opposite number in the Department of Health, Education, and Welfare, chose to wait and see what would happen. So did Surgeon General Scheele, her public-health adviser.

Francis said his report would be ready "next March or April." Report or no, O'Connor—never a timid man—decided to keep vaccine production rolling by ordering $9,000,000 worth of Salk shots. He explained his decision as follows during a 1955 Congressional investigation:

"Of course, we were all interested in what the results would be, but we were pretty certain, because . . . we knew the immunol-

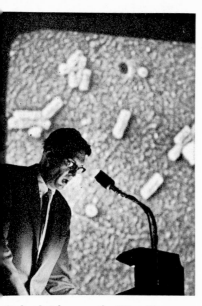

Gerhard Schramm, the West German scientist who broke tobacco-mosaic virus rods, pictured on the screen behind him, into protein collars and nucleic-acid cores. (*By Werner Wolff, Black Star*)

Heinz Fraenkel-Conrat, who discovered that the power of the virus to infect, multiply, and behave as a living creature is confined to its nucleic acid.

Roger Hart looks on while Wendell Stanley infects the leaves of young tobacco plants with a swab containing a solution of tobacco-mosaic virus.

PLATE 9

Upper left: Peyton Rous, first man to discover a true cancer virus (chicken sarcoma). *Upper right:* Francisco Duran-Reynals, the Moses of the cancer-virus workers during their wilderness years. *Lower left:* Maud Slye. She made herself unpopular by emphasizing the hereditary factor in cancer. *Lower right:* John J. Bittner, who proved that a virus was one cause of breast cancer in mice.

PLATE 10

ogy of this disease. . . . As we wound up the field trials in July of 1954, we realized that we could not get an evaluation prior to the end of 1954, maybe . . . into 1955, sometime, and that if the commercial manufacturers shut down making vaccine, the difficulty would be a severe one, because this is a process that requires special personnel. . . . If they . . . did not resume until they knew the vaccine was effective, there would still be a seventy-day lag thereafter.

"Now, the commercial houses took a very proper position, in my point of view, that they could not gamble their stockholders' money against an unknown entity, and so . . . we asked them what their production would be until the end of the year." [3]

The pharmaceutical laboratories' estimate was twenty-seven million doses. This, according to Salk's 1954 scheme of three doses in five weeks, would be enough for nine million children. As he testified, O'Connor now "took a calculated risk with the American people's money, telling them what we were doing."

He promised to buy the entire production up to twenty-seven million doses, meantime driving, as he said, "a hard bargain." The Foundation would pay approximately thirty-three cents a dose. This was hardly enough to pay the manufacturing costs of the product, as, from time to time, big batches had to be poured down the drain when they failed to pass safety tests or lost their potency.

But the $9,000,000 carrot encouraged the manufacturers to lean into the harness and not only try to fill the order but also increase production and do some speculating themselves.

Presently another complication arose. Vaccine left over from the field trial deteriorated in potency. This was believed to be owing to Salk's use of merthiolate in the vaccine as a preservative. The manufacturers had to discard two million doses in this stockpile. The L.B.C.—Laboratory of Biologics Control—informed them, the Foundation, and Salk that, inasmuch as a vaccine without merthiolate was technically a new product, it would require an additional field trial. Salk then injected six thousand more

[3] *Poliomyelitis Vaccine: Hearings before the Committee on Labor and Public Welfare* (United States Senate, Eighty-fourth Congress, First Session, June 14 and 15, 1955), Part 1, p. 104.

children with a new vaccine. The Federal laboratory pronounced it safe and potent.

By January 1955 the manufacturers were submitting protocols and samples of their first production of O'Connor's "calculated risk" vaccine. Protocols, in this terminology, are minutely detailed production reports that show every step of the process, including safety tests.

The suspense in March of 1955 was intense, with the Evaluation Center concentrating on completing its analysis, the date for its report still to be set, and the New York *World Telegram* claiming a scoop by announcing that the report would show the Salk vaccine was a success. Francis replied that the report wasn't written yet. One of the few calm voices was that of John Enders, who had made it all possible. Pursuing the long view, he went out to Ann Arbor and gave a lecture at the University of Michigan. In it he said:

"Most worthy of emphasis, I believe, is the prospect that active investigation will continue for some time to come even if Dr. Francis' report shows that the formalized virus is highly efficient as a prophylactic agent. . . . For a long time, researchers will be concerned with such matters as the duration of immunity, the determination of whether dissemination of the virus is reduced in the community, and whether resistance established as the result of vaccination will be reinforced and maintained, as Dr. Salk believes, through repeated inapparent infection of natural origin."

At the time Enders spoke, however, the short view was more popular. The urgent question was how many children could be vaccinated in 1955, and how much time there would be to vaccinate them before the polio season started. The panicky fear of polio again was in the air and in parents' minds.

O'Connor decided that the vaccine supply would go first to all children who had taken part in the field trial but had not received the vaccine and, more generally, to the nine million or so in the groups with the highest polio incidence—that is, first- and second-graders. Van Riper estimated that there might be enough commercial vaccine to vaccinate thirty million—half the children in the country.

Francis since has conceded a modicum of naïveté in the pub-
licizing of his evaluation of the vaccine—a wholly understandable situation inasmuch as neither he nor anyone else had ever
before had the experience of analyzing some 144,000,000 bits of
information involving 1,800,000 persons while the public was
looking, or at least trying to look, over his shoulder to see how the
data added up. It was a little like an advanced mathematics student trying to do his homework at Forty-Second and Broadway
at five p.m.

Francis did not reckon with the size of the gathering crowd.
There were two audiences, actually—the public and the medical
profession. He had originally imagined, he said, that when he
finished his report he would sit down before a radio microphone
and a television camera in a small room someplace and give a
brief summary of the findings. That, together with some press releases, would acquit him of his responsibility.

The medical profession would receive the information through
its regular channels, medical-society meetings and journals. As a
matter of fact, Francis contemplated prompt publication in the
monthly *American Journal of Public Health,* a natural outlet
for field studies. Science is accustomed to chew its information as
a cow chews its cud, swallowing the data when it is first presented
and then bringing it up for rumination and final digestion. Ordinarily, this allows time for confirmation by fellow scientists and
provides the medical practitioner who ultimately will apply the
worth-while knowledge to his patients a chance to look up the
original article, think about it, and talk it over with his friends.
Until this individual doctor is sold, the most marvelous remedy
isn't worth a great deal.

Francis knew this to be the usual process, but he, too, was
swayed by the unusual character of the project. He had been selected to direct an independent and objective evaluation and he
and his staff had been to such pains to make it so, despite obstacles, that he assumed the medical profession would take his
word for his findings. His staff would do the digesting for them,
he said. Thus, when the American Medical Association approached him during the final stage of analysis and asked if an
A.M.A. committee could preview his findings in anticipation of a

report in its *Journal,* which goes to 180,000 doctors, Francis said no. He had said, plainly, that there would be "no peep shows," and he meant it.

Van Riper later commented that Francis particularly objected to the presence on the committee of one Albert B. Sabin, who repeatedly had made his doubts about a killed-virus vaccine clear and had a live-virus polio vaccine of his own. Anyway, asked Van Riper, what was the point of evaluating the evaluator—a man of unquestionable integrity? [4]

Meanwhile, the Foundation and University of Michigan public-relations people had to make some plans around the busy, preoccupied Francis, both for the medical profession and for the press. "We told him," O'Connor recalled, "that we ought to have some time to set up a proper announcement . . . at a scientific meeting."

It was not practicable to present the report at a regular meeting of a medical or scientific society, it appeared, because the date for finishing the report was flexible. So the Foundation and the University decided to hold their own meeting, in Ann Arbor, and invite leaders of virus research, science, medicine, and public health. The arrangers also entertained the question of how to get the information to the rest of the medical profession. This was settled when the Lilly company offered to put on a $250,000, one-hour, closed-circuit telecast to fifty-four thousand doctors in sixty-one cities, with Francis presenting his findings to them on a live program. This, in effect, would turn the event into a nationwide medical meeting.

Television cables and program time have to be reserved. The next question was on what day and at what time would it be most convenient for busy doctors to pause, go to a near-by theater, and listen to Francis. Tuesday, it was agreed, would be the best day of the week, with the doctors' program coming at six p.m., following a morning news announcement. After conferring with Francis, his public-relations consultants reserved four Tuesdays, the last two in March and the first two in April.

[4] Greer Williams: "Polio Post-Mortem: What Really Happened," *Medical Economics,* August 1955.

Francis had begun writing his report in early March, as soon as the formidable statistical tables were fairly complete. As time went by, only the last two Tuesdays remained as possibilities, and finally only the last one—April 12. He gave the Foundation fifteen days' notice that he would have his report ready on that date. During the last week he wrote at home, to escape a procession of visitors and the ever-ringing telephone. At three o'clock on Friday morning, April 8, he finished. The Francis Report was now ready for stenciling and mimeographing.

By the oddest—and, for many, sentimentally delightful—coincidence, Tuesday, April 12, 1955, was the tenth anniversary of Franklin Delano Roosevelt's death. No diehard Republican can ever be expected to believe that O'Connor did not set the date in memory of his dear friend, or that he didn't see the report until 8:30 that morning, but "that is the fact," according to O'Connor. "We said we would prefer April 5th because it would give us that additional week to get vaccine into the arms of the children," he explained. Francis, "not a Democrat," likewise insisted he didn't know that April 12 was a Roosevelt anniversary.

Possibly the anonymous public-relations people involved did know—they are well paid and frantically try to make events come off in a dramatic way. In any event, criticism of the choice of date as "cheap exploitation" seemed petty to millions of Americans who remembered Roosevelt as the friend of the common people. There was no cause, they felt, for apology on that score.

The meeting was held in the University of Michigan's largest, most beautiful auditorium—the salmon-colored, ultra-modern Rackham Hall. In external aspect, the stage setting was as impressive and dramatic as the news. In fact, the next morning, Wednesday, *The New York Times* would report in a secondary feature story on page one: FANFARE USHERS VERDICTS OF TESTS. MEDICAL HISTORY IS WRITTEN IN HOLLYWOOD ATMOSPHERE.

Behind the scenes, the pace of O'Connor's "proper announcement" accelerated to that of a motion picture run through the projector at double speed. Louis Graff, the science writer assigned from the University News Service, had only twenty hours to prepare an authoritative news release for world consumption on a study that had taken a year to do and had taken Francis three weeks to write up—some fifty pages of textual detail and close to one hundred tables and charts. "Our science writer went through six drafts of the release before he produced one that was okayed by Dr. Francis," said the news-service editor Cleland Wylie. "If there is optimism in the release, it has been approved by the source of the Evaluation Center's report." [5]

The plan was to give newsmen the press release, an abstract of the report prepared by a scientist, and the report itself at 9:15 a.m. The actual release time would be 10:20 a.m., when Francis started speaking. Wylie's messengers brought the first batch of material to the hundred or more reporters waiting in a large rectangular room three floors above the auditorium at 9:17.

Seeing the messengers get off the elevator, some of the best-educated persons in American journalism surged through the press-room door into the hall, shouldering, jamming, and clutching for vaccine news. One of the smartest had the foresight to meet the messengers at the elevator, seize his handout, and then run back to his telephone and typewriter in the press room through another door. Appalled, the messengers backed off, pitching packets into the crowd like oceanarium keepers throwing fish to leaping porpoises.

In a gentleman's agreement, and as a courtesy to the hosts as well as a kind of *quid pro quo* for use of intellectual premises, radio and television news broadcasters had agreed to hold back their oral news flashes until 10:20. As soon as he saw the words "The vaccine works," Dave Garroway of the National Broadcasting Company put Francis's well-kept secret on the air, an hour before the scientist spoke. Garroway justified this breach of confidence by stating that the news was too good to keep. O'Connor himself would find it difficult to dispute him.

The Associated Press, more accustomed to big news, was also more dependable. It was represented at Ann Arbor by the nation's number-one science reporter, Alton L. Blakeslee, and by the local correspondent, and its first telegraphed message read thus:

[5] Cathy Covert: "Reporters Sizzling Over Polio Chaos," *Editor & Publisher,* April 16, 1955, p. 10.

BULLETIN
     ADVANCE FOR USE AT 10:20 A.M. TODAY
POLIO (TOPS 3)
(ADVANCE) ANN ARBOR, MICH., (AP)—THE SALK
VACCINE IS SAFE, EFFECTIVE AND POTENT, IT WAS
OFFICIALLY ANNOUNCED TODAY.
END ADVANCE
         JC919A 4/12

By the time Francis spoke, there were church bells ringing in some towns. One courtroom observed a moment of silence. Department stores delivered the news over their public-address systems. In whitewash paint, a shop keeper daubed on his window: THANK YOU, DR. SALK. Parents and teachers wept. The little Polio Pioneers looked proud. Prayers were offered and candles were lighted for Jonas Salk, the Jew, and Basil O'Connor, the Irish Catholic, who had conquered polio in the name of an Episcopalian, Roosevelt. What man could say he was not thrilled and overjoyed when he heard Dave Garroway—no man for a gentleman's agreement—bring this great news to the waiting world of polio-conscious people? It was as if a war had ended.

At 10:20 a.m. Francis, a man of his word, began reading his report to his five hundred assembled colleagues and to a battery of sixteen television and newsreel cameras on a long wooden platform erected at the rear of the auditorium. Here, under a darkened ceiling, whence shone small lights like planets in the sky, the atmosphere was more sedate. The number-one dignitary of American Science, Dr. Detlev W. Bronk, president of the Rockefeller Institute for Medical Research, presided.

Francis spoke from a lectern emblazoned with the great maize-and-blue seal of the University of Michigan. The lectern cut the epidemiologist off at his breast pocket, making him appear small as he stood there in a black suit, white shirt, and gray tie, adjusting his horn-rimmed glasses and looking sober as the spotlights played on him. As if in counterpoint to the supersonic pitch of excitement, Francis the scientist clung to understatement as a drowning man to a straw. He talked slowly, in a conversational tone, with no forensic high jinks, showing charts and tables projected on a movie screen, and discussing them with the aid of a flashlight pointer. He thus continued for one hour and thirty-eight minutes, ending just before noon.

In the press room, three floors above, the reporters pawed frantically through his text, trying to understand it, to be accurate, and to make their deadlines.

The whole event had a mad touch of the impossible about it. There were many comments on this. Blakeslee's was the most charitable. Appraising the "great hullabaloo over a fairly minor disease" as inevitable, he said: "It would have been sensational news had one person merely whispered it calmly to another."

One had to be patient and listen carefully to get the full import of what Francis said. He went into the infinite details of the plan of the study and analysis of data. One fact of significance, easy to overlook, was that the vaccine used was of variable quality in its capacity to produce antibodies, a few batches being "essentially devoid of antigenic activity." Generally, the vaccine was less potent for Type I—the most important—than for II and III. The Salk vaccine was anything but a standardized product. It was potentially capable of producing false confidence as well as immunity.

Finally came the news—the "Summary of Estimates of Effectiveness of Vaccine."

In the first place, the vaccine *did not* work to prevent non-paralytic poliomyelitis—"There was no significant difference between vaccinated and non-vaccinated among children who had polio but no paralysis."

In paralytic polio only, "an estimate of 72 per cent effectiveness was obtained in the placebo areas and 62 per cent in the observed areas."

Francis found that against spinal paralysis, the vaccine was 60-per-cent effective, and against bulbar paralysis, 94-per-cent —"an extremely successful result." These were his only superlative words. Finally, he said:

"From these data it is not possible to select a single value giving numerical expression in a complete sense to the effectiveness of vaccine as a total experience. . . .

"There is . . . greater confidence in the results obtained from the strictly controlled and almost identical test populations of the placebo study areas. On this basis it may be suggested that the vaccination was 80–90 per cent effective against paralytic poliomyelitis; that it was 60 to 70 per cent effective against disease caused by Type I virus and 90 per cent or more effective against that of Type II and Type III virus. The estimate would be more secure had a larger number of cases been available."

When Francis finished reading, there was restrained applause. Eventually, there would be some criticisms—for example, of the failure to provide for rapid dissemination of the full text through the A.M.A. *Journal* or some other publication that would reach the nation's family doctors and pediatricians. But most would agree with Sabin when he said: "There is not a colleague of Dr. Francis who is not greatly impressed and deeply grateful for the stupendous amount of work that he and his associates have done. Perhaps never in history before in analytical epidemiology has anyone done a job such as he has done." Nobody could fairly accuse Tommy Francis himself of sensationalism, or lack of a scientific attitude.

Indeed, Francis was so tentative and guarded that, had it not been for the excited press release, it might have been said that, if anything, he sold the vaccine short. A 60–70-per-cent effectiveness against Type I, the cause of most paralytic polio, promises no great cure-all; turned around, it means 30–40-per-cent ineffectiveness.

Salk, greeted with a great ovation, now spoke. Conscious that manufacturers had been stockpiling vaccine in a calculated risk, Salk mildly protested: "It is not gambling in which we have been engaged, but rather in pursuits in a field of science." He reemphasized "the margin of safety" that "makes possible the prediction, rather precisely, of the time required to render each preparation free of living virus. . . . It might be said that this aspect of the problem demands little, if any, further attention."

He turned to his new studies, showing that the potency of some of the field-trial vaccine was low owing to the merthiolate antiseptic, since eliminated from the commercial vaccine. Next he took up the question of dosage. He recommended a new system—the first two injections one month apart and the third seven or so months later. This produced the highest degree of protection, he had found.

Thus, polio prevention would start with the 1955 season with a new vaccine—no merthiolate—and a new treatment system—partial protection with two shots in the spring and complete protection after the third shot in the fall. Salk commented to the press: "Theoretically, the new 1955 vaccine and vaccination procedures may lead to 100 per cent protection from paralysis of all those vaccinated."

This would compare with smallpox and yellow-fever vaccines, 95-per-cent effective; tetanus toxoid, 95-per-cent; and diphtheria toxoid, 90-per-cent. In biology, nothing is 100-per-cent. But it was an overly stimulating day, and a scientist should be entitled to some hyperbole in a moment of triumph.

Salk did leave an unanswerable question unanswered. How long would immunity last with his vaccine? He hoped it would be long-lasting, but: "Time alone will tell." Detectable antibodies had persisted two years in some of his earliest subjects.

By telegram Dr. William G. Workman, director of the Laboratory of Biologics Control, had invited fifteen leading virologists to meet with him in Ann Arbor following the reading of the Francis Report and advise him on licensing of the vaccine.

Therefore, as soon as Salk finished speaking, a dozen virus hunters withdrew from the Rackham Hall program and went to a near-by hotel to decide the 1955 course of vaccine events. Salk and Sabin were among them, as were Francis, Bodian, Hammon, the gamma-globulin man, and Joseph E. Smadel, then the leading virologist at the Walter Reed Army Medical Center, now associate director of the National Institutes of Health. John Enders was invited, but was not seen in Ann Arbor this day.

Workman informed the group, most of them National Foundation grantees, that a press conference and license-signing ceremony had been arranged for Mrs. Hobby at the Department of Health, Education, and Welfare in Washington. A long-distance telephone line would be kept open so their decision could be telephoned to Surgeon General Scheele as soon as they reached it. The Surgeon General would then make the recommendation to Secretary Hobby. By law, she was the signing officer.

Again the pressure was on, as it had been in the press room that morning and the Evaluation Center for the past year. The committee had a good two hours to think about and discuss the fifty-page Francis Report plus all its tables and charts, to look at the manufacturers' fifty- or sixty-page production reports, and to go over the L.B.C.'s tests of vaccine samples submitted. Forty lots from five companies—some 10,500,000 doses—awaited clearance. The L.B.C. had fully tested six lot samples in monkeys and tissue cultures and found them safe. All lots had been tested by the companies, of course. As the experimental phase was over, Salk no longer would be required to make tests in Pittsburgh.

What Workman proposed to do was what his Laboratory always had done when a new vaccine passed the experimental stage and reached the one of mass production. This was to license each batch, on the basis of protocol review alone. His Laboratory really wasn't set up to test everything, except in experimental situations such as had existed up until now.

There were questions from the committee. Some members counseled delay and stressed the desirability of a full discussion, however long. Some recalled the live virus that had survived the formaldehyde in the first batches of vaccine. They were reassured that this problem had been corrected through improved techniques. Sabin suggested getting rid of the dangerous Mahoney strain before going ahead with commercial distribution of a vaccine.

Somehow three crucial points did not come into focus—at least not forcefully. One was that the vaccine to be used in 1955 was different from the one that had been field-tested in 1954. Salk's tests indicated that the new process was an improvement, but this had not been confirmed through wide experience. So 1955 inevitably would be a year of further field-testing, this time with "calculated risk" vaccine.

Secondly, a part of the minimum requirements imposed on the manufacturer called for consistent performance before his vaccine could be considered for clearance. This meant the consecutive production of a series of batches passing all safety tests. The L.B.C. could not tell whether consistent performance was, in fact, the case because it required protocols and samples only on batches that had met the manufacturers' own safety tests. It had no current information on any discarded lots. During the spring of 1955, as during the spring of 1954, "Each producer had had difficulties in processing and testing materials at various stages of production." So Scheele would report to Mrs. Hobby in another seven weeks, when there was cause to pause for second thought.

Thirdly, as Scheele also later pointed out, "An important factor in the decision to license, moreover, was the evidence of safety and efficacy presented by the field trial evaluation." On this basis, Workman recommended to the committee that thirteen lots of vaccine (six Cutter, two Lilly, three Parke, Davis, and two Pitman-Moore) be approved, though some had had only the factory safety tests—none by the L.B.C. in Bethesda.

It requires some hindsight to see this failure of logic. The assumption that the 1955 vaccine would be entirely safe because the 1954 vaccine had been safe would have been justified only if the same safety-testing procedures had been observed. Actually, the conclusion on April 12 was that, because great care had resulted in great success, it no longer was necessary to be so careful.

But while some of the best brains in biology tried on an afternoon in Ann Arbor to think against time, word came over the leased wire that Mrs. Hobby was getting a bit warm sitting under the bright lights of the television and movie cameras, waiting to sign the product licenses. Scheele already had canceled her press conference, explaining: "Things are running late in Ann Arbor."

It was inescapable that somebody would say: "We mustn't keep the lady waiting."

The gentlemen, Sabin included, unanimously recommended that the vaccine be licensed. Workman informed Scheele by phone. Scheele made this recommendation to Mrs. Hobby and she had her picture taken signing the product licenses at 5:15 p.m. Said she:

"It's a great day. It's a wonderful day for the whole world. . . ."

* 25 *

DARKNESS OVER
POCATELLO

DURING the next two weeks the Laboratory of Biologics Control cleared ten million doses of Salk vaccine. Children stood in line at school to get their shot. The National Foundation's vaccination program for first- and second-graders moved into the fast lane and, as Francis said, everybody was "trying to get into the act." Rarely did anyone hear or heed such words as these from a cautious family doctor: "Sounds good, but let's wait awhile and see how it goes. I like to be the last man, not the first, to use a new drug."

The national mood remained one of elation. Drug-stock prices immediately rose, but failed to hold their gains. The biggest questions were how much vaccine there was, who was getting it, and how to get it for "our town," "my children," and "for me." Congress saw a chance to do something for its constituents. Soon polio was being treated as a national emergency, though it never was, really.

A few adults were able to get the vaccine for themselves. Others got it for infants a year or so old. Most of the vaccine seemed to be going to the Foundation, as scheduled.

There was much discussion of price, and many warnings against a vaccine black market that never materialized. There was a tremendous public demand that no one, including the Foundation, was prepared to fill.

A Senator, finding that the government had no vaccination program whatsoever, asked for Federal control of the supply. President Eisenhower now ordered Secretary Hobby to set up a voluntary allocation system. There was some talk that sixty million could be vaccinated by summer's end. Basil O'Connor, however, reduced the Foundation's purchase commitment to eighteen million doses, enough to provide two shots for nine million children by the beginning of the polio season.

"No more scoops," remarked Salk. He turned down offers of cash, farm tillers, automobiles, chances to endorse baby products, magazine bids for "the inside story," and five Hollywood offers to buy his life story. All the weary young doctor wished to do, he said, was get back to his research work.

But Jonas Salk now belonged to the public, to humanity, more than to science. We loved this young man in white—a hero of test-tube magic, a savior of little children, yet a modest person who asked nothing but to be left alone with his cherished research. A Congressman proposed a bill to give Salk $10,000 a year for life. Salk said he would put any money that he received into research. Nothing came of the proposal. Eisenhower reflected the general sentiment when, in mid-April, he summoned Salk to the White House to receive a Presidential citation, one of numerous honors to come.

Mrs. Hobby was there. Surgeon General Scheele was there. Basil O'Connor, who had made it all happen, was there. Later, Salk reportedly told friends: "There we stood, my wife, three boys and myself, in the Rose Garden of the White House, while the president congratulated me. I thought to myself, 'What am I doing here?' I'd been told beforehand to confine myself to a straight thank you, but I couldn't do it. I felt I had to acknowledge my associates and all those others who had made the vaccine possible. So I said what I felt." [1]

[1] June Krieger: "What Price Fame—to Dr. Salk?" *The New York Times Magazine*, July 17, 1955.

But on that day, in bitter counterpoint to glory, tragedy was overtaking the Salk vaccine and some who received it. In a certain few places the vaccine was crippling children.

The thing that had happened with Maurice Brodie's vaccine when Salk was a medical student and had broken Brodie's heart —the thing Salk had so consciously worked to keep from happening with his vaccine—the thing he repeatedly promised would not happen, *could not* happen—*did* happen as soon as the vaccine was out of his hands. The Salk vaccine, as manufactured by the Cutter Laboratories in Berkeley, California, showed signs of producing the disease it was designed to prevent.

The Mahoney virus—the polio virus Sabin had warned against —for the time being outwitted science.

The year 1955, because of the Francis Report, will remain a great one in the history of preventive medicine. The Cutter incident will fade away as—an incident. The history of vaccination reveals many accidents. But the National Foundation had taught us to take every case of polio seriously, to regard it as a child, not an incident. The children and adults stricken by the Salk vaccine were polio victims, too.

Something had gone wrong. For the next three months the Salk story makes sad reading. The bad news began incubating in a one-year-old Chicago child on April 16, four days after the Francis Report. On that day this tot received a sample of the Cutter vaccine. On April 21 he was ill and his doctor diagnosed the condition as polio. On April 25 there was paralysis.

Dr. Harold M. Graning, the Public Health Service's regional medical director in Chicago, called Dr. Workman in Bethesda and told him of the case. It did not alarm Workman particularly. The Francis Report had showed there were bound to be coincidental cases at this specific time—in children who were carrying the polio virus before the injection. One cannot expect protective antibodies before two weeks; prior infection can cause polio to appear any time up to a month after vaccination. Francis had thirty-four such cases in his 441,000 vaccinated children in 1954—about one in 13,000.

More could be expected in 1955.

And there were more. And some *were* pure coincidence.

But at noon on Tuesday, April 26, almost two weeks to the minute from the time Francis finished reading his April 12 report, Dr. Robert Dyar of the California Health Department called Bethesda. By far the best account of Dyar's message and the ensuing events on April 26 and 27 appeared in the *Saturday Evening Post*: [2]

. . . Two seven-year-old San Diego boys vaccinated in the polio foundation's school program had paralytic polio. At two P.M. he called again to report a case in Ventura —a year-old boy—and late in the afternoon he was on the wire again with word of two cases, a year-old boy from Napa and a four-year-old boy from Oakland. All the California youngsters and the baby in Chicago had received Cutter vaccine, and all six had suffered paralysis within six to nine days after vaccination.

By 5:30 P.M. on the twenty-sixth the news had been relayed to Dr. James A. Shannon, then assistant director —now director—of the National Institutes of Health, the research branch of the Public Health Service. Shannon called a meeting at his office that evening. It lasted from 7:30 P.M. until 4:30 the next morning, and was a session that none of the participants will ever forget. Eight men were present, including Doctors Shannon, Haas [3] and Workman, Dr. David E. Price, an assistant to Doctor Scheele, and Dr. Alexander D. Langmuir, chief of the epidemiology branch of the Communicable Disease Center at Atlanta, Georgia.

The seriousness of the problem facing them was obvious. Six children among the thousands who had received Salk vaccine had been reported ill with paralytic polio. All of them had been inoculated with vaccine made by the Cutter Laboratories. Several hundred thousand more youngsters were scheduled to receive shots of

[2] Steven M. Spencer: "Where Are We Now on Polio?" *Saturday Evening Post*, September 10, 1955.

[3] Dr. Victor Haas, director of the National Institute for Allergy and Infectious Diseases, of which the Laboratory of Biologics Control then was a part.

Cutter vaccine the next day, April twenty-seventh.
Should these inoculations be called off or not?

"We had a tough decision to make," said Doctor Shannon in recalling the tense atmosphere of the meeting,
"and we felt under pressure to make it in a hurry. We had
to play safe, and at the same time we didn't want to
wreck the whole immunization program."

There were three possible explanations for the illness
of the vaccinated children: (1) Coincidence, since the
polio season was just starting in California; (2) "provocation," in which inoculation with any material may stir
up polio viruses already in the body and cause paralysis;
or (3) live viruses in the vaccine itself.

In an attempt to nail down the facts, the conferees at
Bethesda held several long-distance conversations with
the health officers in California. Did the children really
have polio? they asked. Who had seen the patients and
how well was the diagnosis verified? Did paralysis first
appear where the inoculation was made?

Answers to these questions strongly incriminated the
vaccine. For example, it was found that all five of the
California children became paralyzed in the left arm,
which had received the vaccine. This was suggestive,
since arms are less often paralyzed than legs.

Still, the case against the vaccine was not airtight. The
scientists picked the information apart and argued this
point and that, meanwhile gulping coffee and piling the
ash trays high with cigarette butts. At two A.M. Doctor
Shannon polled them on what they thought should be
done. As Doctor Haas said later, "Opinions shaded from
'wait and see' to 'stop the program right now.'"

Finally, at three A.M., they routed Doctor Scheele out
of bed, told him they stood divided, and asked his advice. Doctor Scheele suggested they consult additional
experts, such as Doctor Salk and Doctor Francis. . . .
After discussion as to whom else they might call in, they
broke up at 4:30 and went home. At eight A.M. Doctor
Haas was back in his office arranging a telephone con-

ference, the quickest way to gather opinions from out-of-town men. Doctor Salk and Dr. William McD. Hammon, professor of epidemiology at the University of Pittsburgh, were on a line from their city. Dr. Howard J. Shaughnessy, professor of public health at the University of Illinois, talked from Chicago. Plugged in at Washington were Dr. Joseph E. Smadel, of the Army Medical Service Graduate School,[4] Doctors Francis, Haas, Workman and others.

"All agreed the Surgeon General should take some action," Doctor Haas recalls. "But they couldn't agree on what it should be. They were not even of one mind on whether he should stop the use of Cutter vaccine. They preferred not to halt the whole program, but they said they would go along with whatever the Surgeon General decided to do."

What a decision to ask a man to make! In the first place, this really had been Basil O'Connor's show all along. The Public Health Service and National Institutes of Health had played only a secondary role in the introduction of the vaccine. Now, of course, they had a legal responsibility to protect the public, as laid down in the so-called "virus law" of 1902, regulating the safety, potency, and sterility of any virus serum or vaccine of any kind to be shipped in interstate commerce. This law rose out of an incident in St. Louis—some children were killed by tetanus in a contaminated diphtheria antitoxin.[5]

But the biologics-control act gave Scheele no authority to order a company to stop selling a product already licensed. He could suspend the company's license, but not without legal evidence and time-consuming formal action. He would have to depend on the company's voluntary co-operation.

There is no record of what went through the Surgeon General's mind—the calm and smiling Scheele is a man of colossal restraint and shock-proof benignity. But it would have been understandable had he some twinge of regret that Harry Truman had appointed him to succeed old, bold Thomas Parran, the veteran

[4] Now assistant director of the National Institutes of Health.

[5] "Virus" was here used in its older sense, meaning disease-inducing poison.

microbe hunter and anti-syphilis campaigner, who was replaced, presumably, because of the rising interest in chronic diseases, such as cancer and heart ailments.

The American people naturally look to the Surgeon General for leadership in public health. The Public Health Service, manned by career officers just as the Army or Navy are, has a brilliant record of laboratory and field research and achievement. But, administratively, it has an equally long record of pussyfooting actions, as has many another arm of bureaucracy. P.H.S. administrative officers are sensitive to the proddings and probings of Congress, respectful of the rights of private enterprise, and constantly deferent to states' rights, as personified to them in state and local health departments.

Scheele's action on April 27, 1955, was decisive. At ten a.m. he wired the Cutter Laboratories, requesting withdrawal of Cutter polio vaccine from the market. By 10:38 the Laboratories had contacted all distributors. Robert J. Cutter, president, said: "The only proper and safe course is to immediately stop any further use of the Cutter poliomyelitis vaccine until the facts can be established."

Scheele at the same time appointed Alexander Langmuir to head a Poliomyelitis Surveillance Unit to keep a continuous watch on polio cases, vaccinated and unvaccinated (it has done so ever since). Also, he dispatched Drs. Karl Habel and William Tripp to investigate vaccine production in the Cutter plant.

There was nothing more at this point that a public-health man could do except take the public that paid his salary into his confidence. Parents had to know the full story because it was *their* decision—not Scheele's, not Salk's, not O'Connor's—whether to have their children vaccinated.

Here, as the press soon recognized, Scheele pussyfooted. For example, he did not disclose, as he later reported to Mrs. Hobby, that there was "strong presumptive evidence" at the time that these cases were probably not coincidences but the fault of the vaccine.

Rather, he announced the stop on Cutter vaccine as a "safety precaution," and said the action did not indicate that the vaccine was in any way faulty. In fact, there was "nothing unusual" in the

United States polio incidence at this time. The vaccination program would continue as planned. Scheele said: "I want first and foremost to assure the parents of children who have received an injection of poliomyelitis vaccine this spring that in the very best judgment of the Public Health Service, they have no cause for alarm."

This "very best judgment" quickly became a source of great wonderment. Cutter cases continued to turn up in the next several days. There *was* cause for alarm, and parents lay awake nights wondering whether they had made the right decision in believing polio-vaccine propaganda. What had happened? Whom could they believe now? O'Connor? Salk? Scheele?

They could do nothing but worry and fume. But other parents could do something and, in countless instances, did—steer clear of Salk vaccine! Alton Blakeslee reported: "But, by the hundreds of thousands, parents and doctors shied away from it. The potent seed of doubt had been planted. It took root; it was slow to die." [6] *The New York Times* said there was no public hysteria. That was true—but there was darkness over Pocatello.

While the health officials were still talking in Bethesda, news came from Pocatello, Idaho, of two more cases, one fatal. Susan Pierce, a first-grader, aged seven, had been vaccinated on April 19 and had come down with polio on Sunday, April 24. On Wednesday she died of fulminating bulbar polio. And on this same April 27, while Scheele was announcing his decision, three more Idaho children came down with polio following vaccination.

It wasn't polio season in Idaho. All these cases received Cutter vaccine. In the majority of cases, paralysis began in the vaccinated arm. In the next few days and weeks, events made Scheele eat his words.

Between April 23 and June 7 there were twenty-two cases of polio in children vaccinated in Idaho. Two died. Between May 4 and 27 there were fifty-three cases of polio in family contacts or associates of these vaccinated children. Three died. One was a thirty-five-year-old father in Boise, a man named Rockne, who apparently got polio from his two vaccinated children. Another

[6] Alton L. Blakeslee: *Polio and the Salk Vaccine* (New York: Grosset & Dunlap; 1956).

was Mrs. Annabelle Nelson, a thirty-three-year-old mother whose two children had been vaccinated. A third was a six-year-old who had played with vaccinated children. They were polio victims.

Meanwhile, other cases and other deaths were occurring in other parts of the country—a nurse's four-year-old son, paralyzed; an expectant young mother in Atlanta and a famous surgeon's little grandson in New Orleans, both dead. Cutter vaccine again.

Langmuir finally summarized the Cutter cases as follows: "A total of 204 vaccine-associated cases occurred. Of these, 79 were among vaccinated children, 105 among family contacts of vaccinated children and 20 among community contacts. Approximately three-fourths of the cases were paralytic. There were 11 deaths, making a case fatality rate of five per cent."

Within the first month after licensing, five million or more Americans received their first Salk vaccine, about four million as part of the Foundation program. In this number there were bound to be some coincidental cases within the month, in association with all five makes of vaccine. There were, too. The grand total was 113—about one in fifty thousand and not a bad record, really.

Only in the cases associated with certain batches of Cutter vaccine and in seven Pennsylvania and Maryland cases associated with one batch of another company's vaccine were the numbers out of line with what might be expected through chance.

Though many officials and people in general did their best not to think of the Cutter cases—some even seem to resent the victims for spoiling the story—Salk did not turn his back on the sorrowing families in the West. "I know it's purely emotion," he told a friend, "but I cannot escape a terrible feeling of identification with these people who got polio." Trapped within him, intimates saw, was a sense of deep sadness and disappointment.

The Cutter Laboratories, too, expressed "deep concern" for the polio victims among the slightly more than four hundred thousand who had received Cutter vaccine. Some observers felt that the Cutter firm had been carried away in the eager rush and had moved its product into the market too fast. Yet there was much more here than could be covered by the word *commercialization*.

The company's laboratory workers had made the vaccine and used it on themselves and their families—without accident.

O'Connor's first statement of record, May 7, was a disclaimer of any Foundation control over manufacturing or testing of commercial vaccine: "This is the sole responsibility of . . . the U.S. Government." On May 23, at a Lasker Award luncheon in New York, he said he had been "charged with being inarticulate. . . . Maybe it's good to be inarticulate when everybody else is losing self-control. . . . Nothing that has been said affects the safety of the vaccine."

The verbal brickbats flew fast and hit hard. A Congressman called the program "soap opera." Columnist Walter Lippmann said: "Officials went off half-cocked." Adlai Stevenson said the vaccine program was "a mess." The respected *New England Journal of Medicine* referred to the "polio panic." Medical wags talked about the "Infantile Foundation for National Paralysis."

Embarrassed by a lack of vaccine and a lack of time to inform themselves, and shocked by the "TV spectacular" as a substitute for sober reading and reflection on the Francis Report, the medical profession was especially bitter in its remarks. An unnamed California physician gave striking expression to his colleagues' feelings in the following rich mixture of indignation and fine phrasing:

"I doubt that there has been another development in medical science heralded with such atrophy of reason and misuse of rhetoric. . . . By comparison, a cure for cancer should throw the public into such a protracted, horn-blowing, blubbering tizzy as to threaten total extinction of our waning art of conversation. . . . It was a unique and distasteful experience in my medical career to wait, shoulder to shoulder with a frenzied public, for an announcement concerning a development in my own professional field. . . ."

Thus began the ordeal of Jonas Salk. He felt that he had no choice but to go to Washington and defend his vaccine against what *The New York Times* editorially described as Public Health Service "bungling." He confided that, in his own career, he felt as if he were "treading water until the waves recede." To some he appeared more like a strong swimmer caught in a fast-running

tide. He could swim hard, but he could not turn it or make progress against it.

June Krieger pictured Salk as profoundly disturbed: "He is trying hard to keep himself and the scientific method with which
he identifies himself from being sucked into a whirlpool of publicity, politics and pressures. . . . He talks continually about getting
out of the limelight and back to his laboratory. . . . 'It's not a
question of modesty,' he says. 'I want to clean up this vaccine job
and get on with other things.' "

In May, following the April 27 stop on the Cutter vaccine, the
meetings in Washington came thick and fast. Scheele and Shannon called one committee meeting after another. The polio experts were going to have to tell them what to do. Again, great
names of virology were involved—Bodian, Enders, Francis, Hammon, Paul, Sabin, Shope, Smadel, and, of course, Salk. Likewise
in May, Senator Lister Hill and the late Congressman Percy Priest
began hearings on a $25,000,000 Federal bill to buy Salk vaccine
and give it to the needy—hearings that from time to time
turned into painful question-raising. For example, Representative
Charles A. Wolverton of New Jersey stated the pivotal question
when he said:

"I am just trying to find out whether there is a deficiency in
the formula of Dr. Salk or whether it is in the manufacture of this
formula."

This was precisely the question that bothered Scheele, Cutter,
Salk, and their colleagues. In a May 5–6 meeting, with manufacturers' representatives present to tell their side, the scientists
learned something that disturbed them greatly. All six vaccine
makers—not just Cutter—were having trouble killing the virus in
consistent fashion. This was news to Workman and his Laboratory
of Biologics Control.

True, some had much better performance records than others,
the percentage of unsafe batches of vaccine running from two to
twenty-one per cent after nine days or more of formaldehyde
"cooking." This led Salk to blame the manufacturing process in
the Cutter Laboratories, rather than any failure of his "margin of
safety" theory.

Nonetheless, all had *some* trouble. They hinted that a theory was not much good unless it proved out in practice. "Every batch of vaccine is a damned research project," someone complained. "That's the way it will have to be, then," said Salk.

There wasn't much question but that the burden of fuller inquiry was on the L.B.C. and not the manufacturers, who felt obliged only to fulfill the minimum requirements as laid down. One health authority explained: "It should be understood that commercial firms are not more explicit than the occasion demands when discussing matters that lend themselves to misinterpretation by the public."

One thing the manufacturers were explicit about: all considered themselves plain lucky they hadn't had a Cutter Incident of their own. The comment of a Lilly spokesman was pertinent: "We've certainly taken more precautions to make this vaccine safe than for any other vaccine in history." Explaining his company's success in keeping live-virus vaccine going into the incinerator rather than the channels of trade, one Lilly worker said: "Man, we test the stuff to death."

Considering that there are upwards of ten million virus particles in one vaccine dose and that the last one requires just as much killing as the first, such testing appeared justified. Most of the trouble centered on the Mahoney strain. The questions were whether the formaldehyde was reaching every virus particle and whether some viruses were more resistant than others.

John Enders, who finds little to say in such a heated atmosphere as existed behind the closed doors at Bethesda, made a recommendation: stop the Foundation's entire vaccination program until something safer than the Mahoney strain could be found for the Type I part of the vaccine. On May 7 Scheele called a halt to all polio vaccination. However, he insisted that his move did not mean the vaccine was suspect.

This halting action Salk deplored with articulate anguish. Nevertheless, he confided that he made a point of not losing his temper, but using it. On some occasions, when angry, he would return in his quiet way to his hotel and write out a reply to his critics. Then he would throw it in the wastebasket and go to bed. Many people remarked on how well he conducted himself in these most trying circumstances.

What went on in the meetings, particularly the one of May 5–6 attended by O'Connor, participants have been reticent to discuss. Under the Hobby regime, security regulations were strictly enforced, and the great scientists had to be fingerprinted and "mugged" and wear badges in order to act as consultants. This became an excellent excuse for not talking to reporters. There were other reasons.

Some of the scientists were acutely afraid of what the public might think of its health authorities. They loathed the situation they found themselves in. General results of the arguments are known:

A week later Scheele reversed the situation and released 4,500,-000 doses of Parke, Davis vaccine and and 3,500,000 of Lilly vaccine. The "on-again-off-again" polio-vaccine program was "on again." But in another day or two Wyeth and Pitman-Moore, after a long period in which all tests showed the vaccine to be safe, reported that they were again having trouble killing the virus. Scheele now predicted, with fine accuracy, that there would be a reduced supply of vaccine for some time to come.

One can easily see what this did to O'Connor's fast-lane plan to vaccinate nine million children before the 1955 polio season. Roadblocks and detours wrecked it (as a matter of fact, the Foundation was not able to complete its commitment to first- and second-graders until 1956).

Of the seven committee meetings between April 29 and May 26, the record shows Salk attended six. He walked out on the fifth and returned to Pittsburgh, telegraphing Scheele that he would not come back until a committee with power to act was formed. A firm hand was needed. On the day Salk stayed home, May 23, O'Connor put on pressure by wiring Scheele that the results of the Cutter investigation should be released, hinting that it held the key to the question of safety-testing.

Presumably, he referred to the fact that on that same day Dr. Louis P. Gebhardt of the University of Utah confirmed the presence of live virus in a vial of the Cutter vaccine distributed in Idaho. Gebhardt injected the vaccine into four monkeys; one died of paralytic polio. He put it in tissue cultures, and infected them, too.

Scheele replied that the Cutter investigation was not yet complete. But he did appoint a new technical committee consisting of Bodian, Salk, Shope, Smadel, Shannon, and Workman (soon to be replaced by Dr. Carl L. Larson). He asked the new committee to draw up new requirements for a safe vaccine. It met all day on May 24 and until 2:30 a.m. on May 25, emerging with a new and more exacting set of requirements. The manufacturers readily agreed to them.

Essentially, the tightening up consisted of more safety tests per batch, using live monkeys and monkey-kidney cultures, both by the manufacturer and the Federal laboratory. Now, definitely, the reliance would be on each and every test and not on the Salk theory of the built-in safety factor—namely, that the curve of formaldehyde inactivation of the virus follows a straight line reaching zero about three days after the last live virus can be measured, and therefore that if "cooking" is carried to the ninth day or beyond, no live viruses possibly can survive.

The trouble was, they did. In consequence, it now would take a total of one hundred and twenty days, not the previous seventy or ninety, to produce and test one batch from Berkeley to Bethesda. If it would be four months before any new vaccine could be ready, obviously there would not be much of a program in 1955, except with vaccine that had been cleared, or could be re-cooked and re-cleared.

The Surgeon General did not confirm the Gebhardt report until June 5. At last what discerning newspaper readers had come to believe was officially admitted. There was live virus in some of the Cutter vaccine, and this—not coincidental infection or provocation of latent infection—was the probable cause of the California and Idaho polio epidemics.

Insiders sympathized with the Surgeon General's predicament —"We were all caught in a trap," observed one local health officer. Salk was caught, too.

Many also remarked that Scheele's public relations were terrible. (The rule is simple enough; to enjoy public confidence, confide in the public).

The first of some forty damage suits, amounting to many millions of dollars, already had been filed against the company. The

California courts eventually held the company blameless for the accident of live-virus contamination, but nevertheless found it financially liable for damages under the laws of warranty, which hold commercial enterprises responsible for the safety of their products.

No special reason for the Cutter accident could be brought to light through plant inspection, Scheele revealed when on June 10 he made a full (162-page) report to Mrs. Hobby, by this time under heavy political fire for letting the government also become trapped. She had made an incredible statement to the press: "No one could have foreseen the public demand for the vaccine." This was equaled by her words in her letter of resignation to the President in July: "There is nothing I would have done differently." Scheele continued another year and then resigned.

The Scheele "white paper" was written with courage, yet was tactful. It did not spare the Laboratory of Biologics Control, but, in fact, recommended its complete reorganization (this was done; Carl Larson became its director, and Workman his assistant). "The records required of the manufacturers," said Scheele, "were inadequate to permit realistic assessment of consistency in the performance of each establishment."

The press further interpreted the report as implying criticism of the Foundation. "Events which in the traditional course of scientific development would have covered years were telescoped into months and, as a result, both successes and failures have been magnified," Scheele said.

The report made it fairly clear that nobody but Salk was any longer impressed by the so-called built-in factor of safety. "The original concept of vaccine preparation was that the process itself assured a wide margin of safety. . . . The total experience of the manufacturers now reveals that the process of inactivation did not always follow the predicted course."

Apropos of Salk's tendency to stand guard over his vaccine whenever it came under critical discussion, June Krieger astutely remarked: "He still seems to regard the vaccine with something of the emotional feeling of a mother toward her child." Her observation recalls an analogous situation in the dawn age of vaccination. Remarking on his own obstinate refusal to accept criticism of his smallpox vaccine, Edward Jenner revealed: "I cannot bear to see my darling child whipped with so much as a feather."

Salk said: "As I have previously indicated, theory and practice have coincided in the laboratory and under conditions of large-scale production." The manufacturers blinked their eyes and said nothing.

Salk's theory underwent another wringing out when Congressman Percy Priest called for a panel hearing of fifteen scientists and health authorities, June 22–23.[7] In all probability, it was one of the most learned Congressional hearings ever held, including as it did two great virus hunters and Nobel winners, John Enders and Wendell Stanley.

John Paul of Yale, as panel chairman, at once sought to disabuse the committee of the popular belief "that science is a fixed thing" and that if scientists disagree, "one man is right and the other is wrong." Until all the facts are in, he said, it is merely a question of various interpretations of available data.

It fell to Stanley the chemist to pick the raveling in the Salk safety theory. There is probably as much professional jealousy of Stanley's fame as there is of Salk's, but when Stanley talks, his colleagues listen. He is well informed, reasons closely, and, while he will stick his neck out, he has shown some willingness to retract when the evidence goes against him.

Stanley said to the committee:

> . . . About this shadow-line zone between safety and danger. Eventually what is taking place here is a chemical reaction, a combination between formaldehyde and poliomyelitis virus in a medium in which the virus makes up one part per thousand of the protein. Formaldehyde reacts with all of the protein, and not only the virus nuclear protein. . . .
>
> The chemist will tell you that in such a reaction it is theoretically impossible to wind up with a situation in which you have no active virus. . . .
>
> This curve which has been shown is one which will

[7] *Poliomyelitis Vaccine: Hearings before the Committee on Interstate and Foreign Commerce* (House of Representatives, Eighty-fourth Congress, First Session, June 22 and 23, 1955), Part 2.

bend. On that basis alone, the manufacturers' data indicate that they find that to be the case in truth.

From a biological standpoint, there is also the possibility of viruses of differing resistances. . . . A virus . . . very resistant to an inactivating agent may survive. . . . From this chemical and this biological standpoint, then, you have this no man's land where it is difficult to determine whether or not the virus is active and will cause disease, or has been inactivated and will not. . . . So this is a very tricky business.

Stanley had joined the issue. Salk's early confidence in the absolute safety of his vaccine was based not so much on an elaboration of safety tests in monkeys and tissue cultures, for here one soon enters the zone of undetectability, but on his theory that formaldehyde killing of the virus followed a straight-line "curve" that, sufficiently extended, must reach zero.

As one consequence, the Cutter firm's mistaken assumption that it was operating on a wide margin of safety resulted in a polio attack rate in Idaho of one case for every two thousand vaccinated. This was about four times higher than the natural incidence of polio in that state in any of the previous six years.[8]

Salk stood up to Stanley. "I was a chemist once," he said, "so I shall not talk as a physician for a moment." He maintained, as he had before, that there was a "point of no return" in the chemical effect of formaldehyde on the virus. Up to a point, the action was reversible and the virus might come alive again, but beyond that, he said, there were "irreversible complexes that eventually go on to death." He said it was not in all instances the kind of simple chemical reaction Stanley referred to. Salk continued: "We do know that it is possible to make vaccine and to inject every last cubic centimeter into children. . . . I say these things merely to counter some of the theoretical discussions, which is all very interesting and very nice, but let us not lose sight of the forest for the trees. . . ."

Dr. Thomas Rivers—who in 1935 had sat in judgment on

[8] Lawrence J. Peterson, Woodrow W. Benson, and Frederick O. Graeber: "Vaccination-induced Poliomyelitis in Idaho," *Journal of the American Medical Association*, Sept. 24, 1955.

Brodie and Kolmer—jumped into the argument and diverted it. He had verbally tilted with Stanley before, as microbiologist versus chemist. As chairman of the National Foundation's Vaccine Advisory Committee, Rivers had given O'Connor and Salk the green light in the fast lane.

Referring to earlier testimony, Rivers first turned on another old adversary, saying: "Mr. Priest, Dr. Sabin has admitted that a safe vaccine can be made. Right after that he suggests that we stop making a safe vaccine and make a safer one. . . . I should like to make a plea that . . . we do not stop making the safe vaccine."

Rivers now doubled back on Stanley and, as a physician, sought to disqualify the chemist for a lack of knowledge of the long history of formaldehyde as an "old friend" in the inactivation of both viruses and bacteria for various vaccines. He challenged Stanley to come up with a better inactivator.

Sabin now took up the challenge. He had first learned about viruses from Rivers, he said; "therefore I make my statement with trepidation. . . . But he has one ear in which he does not hear well and I think this is the one." Sabin explained that he had said that it had been shown a safe Salk vaccine could be made, but not with regularity.

Then he thrust a verbal stick between the legs of both Rivers and Salk: "Dr. Rivers also knows that some vaccine can be made safe, and others not. Dr. Smadel here has had an experience in making a vaccine against Venezuelan encephalitis with formalin, and it passed the animal tests. But when inoculated in human beings, it produced disease."

Rivers replied that he heard too much with his good ear. Representative Wolverton then began a line of questioning directed to ascertaining whether the assembled scientists were more on Salk's or on Sabin's side.

"My point," said Sabin, requested to state his position, "was that if we have another Cutter Incident the . . . loss of public confidence in the vaccine, which was very high to begin with, and the difficulties which we have now, would become magnified. . . ."

Presently Enders, in one of his rare comments, summarized the situation:

> One, there has been some doubt cast on the process of inactivation of the virus. We do not know absolutely whether it works according to theory. . . .
>
> Two, the safety tests may not be sensitive enough to detect the amount of virus that is sufficient to infect a few human beings who are unusually sensitive.
>
> And, three, we do know that somehow . . . in the Cutter case . . . , in spite of the processing, in spite of the safety tests, live virus did get through . . . with the production of disease.
>
> Now, new safety tests may take care of that. They have not been tried so far as I know.

The question, as Enders and others explored it, fell into two parts: (1) Should an effort be made to replace the Mahoney strain in the vaccine with a safer one? (2) Should the whole vaccination program be stopped awaiting the results of this effort?

Sabin went on to define the moral issue: ". . . I cannot ask anyone to come forward and take the chance this year of getting paralytic polio which he otherwise might not have, because in so doing he would be doing a great service for perhaps 2,000 others who would be prevented from getting polio this year."

The vote—the discussions and a polling of the scientists continued into the second day—was unanimous in approval of an effort to find a satisfactory substitute for the Mahoney strain.

On the question of stopping the program or continuing it, Stanley and other chemist, Manfred M. Mayer of Johns Hopkins, disqualified themselves on the ground that they were not physicians. Salk himself abstained, explaining that he wished to retain "my role of investigator who provides facts. . . ." As chairman, Paul also abstained.

The vote was eight for continuance of the program and three for stopping it. Enders, Sabin, and Hammon (voting by proxy) formed the minority.

As the hearings ended, O'Connor rendered a public opinion. He said Sabin's attack on the vaccine was "old stuff," but the Foundation would continue to support Sabin's research on a live-virus vaccine. He added: "Those who would prevent its [the Salk vaccine's] use must be prepared to be haunted for life by the crippled bodies of little children who would have been saved from paralysis had they been permitted to receive Salk vaccine."

It was an ironical statement, indeed, to some who noted that California and Idaho had abandoned their vaccination programs because of crippled bodies in San Diego, Oakland, Napa, and Ventura, and in Pocatello, Boise, and other towns. Lawrence J. Peterson, Idaho State Health Director, said: "We have lost confidence in the Salk vaccine." He did not blame the Cutter Laboratories, he said, but the procedure outlined by Dr. Salk.

The vaccination program, a typhoon-battered ship with sails torn and seams opened, moved forward into calm waters. In general, the story the press told and the public believed was that Salk was a hero and Sabin a villain—that the Salk vaccine would conquer polio, and it was too bad the Cutter production mishap had to happen—that if the Public Health Service had lived up to its responsibilities, the Foundation's program would have been a complete success.

Now, however, there was considerable doubt among doctors about vaccinating at the height of the polio season, for fear of provoking polio. Massachusetts had a full-scale Type I epidemic, with 3,819 cases for the year, or 77.5 per 100,000. The peak was in August. The vaccination program had been started and then stopped, and there was much bitterness among Boston's medical men, some of whom suspected the vaccine of having set off the epidemic. This dark suspicion apparently was groundless.

Against the great hopes and expectations of the spring, the National Foundation at the end of 1955 could count 7,000,000 children vaccinated "at least once," including the 441,000 in the 1954 field trials. But relatively few had received a second or third shot.

The new technical committee meanwhile had been busy. In November it suggested, for the first time, that the probable cause of live virus in the killed-virus vaccine was "clumping." If the tissue culture containing the virus harvest stood too long before the formaldehyde was added, virus particles became buried in clumps of kidney cells, where the antiseptic could not reach them. Salk

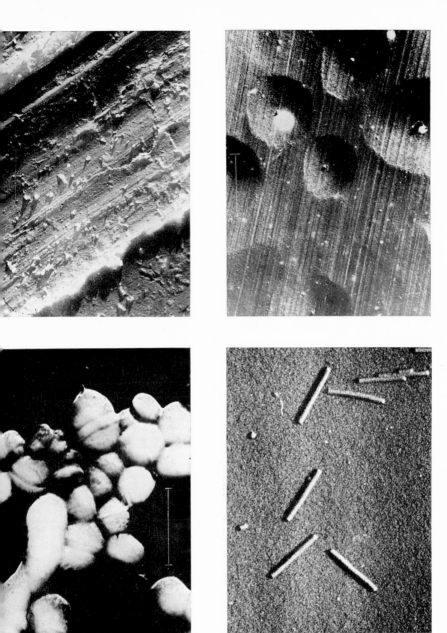

...e electron microscope, with magnifications up to 200,000 times natural size, brought virus
...rticles well within visual range. Yet virologists could see precious little until Robley C.
...illiams metal-plated infinitely small objects. *Upper left:* The surface of a used roller bear-
...g plated with a thin coat of chromium. *Upper right:* A polished diamond face plated by
...illiams. *Lower left:* The grotesque shapes of chromium-shadowed *Staphylococcus aureus,*
...e bacterium causing boils. *Lower right:* Uranium-plated tobacco-mosaic virus, previously
a vague bit of straw under the electron microscope.

PLATE 11

Upper left: An old friend, the cowpox (vaccinia) virus, magnified 50,000 times. *Upper rig[ht:]* Closely packed polio viruses, uranium-shadowed and magnified 100,000 times. *Lower le[ft:]* The PR8 influenza virus, first discovered by Francis, in a magnification of 100,000. *Lou[er] right:* The hexagonal head and tadpole-like tail of the T-4 bacteriophage, 50,000 times [its] size.

PLATE 12

apparently had not encountered the problem in making small batches rapidly for experimental use. Thus, there had been nothing in the original minimum requirements to prevent this phenomenon, learned only from tragic experience.

The committee remedied the matter by requiring ultra-filtration of the tissue-culture fluid just before the formaldehyde is mixed in, and again when the "cooking" has proceeded to the point where the virus is no longer detectable by the "crude" tests. This precaution has a booster effect on Salk's theoretical "margin of safety," so to speak; during the remaining days of cooking, no virus can hide out and keep it from theoretical operation.

Also, more sensitive safety tests were introduced, including one in which the laboratory worker induces a man-sized sensitivity to polio in a monkey by injecting him with the hormone cortisone before testing the vaccine on him. In this way, vaccine previously considered to be thoroughly killed occasionally will infect a monkey. If so, it is rejected.

It is a great credit to all concerned with making the vaccine safe that since early May 1955 and continuing through 1956, 1957, and 1958, no more vaccine-induced polio cases have shown up in the course of 200,000,000 injections, as far as Langmuir and his Poliomyelitis Surveillance Unit have been able to find. As he has pointed out, however, single cases might be missed. Because of the presence of coincidental cases at all times, it would take a series of several to arouse suspicion.

Today there is every evidence that the vaccine is as safe as Salk said it was in the first place. Smadel remarked that, while the vaccine might have been characterized as "witch's brew" during the period of stress, it would now compare to Grade A pasteurized milk. The occasion of his remark was a scientific meeting and banquet for scientists from all over the world at the Starlight Roof of the Waldorf, held in celebration of Basil O'Connor's sixty-fifth birthday anniversary, January 8, 1957. Just about all the great virologists were there. An anonymous donor gave the New York Academy of Sciences $54,000 to stage the three-day event. Some amazed scientists came five thousand miles for a ten-minute discussion of someone else's thirty-minute report. Salk, Sabin, Stanley, Bodian, Howe, Francis, Shope, Paul, Koprowski, Robley

Williams, Fraenkel-Conrat, and Goodpasture were there—but not John Enders from Harvard. He was invited, but "couldn't make it."

Though he never has said so in public and is not apt to, there is evidence that Enders, a kind man but an independent one, thoroughly disapproved of making a great public spectacle of a research effort to prevent a disease. A number of intelligent persons, laymen as well as scientists, agreed with him.

ARE WE CONQUERING

POLIO NOW?

By the beginning of 1959 approximately 70,000,000 Americans under forty, or well over half of the 110,000,000 in this so-called "polio age group," had received one or more injections of Salk vaccine. But of the children under five, who since the vaccine's advent have superseded the five-to-niners as the group with the highest polio incidence, less than half had had the three injections needed for maximum protection and about one third had had no vaccine at all.

Inasmuch as people have such a great emotional and financial investment in the vaccine—poliomyelitis could well become the first disease to be wiped out through voluntary popular support of research—the public deserves objective answers to questions that still remain after five years. The safety question has been disposed of—there has been no repetition of the Cutter incident. There are others:

1. *Just how good has the Salk vaccine been since 1955?*

The thing that impresses epidemiologists such as Dr. Alexander Langmuir of the Poliomyelitis Surveillance Unit is not one year's good results, but consistent results from one year to the next. The vaccine meets this test. The vaccine—a somewhat different one from that tested in 1954—has been from 60- to 90-per-cent effective in reducing paralytic polio among vaccinated persons, according to a statement made at the end of the 1958 polio season by Surgeon General Leroy E. Burney of the Public Health Service. "Only 12.7 per cent of the total of paralytic cases in 1958 had received three shots of the vaccine," Burney said. "This is an effective rate of about 87 per cent."

It was also impressive that the seven- and eight-year-olds who received vaccine in the 1955 school vaccination program had a lower polio attack rate in 1956, 1957, and 1958 than children in the age groups above and below them, though these first- and second-graders were in the five-to-nine group most frequently hit by polio in the pre-Salk days.

At first it seemed that mass vaccination was responsible for a general decline in polio, in both vaccinated and unvaccinated. Here, from the records of the National Office of Vital Statistics, is how the trend appeared, with vaccination years starred:

YEAR	TOTAL POLIO CASES	RATE PER 100,000 POPULATION	PARALYTIC POLIO CASES
1947	10,789	7.5	
1948	27,677	19.1	
1949	42,306	28.4	
1950	33,267	22.0	
1951	28,525	18.6	
1952	57,740	36.9	
1953	36,028	22.5	
1954*	38,694	23.9	
1955*	29,324	17.6	10,630
1956*	15,463	9.0	6,710
1957*	5,485	3.5	2,499
1958*	6,061	—	3,140

As may be seen, a general five-year decline of polio ended in 1958 with a small increase. The paralytic cases, reported separately only since 1955, are a more significant index than total cases for two reasons: the vaccine does not protect against non-paralytic polio, and, furthermore, much that was diagnosed as "non-

paralytic polio" in former years is now reported as aseptic meningitis, or virus meningitis, because of some of the newly found
Coxsackie and ECHO viruses (see Chapter 27).

Cautious epidemiologists wonder whether the Salk vaccine,
from 1955 to 1958, was not riding the downhill side of one of the
great natural swings in the epidemic intensity of polio. There
have been extremely low years in the past when there was no
vaccine at all.

The experts are presently inclined to the opinion that polio will
not be stamped out until all, or nearly all, susceptible persons are
triply vaccinated, especially children under five.

2. *Is a fourth shot necessary? If so, when?*

As the result of his experience in giving three injections, the
first two about a month apart and the third seven months or so
later, Salk was convinced his vaccine would produce strong antibodies and a durable immunity. "Time will tell," he said.

In 1958 he was able to show, and others independently confirmed, that measurable polio antibodies remained as long as
three to four years after vaccination. The lower attack rate among
children vaccinated in 1955 likewise bore out his prediction.

Early in 1958 parents were confused when the Public Health
Service announced that a fourth shot was not necessary, whereas
the American Academy of Pediatrics, speaking for child specialists in general, took the position that it was a good idea.

Salk clarified the issue. The public-health officer crusading for
mass disease prevention, he said, is primarily concerned with the
vast number of persons who have not been vaccinated. The general practitioner and pediatrician, on the other hand, "is aware
that time for the accumulation of practical experience has been
limited," and that there is about a ten-per-cent chance that the
vaccine will fail to provide protection, he said. Counsel against a
fourth, or booster, shot "would have little meaning to a parent
whose child might be among the ten."

If there has been a lapse of more than a year following the third
injection, a fourth shot "will do no harm," said Salk. In fact,
"there is no evidence of harmful effect from as many as six injections."

A University of Michigan study showed, by the way, that polio vaccination can be started when a baby is two to three months old, before it loses antibodies passed on to it by its mother, as it will before it is a year old. Thus, the infant can begin life with a thorough conditioning of his antibody-production system at a time when, according to the Francis "doctrine of original antigenic sin," antibody "memory" patterns are laid down for life.

3. *What are the possibilities for a better polio vaccine?*

Speaking strictly from the experience in laboratory and field studies, we know of no evidence as yet that there *can* be a safer or more effective polio vaccine than Salk's. A number of live-virus polio vaccines are undergoing evaluation. They have one tremendous advantage—they are given by mouth, in a tablespoon of cherry syrup, a squirt from an eyedropper, a sip of milk, or a capsule. No hypodermic needle is involved.

Two live-virus vaccines have been widely tested in humans.

One is the discovery of mild-mannered, well-liked Dr. Hilary Koprowski, director of the Wistar Institute, an independent microbiological research organization in Philadelphia. Koprowski stayed out of the Salk-Sabin controversy and all other public arguments, it appears, but he actually was the first man in the post-war field of polio-vaccine development. While working at the Lederle Laboratories in Pearl River, New York, he attenuated viruses of Types I and II in 1948 by passing them through the brains of mice and cotton rats. He made his first human tests on three children in 1950. These strains, of course, inherited the old problem of cultivation in nerve cells—that is, neurotropism and the danger of post-vaccination encephalitis.

Happily, this feature soon was left behind. A Lederle associate, Dr. Manuel Rocca Garcia, opened up a new possibility by adapting a Type II polio virus (MEF-I) to cultivation in hen's eggs. This would have been a great forward step, because it would have solved the nerve-cell problem and because hatching eggs are far cheaper than monkey-kidney tissue cultures, but this chick-type virus lost its antibody-producing power.

Koprowski moved his mouse Type I virus into chick-embryo tissue cultures, but it did not seem to multiply well and he eventually had to switch the virus to monkey-kidney tissue cultures. In this last step he was vastly aided by a technique for cultivating thoroughbred viruses introduced in 1953 by Drs. Renato Dulbecco and Marguerite Vogt of the California Institute of Technology, in Pasadena. In what seemed to be the more or less ultimate refinement of the Enders "green thumb" method, Dulbecco and Vogt found a way of culturing polio viruses in shallow glass dishes covered with a single layer of living monkey-kidney cells. This enabled them to spot single plaques, or colonies, of viruses that had multiplied from a single virus particle! Now the virus hunters could work with "pure cultures," in the same sense that bacteriologists used the term in their culture of bacteria on plates of jelly.

Koprowski tested his Type I attenuation, now known as SM N-90, in 227 adults, children, and babies without ill effect. He then recaptured the virus from the feces of one person, C80, whose name he abbreviated as "Chat." This Chat strain produced antibodies, but Koprowski reported in 1957 that tests showed it did not produce paralysis when injected into the brains of monkeys. Furthermore, it was less infectious than SM N-90.

The Wistar Institute now made a Chat vaccine for a field trial in the Belgian Congo. Some 244,596 African children and adults received the vaccine by mouth, again without signs of harm. In addition, a Type III vaccine containing a virus attenuated by John Fox of Tulane University was tested on 2,511 Africans.

The second attenuated live-virus vaccine is that of Albert B. Sabin of the University of Cincinnati. Recognizing the value of the Dulbecco plaque method, Sabin set out in 1953 to see what kind of attenuated viruses he could culture from single viruses and single colonies grown in monkey-kidney cells. He learned that there is a tremendous individual variation within a given type of polio virus, even when all particles descend from a single one.

By 1955 Sabin was able to select non-virulent, or attenuated, strains for each type of polio virus—I, II, and III—and hence produce a "purebred" live-virus vaccine offering the promise of all-round protection. By 1957 he had tested this vaccine on 10,000 monkeys, 160 chimpanzees, and 243 humans. The volunteers were mostly inmates of Federal penitentiaries, but Sabin, his wife, and his two small daughters were the first to receive his vaccine.

All appears to have gone well thus far with the Sabin vaccine.

With some encouragement from the World Health Organization, the vaccine has been administered to four million persons, particularly in Russia and Central and South America. Sabin found that the Type II virus tends to interfere with Types I and III, and therefore he feeds his three attenuated viruses to the vaccinee one type at a time, about three weeks apart.

What are the comparative advantages and disadvantages of killed-virus *v.* live-virus vaccine?

Sabin frequently has pointed out that the Salk vaccine does not eradicate the ubiquitous polio virus from the bowels of the vaccinated population. The Salk vaccine builds antibodies in the blood, and these head off paralysis, but the virus apparently can still live and multiply in the intestinal tract. In contrast, Sabin claims that a live-virus vaccine given by mouth—eliminating the needle—will keep wild polio viruses from passing through by creating a local, or cellular, resistance in the walls of the intestines. Thus, he assumes that a live-virus vaccine ultimately could lead to the extinction of paralytic polio viruses by eliminating any possible carrier state. This seems to have been the case with smallpox and diphtheria vaccination. Locked out of a large part of the population, the infectious agents cannot move on and propagate freely, and hence they die out.

Koprowski appears inclined to agree with Sabin that children immunized with a live-virus vaccine by mouth cease, or almost cease, to be wild-virus carriers.

But in science the burden of proof for such a claim falls on the claimant, as we have said before; thus, Sabin, who has been the spokesman in this matter, finds himself in precisely the same position as Jonas Salk when the latter said a killed-virus vaccine could produce an immunity as good as or better than natural polio infection: he has advanced a special theory that seems to fit his case, and conclusive evidence is not yet at hand. Sabin could be right about local immunity, but few, if any, microbiologists will take a strong position on the question. Perhaps they remember Mary Mallon, an Irish housemaid, who was naturally immune to typhoid fever but carried the disease into many homes. She became better known as Typhoid Mary. Indeed, there is some evidence that a natural immunity, produced by ex-

posure to wild polio viruses, does not necessarily prevent the immune individual from carrying the virus and transmitting it to
others. Could better results be expected from an attenuated virus
passing through the intestine?

Here we come to the greatest potential danger of a live-virus
vaccine, and one that Sabin has discussed freely: "The real issue
that remains to be resolved concerns its safety—safety not only
as regards the viruses that are initially swallowed but those that
may be excreted in a changed form and spread to others."

A presumed advantage of a live virus over a killed one in a vaccine is that, once in the body, it multiplies and therefore provides
a much more solid immunity due to greater stimulation of antibody reaction. However, when the multiplication takes place in
the intestinal tract, the attenuated virus can escape into the outside world and infect others in addition to the person vaccinated.
This would be of no moment if the physician knew that the escaped virus was still attenuated. But it is possible for a virus that
has mutated from a virulent to a non-virulent form to mutate in
the other direction; it has happened in monkey tests, though not
in human tests, as far as is known.

Introduction of such a polio vaccine for general use in the
United States still faced an uphill climb midway in 1959, when,
following a world health conference on live-virus polio vaccine,
Surgeon General Burney of the Public Health Service stated the
"need for controlled studies." Not only safety but effectiveness
remained to be proved under the same kind of scientific scrutiny
that the Salk vaccine faced. The question of whether the Sabin
and Koprowski vaccines do, in fact, prevent paralytic polio remained unanswered.

4. *In view of the* "Cutter incident," *was Basil O'Connor's* "calculated risk" *justified?*

This is not a scientific question, precisely, but it involves the
public's health and has been in the minds of many thoughtful
people. Many others, of course, probably would prefer to let the
ultimate success of the Salk vaccine speak for itself, and pass over
the critical judgments of physicians and scientists who applauded
the ends but took issue with the means.

One thing should be said in all fairness, from the viewpoint of vaccination history: there is some question whether the Cutter incident could have been avoided under any circumstances. One thing we have learned over and over from the story of the virus hunters is that, at some point, the introduction of a new vaccine usually spells trouble for the vaccine advocates, the vaccine maker, and at least a few of the vaccinated. This was true for smallpox, rabies, and yellow fever. Polio was no exception.

The simplest test of an effort to achieve a stated goal is whether that goal was achieved. By placing an order for mass production of Salk vaccine in 1954, before the field trials were complete and the Francis Report available to the medical profession, O'Connor planned to provide protection against polio for nine million first- and second-graders before the 1955 polio season began, and also to encourage the manufacturers to expand production and make vaccine available for many millions of other children. As he said in *Polio Facts for Speakers and Writers*, published for the 1957 March of Dimes:

"The common-sense thing to do would have been to wait for the report on the field trial . . . before placing such a huge order. The uncommon sense used by the National Foundation made it possible to go ahead without waiting for that report, so that if it were favorable, there would be vaccine on hand to save young arms and legs and young lives from polio—starting in 1955, not 1956 or later."

We already know the toll of the Cutter vaccine, which was a part of the purchase order. It is likewise a matter of record that when the 1955 program came to a halt, less than a month after it began, some four million children had received vaccine, and by the end of the polio season the number had increased to seven million. Hence, the objective was not fulfilled.

Contrariwise, it was not the Foundation's objective to cause parents mental anguish, shake public confidence in science, embarrass public-health authority, or offend the American medical profession. Again it is a matter of record—these things happened. There was much critical comment on all this.[1]

The big build-up and the big let-down, the traumatic wrench

[1] Paul Meier: "Safety Testing of Poliomyelitis Vaccine," *Science*, May 31, 1957.

of public emotions from joy and high hope to disappointment and mistrust, can scarcely be said to have advanced public acceptance of polio vaccination for all under forty. In fact, an opinion survey made for the Foundation later showed evidence of "buyer resistance," as well as the general apathy that vaccination crusaders always have faced.

If anything, the buyer resistance was more marked among doctors than parents—until the beginning of 1957, when the American Medical Association joined with the Public Health Service and the National Foundation in an all-out campaign to "finish the job." Despite great strides, the job is still unfinished.

We can hardly escape the conclusion that the calculated risk was miscalculated. As Leonard Scheele wryly noted in 1955, "You cannot make viruses meet deadlines." The following statement, made four years ago, still holds:

> What the N.F.I.P. did wrong was this: It surrendered to the anxiety of parents looking over its shoulder; and it drove its immunization program beyond the tolerance limits of the diverse system through which the vaccine had to pass to reach the children of those parents. This system involved all kinds of people: scientists, pharmaceutical personnel, government workers, state health officers, medical society officials, and private physicians. All needed to be considered—but not all were.[2]

Putting the development of the vaccine back into the context of a scientific advance of knowledge would have required someone as strong as O'Connor to stand up to him—and to public opinion—and say in a firm, friendly manner: "Now, wait a minute, Basil." There were a few scientists who thought Salk should have been the one to do so. This brings us to our final question.

5. *Is Jonas Salk all the hero the public made him? What do his fellow scientists say?*

The Salk vaccine made Jonas Salk, the quiet, studious boy born at Madison Avenue and 106th Street, New York, one of the most famous medical scientists of all time. There were many indications in 1955 that he felt more like a victim than a hero of the

[2] Greer Williams: "Polio Post-Mortem: What Really Happened," *Medical Economics*, August 1955.

National Foundation's success story, but to the public he looked just about right for his role. He proposed to save little children, he renounced personal financial rewards, he bore fame modestly, he faced the Washington ordeal with determination and yet held his temper, he spoke with eloquence in defense of his vaccine. He became a public saint.

It may seem incredible, but it is nonetheless true: many giants of virus research, the heroes of other chapters in this book, do not share the great admiration for Salk. There seem to be three issues involved.

In the first place, some insiders have expressed considerable resentment that "Jonas Salk got all the credit for making a polio-myelitis vaccine based on a discovery by John Enders." And, of course, it wasn't all the discovery of Enders either. There were Weller and Robbins, and equally important work was done by the Johns Hopkins group, Bodian, Howe, and Mountain, plus others.

Does Enders share this resentment? His reply was revealing. "My goodness, no," he said with surprise and then a chuckle. "I thought *I* was getting too much publicity." In such matters, he likes to quote Hans Zinsser:

> As a rule, the scientist takes off from the manifold obser-vations of his predecessors, and shows his intelligence, if any, by . . . selecting here and there the significant stepping stones that will lead across the difficulties to new understanding. The one who places the last stone and steps across to *terra firma* of accomplished discovery gets all the credit. Only the initiated know and honor those whose patient integrity and devotion to exact ob-servation have made the last step possible.

When Salk discovered that the Foundation staff and the press were attaching his name to the vaccine in 1953, he protested to O'Connor. The Foundation then made some effort to avoid the term, mainly to please Salk. There was nothing it could do. Ac-tually, the press and just people talking about the Salk vaccine named it—that and the fact that the four-letter word fits well into headlines. Had it been the Koprowski vaccine, the name wouldn't have been nearly so popular.

Were it only a question of who gets the credit, as important as being first is to a scientific investigator, we might dismiss the question as merely one of professional jealousy. However, the feeling runs much deeper—some reveal a surprising amount of bitterness. Is it that virologists saw Salk as a too willing servant of Basil O'Connor's ambition to conquer polio and of the fund-raising and publicity techniques that went with it? The *New England Journal of Medicine* for June 23, 1955, seemed to imply this. "In the final analysis it is physicians who must assume some of the responsibility for allowing themselves to be drafted by methods of the modern impresario into a scientific version of grand opera. . . ."

The editorial went on to imply that, to avoid pushing research too fast or too far, the scientist must submit to the jurisdiction of his colleagues first and last, rather than commit himself to a course that leaves no opportunity for him to hold back, change his mind, or simply say: "I was mistaken."

On a third, somewhat related issue—the source of the vaccine's safety—there has been an increasing amount of published evidence and opinion in scientific journals to the effect that Salk was mistaken about his theory of a "margin of safety," or a built-in safety factor in the killing of the virus. The vaccine as presently made—without mishap since 1955—does not depend on the "margin of safety" for its safeness. It depends on safety-testing. At this writing, however, Salk has not retreated from his position that his theory is valid. The whole course of events in developing, testing, and manufacturing the vaccine was predicated on his certainty that a safe vaccine could be made.

To be sure, many of his scientific critics' misgivings rose from his claim that a lasting immunity could be obtained with a killed-virus vaccine, as opposed to the classic position of microbiologists that the only lasting immunity against an infectious agent is the result of infection with that agent, in some living form. Others had made killed-virus vaccines—against influenza, for example. But before Salk, no one claimed that they would produce anything but a short-term immunity of a year or so at best.

Yet, nobody can be sure at the moment that, on this score, Salk will not go down in scientific history as a man who made an original contribution and not simply a "biological engineer," as Earl Ubell of the New York *Herald Tribune* called him. At present the evidence is running in Salk's favor: antibodies produced by a killed-virus vaccine persist for at least three or four years in the majority of cases, it would appear. This does not seem to be true, on the whole, of other killed-virus vaccines. Though Edward Jenner claimed lifelong immunity for his smallpox vaccine, three years is now considered the upper limit of dependable protection with this live-virus vaccine. So, in the end, Salk may be a true pioneer, though it may take a few more years to establish the fact.

It always has been the fate of the pioneer to be attacked by persons whose knowledge and authority he has disturbed. Usually there is some room for fair criticism, even though in the balance the net gain he has made weighs heavily in its benefit to mankind. Here there seems to be a curious analogy between what happened to Jenner and Salk.

Jenner took a position contrary to the belief of his fellow physicians that the only way to immunize against smallpox was to have at least a mild case of it. Jenner said that it could be done with cowpox from a dairymaid's hand, without harm and with immunity for life.

The more he defended his claims, however, the more he felt under attack. In his own hands his vaccine worked marvelously well. He was neat in his use of it and did everything just right. As soon as cowpoxing passed into other hands, there was trouble. There was contamination. And the vaccination failures piled up. Though the public and most of the medical profession embraced Jenner's vaccine and lent him moral support in his sense of rightness, questions of safety and potency were continually raised by men whom he saw as enemies. In actual fact, his own friends also had questions that they wished satisfied. It did not occur to Jenner that he could be right in his over-all observation and wrong in his explanation, or right in general but wrong in some particulars. The ill words fell thick and fast, and they hurt him deeply. But they did not diminish the ultimate significance of his discovery.

Just possibly Jonas Salk—like Jenner—is as great a human being as he is a scientist. Salk has kept his feelings to himself, but in all probability he would prefer to be honored as a scientist. The public, of course, honors him the more as a scientist because it likes him as a human being. Science—impersonal, less sentimental, not obliged to commit itself—will take its time in making up its mind. For *this* the crusaders will have to wait.

ARE WE LICKING THE COMMON COLD?

"THERE is just one way to treat a cold," said the model physician and medical aphorist Sir William Osler, "and that's with contempt." This prescription—fifty years after Osler's death—still is as good an insurance of a favorable outcome as aspirin, hot lemonade, or whisky, or any remedy yet devised. Yet somehow it fails to satisfy at least three classes of people:

Victims of the common cold;

Their employers on days when the victims are absent from work;

Virus hunters who, after thirty years of brilliant advances in disease prevention, can still be brought to account with one question: "But what have you done about the common cold?"

Over-all, the problem is as obvious as a running nose. A little arithmetic demonstrates its size. Some authorities estimate that we average three cold-like infections a year. The average is higher among small children, who have five times as many as adults. All told, this would mean at least 550,000,000 colds a year. The common cold is the only disease with a case rate exceeding the population available for attack. It is the most prevalent of all illnesses—more prevalent than all the others combined, as some see it.

If each person endures each cold for four days—a reasonable estimate, since it may last a week or more—then this is 2,200,-000,000 days of feeling awful. Certainly it makes management feel awful when it sees the employee-absentee rate climbing to its annual peak in January and February, when colds are at their worst. The Common Cold Foundation, a New York non-profit group that seeks to stimulate industry to spend more money on cold research, reports that the average worker loses two and a half days a year due to colds. During the peak winter months one of every four employees will be absent one or more days.

It is impossible, of course, to say how many use a cold as an excuse for a sudden and acute loss of interest in going to work on a Monday morning. But industry loses 150,000,000 workdays a year, at a cost of $2,000,000,000 in wages, as the result of colds, the Foundation estimates. It adds another $3,000,000,000 in lost production and medical expenses, for a grand total of $5,000,000,000 as the annual cost of the common cold. To what extent such figures may withstand the scrutiny of economists and statisticians we do not know, but it is a fact that the cost of cold medicines—drops, sprays, syrups, and pills—has been put at nearly a quarter-billion dollars a year. The object of all these is not a cure—there is no cure—but relief from discomfort.

There always has been debate about what the common cold is or is not. To most of us, it means a head cold and its attendant discomforts—a nasal catarrh; a chilly feeling; sneezing, coughing, and nose-blowing; a thick, stupid feeling; and a desire to lay down our load.

Yet, confusingly enough, we also have sinus colds, sore throats, laryngitis, ear infections, eye infections, croup (in children), bronchial colds, chest colds, summer colds, grippe, intestinal flu, and related affections that some doctors call "febrile catarrh." Some would separate the common cold from any other infection of the breathing-passages that produces fever. With many colds, there is no fever. But the distinction is not clear because often the temperature does rise a degree or so above normal with an ordinary head cold. Some experts now believe that the same viruses produce runny noses without fever in some and runny noses with fever in other persons.

Old-fashioned medical thinking actually supports the modern research concept that a cold is not one disease, but one outcome in a whole complex of respiratory infections characterized by a sudden temporary alteration in the physiology of the mucous membranes lining the nose, sinuses, ears, eyelids, throat, and air passages into the lungs. The membranes become inflamed and swollen and discharge abnormal amounts of mucus.

Some colds are mainly allergies, reactions to irritants such as ragweed pollen. Some are psychosomatic, coming as the immediate result of anxiety, frustration, or disappointment. Any kind of physical or mental stress may lower resistance to virus infection. Exposure to cold—that is, to low temperatures—is certainly one form of stress. However, as we shall see, there is some question about the effect of drafts, particularly from the British, who probably sit in more drafts than Americans.

Few, if any, common colds are caused by the larger microbes— bacteria. For this reason, vaccines made from a variety of killed bacteria, available for many years as "cold shots," are worthless in building immunity against virus infections, yet may be useful in chronic or repeated colds by cutting down on bacteria causing secondary infections.

Viruses are the primary cause of colds. German and American scientists established this fact as early as 1914 and 1916. It since has been abundantly verified, among other things by the fact that the antibiotics, generally effective against bacterial diseases, have no effect on colds. The virus will pass through a bacteria-proof, unglazed porcelain filter. The nasal secretions of cold patients, when reduced to a clear filtrate, will still cause colds in susceptible persons.

The British scientist Dr. William J. Elford, who did so much to put filterable viruses on the map, took the measure of a cold virus in 1951. Using collodion-membrane filters graded according to the size of their ultra-microscopic pores, Elford showed that the single virus particle was between thirty and seventy millimicrons in diameter. Modern research with the electron microscope hasn't greatly changed this estimate. Cold viruses mainly fall in size be-

tween those of polio—a millionth of an inch—and influenza—
about four millionths of an inch in diameter.

There cold research seemed to have bogged down until the last
few years.

The common cold was caused by a virus, but what virus—or
which viruses?

Some top-notch microbiologists have attacked the common-
cold problem. The man or men who found either its cause or its
cure would surely rate a Nobel Prize and, most assuredly, the
undying gratitude of the whole world—all of it prey to the common cold.

Dr. Alphonse R. Dochez and his Columbia University group
spent the better part of ten years on cold research and wound up
with one experimental animal. In 1930 Dochez transmitted human colds to chimpanzees. This was a first requisite, of course.
Ferrets and mice will catch influenza, but only a chimp is definitely susceptible to man's cold in the head. At today's prices—
about $700—an ape is hardly a suitable guinea pig, however.

The following year Dochez filtered a cold virus that for a time
survived in an early form of tissue culture. But it died out, analogous to the way common colds, at first epidemic, soon die out
in completely isolated communities and do not reappear until
there is fresh contact with the rest of the world.

With the 1931 advent of Dr. Ernest W. Goodpasture's technique of cultivating viruses in hatching eggs, there was new hope
that the cause of colds could be tamed and propagated for laboratory study. The flu viruses flourish in chick embryos, as do
some thirty others. From time to time between 1936 and 1950,
medical scientists could read in their journals or listen at their
meetings to the research equivalent of a "trail bark" or even a
"tree bark"—thrilling sounds that require no interpretation to
hunters to hounds.

Drs. Yale Kneeland of Columbia, Norman H. Topping, now at
Southern California, Morris Pollard of the University of Texas at
Galveston, and, most recently, Thomas G. Ward, now of Notre
Dame, all reported success in chick-embryo cultivation of a cold
virus. In each case, however, at some point in passing it from one
culture to another, the hunter lost track of this ultramicroscopic

will-o'-the-wisp. Unlike other isolated viruses, it could not be dried or frozen and mailed from one laboratory to another for contemplation by other scientists.

In 1946 a British virologist of the National Institute for Medical Research, Dr. Christopher H. Andrewes, a member of the team that in 1933 discovered the first human-flu virus, decided to have a crack at the common cold.

When the United States Army moved out of Great Britain at the end of World War II, it left, among other things, a group of prefabricated huts at Salisbury—they had been staffed as an Army hospital by Harvard Medical School. Andrewes set up a Common Cold Research Unit in these buildings and, during the next four years, succeeded in enticing two thousand volunteers—both men and women, many of them college students—to come to Salisbury for a ten-day "holiday" and to have an experimental cold and to submit to various tests. The study turned up some intriguing facts and enjoyed good publicity.

Colds are catching, in person-to-person or nose-to-nose transmission of filtered nasal secretions, often air-borne. But only fifty per cent of the volunteers developed colds when exposed, Andrewes and his co-workers found. In many instances, a volunteer seemed to be coming down with a cold on the second or third day after exposure, and then all symptoms suddenly disappeared—the cold spontaneously aborted. This is probably one reason why people can swear by so many different "sure cures" and be sincere. They feel a cold coming on, they take their favorite remedy, and they get well—and science goes right on looking for *the* cure.

More women than men caught colds at Salisbury, 55 to 43. The almost universal belief that chilling induces colds did not withstand scientific testing, at least with the particular virus under study. Some were given doses of the virus and a hot bath and made to stand for a half-hour in a draft in wet bathing-suits. They then wore wet socks the rest of the morning. Others took a walk in the rain, sat around in their wet clothes, and remained in unheated flats. Americans find even *heated* English flats cold. Still others received this same miserable treatment without the virus.

In two of three trials, the virus plus chilling produced fewer colds than the virus alone. By no method was it possible to increase cold attacks above fifty per cent. And in no case did chilling alone produce a cold. This leaves us with the interesting speculation of whether people catch a cold because they feel chilly, or feel chilly because they are catching a cold.

Andrewes found presumptive evidence that his subjects possessed antibodies to his cold virus in their blood, but these did not necessarily guard them against attacks a few months later, as good antibodies should. He assumed that, because a natural cold infection is so superficial, confined to the outermost layers in the lining of the nose and other air passages, it produces too few antibodies to confer immunity. This suggested to Andrewes that if it were possible to develop an attenuated cold virus, it might also be possible to incorporate it in a vaccine to be repeatedly sniffed into the nostrils, like snuff.

But no attenuated virus emerged. He was unable to cultivate a cold virus. Hence he wound up his study, as others had before him, with no satisfactory test animal or culture medium, no diagnostic test, no certain means of transmission even in humans, no satisfactory immune serum, and no knowledge of what type or strain differences there might be among cold viruses. He later lamented that "pricking a bubble is not news," whereas "a 'cold-cure' is news." Thus, he had no news. Pronouncing the then new antihistamines as worthless for curing colds, he indicated that antihistamine enthusiasts who had been saying good-by to the common cold would be saying hello again and again for some time to come.

As a matter of fact, among virologists it is easy to find pessimists who fear that we shall never see the last of the common cold, any more than we actually had seen the last of influenza epidemics in the flu-less years just prior to the Asian-influenza pandemic of 1957. Such pessimism does not stem solely from lack of progress, but, paradoxically, from the rapid expansion of virus knowledge since 1948.

That was the year that Dr. John F. Enders's laboratory at Harvard, having perfected a test-tube method for the continuous culture and ready detection of mumps virus and then turned to the problems of growing chickenpox and infant-diarrhea viruses in human embryonic and other tissues, impulsively tried polio virus.

It multiplied, too, as we saw. The Salk vaccine was one result of this break-through. But it also opened the way to the discovery of a host of new viruses, including many involved in colds and other common respiratory infections.

Virologists began uncovering, naming, and typing strange viruses by the dozen. Enders's laboratory discovered the first of the so-called ECHO viruses. ECHO stands for "Enteric Cytopathogenic Human Orphans," a name agreed on by a committee of virologists with a certain amount of conscious whimsy. It means that these viruses were found in the human intestine, destroyed living cells, and were not known to cause diseases—"orphan viruses in search of a disease," some called them. Actually, it was the virologists who were doing the searching—for diseases of unknown origin that might be caused by these viruses.

In the five years following the 1948 break-through, Dr. Sidney Kibrick, who succeeded Thomas Weller as Enders's assistant director, examined fecal specimens of 300 patients in Children's Hospital, in Boston—youngsters who presumably had polio. Tissue-culture tests did reveal polio in 173 cases. But they also disclosed strange viruses in 72 of the other 127 specimens. The presence of a virus was deduced from the fact that the living cells in the tissue cultures became swollen and eventually disintegrated. Yet it could not be identified as polio or any other known virus in neutralization tests using standard immune serums for matching purposes.

Eventually the name "enterovirus"—intestinal virus—replaced ECHO in proper virological circles, yet in general usage the first name stuck. The last count on ECHO virus was twenty-five types, any two of which were sufficiently different to produce different antibodies in the blood. The latest evidence indicates that they are responsible for a variety of grippe-like or cold-like infections involving fevers and muscular aches, among other things, including some cases previously diagnosed as "non-paralytic poliomyelitis" and, in all probability, a good deal of infant diarrhea. During the winter of 1958-9 the ECHO-9 type was a popular number, though not with its dragging victims.

But these were not the only "new" viruses responsible for ailments of this sort. Earlier, the Coxsackie viruses had been discovered by Dr. Gilbert Dalldorf, then director of the New York State Health Department laboratory at Albany, now research director of the National Foundation. Dalldorf's find depended not on tissue cultures, but on his use of a different animal host—suckling mice under ten days old.

Late in the summer of 1947 he obtained fecal specimens from two boys—T.T., nine years old, and K.H., three and a half—who appeared to be suffering from paralytic polio. These boys lived in the Hudson River Valley village of Coxsackie (population 2722). The little town appeared to be having a small outbreak of polio, but no polio virus could be isolated from any of its six cases. A variety of tests were tried in the Albany laboratory without success, except when some of the specimens from these two boys were injected into suckling mice. The baby mice weakened, moved in circles, became paralyzed, and died—most of them— after a day. In contrast, polio virus did not faze them. This is an oddity, because adult mice are immune to Coxsackie viruses but are common laboratory vehicles for polio—that is, their brains are.

Dalldorf and his associates combed Coxsackie and other towns and found signs of the strange new virus everywhere. Half of the members of the families of those two little boys had antibodies to this stranger. Again and again it turned up in patients who had either an abortive or a paralytic polio but no sign of polio virus.

Dalldorf put the town of Coxsackie on the map—the microbiological map, anyway—by naming a virus for it. He also succeeded in complicating the polio problem. Some types of Coxsackie definitely cause a pseudo polio, sometimes involving paralysis, sometimes not (these cases are now frequently diagnosed as "aseptic meningitis"). The Coxsackie viruses are not included in the triple-type Salk polio vaccine. While many people become infected with Coxsackie virus and never know it, just as they do with polio, this new virus can be vicious. Type 3 of Group B, for example, causes a fatal inflammation of the heart muscle in infants, Kibrick and others discovered. A half-dozen other diseases have been laid at the Coxsackie door, including certain "flus" and "summer grippes."

Ultimately, two groups of thirty different types of Coxsackie virus materialized, all found in the intestine like the polio and enteroviruses. Some can be transmitted only in newborn mice, but others multiply in tissue cultures.

Still, even this was not the end of the tally, for it does not take into account the discoveries made by the Laboratory of Infectious Diseases, a part of the National Institute of Allergy and Infectious Diseases of the Public Health Service. This laboratory, beautifully situated in green, rolling hills outside of Bethesda, Maryland, itself a suburb of Washington, can be properly described as a world center of research in the common-cold complex. Here in 1953 was discovered the first of another new group of twenty-four adenoviruses, all involved in common respiratory infections.

In consequence of this work—three different families of viruses were found growing in tonsils alone—the common cold is becoming an uncommonly complicated thing. On the other hand, the expanding universe of virus knowledge provides a scientific background for the family doctor when he says: "You have a virus." This is probably the most frequent diagnosis he makes these days. It is a matter not only of fashion but also of fact.

Dr. Robert J. Huebner, chief of the Laboratory of Infectious Diseases and one of the foremost of the "new virus" hunters, in April 1957 remarked: "It is now possible to speak glibly of at least fifty new viruses of man." He suggested there would be more. A year later he counted seventy and then, within a few months, raised the number to eighty. It is still going up. Huebner said:

> More new agents are on the horizon. Untyped agents by the hundreds are accumulating in iceboxes in virus laboratories far more rapidly than they can be characterized and classified. . . . They are not new . . . but newly recognized agents that have long been, and are now, extremely prevalent. . . . Like poliomyelitis, influenza, and many bacteria, these . . . are readily spread by means of ordinary household and community contacts.

As a matter of fact, Huebner is of the opinion that the number of unknown virus infections may be getting larger due to more efficient spreading of viruses—that is, more people, more travel, and bigger schools. The schools are important because the biggest source of adult virus infection is children.

Huebner, forty-five years old, calls himself a general practitioner of virus research, and as such is a better than fair example of the typical virologist who doesn't specialize in a single kind of virus, but moves from one to another as each pops up in an epidemic or in a tissue culture. He is also a leading exponent of team research. Usually each piece of work reported by his group involves the active collaboration and co-authorship of five or more scientists.

Professionally popular, Huebner is a big, muscular man with a square Germanic head, low hairline, flat face, and nose as crooked and precipitous as an Adirondack ski trail. Witty as well as perspicacious, he says: "I have made a profession of looking stupid," meaning that he is more interested in finding new facts than in dreaming up new theories to explain either new or old facts. In this new virus science, theories bear about the same relation to facts as tenpins to bowling-balls. In short, they continually get knocked over.

Huebner divides his time between his twenty-four viruses and eight children more or less in that proportion. The Huebners live on a 160-acre Maryland farm in Frederick County, thirty-three miles northwest of Bethesda. They could not afford a farm in rich, near-by Montgomery County on his salary as a government scientist (now $14,000 a year).

In 1951 Huebner made the down payment on the farm with a $1,000 prize he had won for a Q-fever study, plus unused leave pay saved up from military service. During the Huebners' first summer on the farm, shortly before Berdine Huebner had their seventh child, the barn burned while Huebner was in Texas investigating an epidemic of another Coxsackie virus infection. This one is known as Bornholm disease, pleurodynia, or devil's grippe. A muscular rheumatism of the chest, the disease often provokes its victims to cry: "I can't breathe."

When they had rebuilt the barn, the Huebners found themselves mortgaged for more than the farm was worth. Otherwise, with the calm, competent Mrs. Huebner operating the tractor between babies (now aged five to eighteen), and with Father

Bob helping with the chores before and after his day at the laboratory, the farm has been something of a success as a place to raise children and also Black Angus cattle. The latter are intended as a means of financing the education of the former.

Thus, Huebner, showing up late for a 1958 meeting that he had organized as a means of bringing virologists momentarily abreast of the facts, explained that he had had to truck a young bull to a Richmond, Virginia, stock show. Then, back at the farm, he had picked up Mrs. Huebner, exchanged truck for fast automobile, and driven to New York. The bull costing $400 as a calf, became grand reserve champion and brought $4,200 at auction, he happily announced later at the same meeting.

Huebner arrived at his state of eminence as father, farmer, and, as he says, "hardy virus man" by a series of circumstances that should be of great encouragement to poor boys with natural talent and no background—to wit, no money.

He was born and raised in Cheviot, Ohio, near Cincinnati, the eldest of a motion-picture operator's family of nine children. He began working at one thing and another as a boy. His incredible energy, plus an uncle's help with the tuition, got him through St. Louis University School of Medicine. He not only worked his way, but had to work his way around the dean, Father Shwittala, who had a rule against allowing first-year medical students to work, and periodically attempted to throw Huebner out for this infraction.

Huebner risked the dean's wrath again in his second year when he met and secretly married Berdine, then a nurse. Somehow the marriage escaped the dean's attention, although Huebner became a father before obtaining his medical degree in 1942. In 1944, when he was thirty, he accepted a Public Health Service commission as a regular medical officer. In civilian life he would have been a penniless young general practitioner looking for a place to hang up his shingle.

That same year Dr. Richard G. Henderson, thirty-one, died as the result of a laboratory accident. This was the event that led Huebner to virology. He was chosen to succeed Henderson, who had been working in the National Institute of Health's old Infectious Disease Laboratory with tsutsugamushi fever, or scrub typhus, caused by a microbe known as a rickettsia. He was pulverizing diseased tissues in a Waring blender. The mixer apparently threw off an invisible spray that infected Henderson with the disease. He came down with the fever a week later, and died within a few days.

There had been a number of laboratory accidents to government microbe hunters. When Dr. Rolla E. Dyer, then N.I.H. director, added Henderson's name to the casualty list, he saw that it totaled six dead and 117 disabled in the previous twenty-five years. Researchers had been stricken by meningitis, psittacosis, tuberculosis, Q-fever, tularemia, undulant fever, Rocky Mountain spotted fever—Dyer himself had had spotted fever.

Angrily, he went to see Dr. Thomas Parran, then Surgeon General, and said he wanted a laboratory with every safeguard for its workers which money could buy. Parran told him to go ahead and get it. Dyer went to the commissioner of public buildings and the Bureau of the Budget and he got it.

The result was a model laboratory for work against dangerous diseases.[1] The new Laboratory of Infectious Diseases, costing $1,250,000, was not one laboratory but six, each in a separate wing and completely isolated from the others. Each was sealed, air-conditioned, and ventilated with a one-way air circulation moving out of the corridors into the workrooms and thence into vents and through filters returning the air outdoors. The glass-windowed hoods over the worktables likewise sucked air in through their hand slots—through which the technician could work with a dangerous specimen. This air went out through an electric grill that would incinerate microbes. Always the air moved *away* from the worker.

It was a noble effort to protect hunters from the hunted. Some of the more intricate details proved unimportant, but the new laboratory gave a tremendous forward push to microbiological research under its first chief, Dr. Charles Armstrong, who had introduced the mouse as a handy host for polio.

Some risk of accidental infection will always remain, mainly, it appears, because familiarity breeds contempt. Huebner made

[1] Greer Williams: "Laboratory against Death," *Cosmopolitan*, February 1947.

no noticeable progress against scrub typhus, and, in fact, seemed bent on the reverse. While clearing the bubbles from a hypodermic syringe containing the lethal scrub-typhus germs, he succeeded in jabbing his finger with the needle, through his rubber glove. No infection developed. Nor did he suffer much when, in subsequent investigations, he became infected with murine typhus, Q-fever, pleurodynia, and two kinds of adenovirus infection. Luckily for him, all were mild attacks and did not require hospitalization. A good virus hunter needs good luck.

One of the six units in the laboratory was assigned to the study of the common cold, under Norman Topping. It wasn't that colds were considered dangerous, but an epidemic-proof laboratory is an advantage in keeping experimental animals free of cross-infections and unintended immunities. This was one of the laboratory's grand objectives: to find a suitable experimental host and hence isolate the cause of the common cold. For a time Topping and an associate, Dr. Leon Atlas, appeared to be succeeding, using chick embryos as the culture medium, but the virus vanished.

The Enders tissue-culture technique solved the host problem. Cold viruses grow well in test tubes containing living monkey-kidney cells, and also in other tissues, as experience has shown.

Huebner became chief of virus- and rickettsial-disease research and then chief of the laboratory. Toward the end of 1952 Dr. Wallace P. Rowe, a Johns Hopkins graduate, then only twenty-seven, and his chief got to wondering about adenoids as a tissue-culture medium. Like the near-by tonsils, these lymph-gland tissues in the back of the throat are at the four corners of upper respiratory infection; all viruses inhabiting the gastrointestinal tract and the breathing-passages pass these "four corners."

The two men decided to collect adenoids snipped from the throats of children in Washington hospitals and find out what they would do, still alive, in tissue cultures.

By the next spring they knew. The adenoid cells grew in tissue cultures very well for the first week or so after these scientists placed their test tubes in the incubation room. The cells put out thin sheets of new cells along the walls of the tubes, and even developed cilia, the tiny hairs that grow in the respiratory tract and wave foreign bodies upwards and outwards.

But in three weeks of following the Enders method—that is, changing the media but maintaining the tissue in continuous culture—something else happened. More than half of the cultures showed cell degeneration, and in another week or ten days the cells were completely destroyed.

Rowe, Huebner, and Dr. Joseph A. Bell, the laboratory's chief epidemiologist and oldest man (he is now fifty-five), pondered this phenomenon. What went on? Had these adenoids come to them complete with viruses?

They transferred adenoid culture juice to other types of tissue culture. In almost all cases an identical cell destruction took place. When they succeeded in passing this destructibility through seventeen subcultures over a sixty-nine-day period they were pretty sure they had unmasked a new virus. They were even more certain when they were able to move their—as they called it—adenoid degeneration agent, or AD, among a wide variety of human and animal tissue cultures without losing it.

This was indeed a hardy virus—it met all the tests for a virus. Yet they could not produce a disease with it in various experimental animals—mice, guinea pigs, monkeys, or a chimpanzee. Still, some of these animals, particularly rabbits, did develop antibodies against it, and thus provided the scientists with an immune serum that would neutralize virus growth in a fresh adenoid tissue culture.

This is the scientific bootstrap method by which a virologist identifies his new viruses, as we have pointed out before. If the scientist suspects the presence of a virus in a bit of tissue and can infect a laboratory animal with it, that animal should produce antibodies against the virus in its blood. Now, immune serum from its blood should, when mixed with the virus, prevent the virus from infecting another, susceptible animal. The reaction is ordinarily quite specific—one kind of antibody for each virus. The same result can be obtained by substituting a tissue culture for the animal, putting virus and immune serum into it, and then watching to see whether or not cells are destroyed. If the serum does not neutralize the virus—well, the virologist is still in the dark as to what kind of virus he has on hand, or whether it is a virus at all.

In the beginning, Huebner and Rowe had a virus in adenoids and no disease to tie it to. In fact, they soon found that they had six distinct types of this adenovirus, as it now is known. During the summer of 1953 they found a new lead: they uncovered Type 1 in the post-nasal drippings of a two-year-old with a fever and runny nose. Type 3, on the other hand, came from nasal washings from human volunteers inoculated with secretions from a person who had a head cold without fever. In the way that is characteristic of cold viruses, all further signs of this virus vanished during experimental infection of volunteers, who nevertheless continued to get colds—probably from some other unidentified virus.

But as time went on, Huebner developed a conjunctivitis, or inflammation of the eyelid and eyeball, also known as "pink eye." The same thing happened to a technician also working with the tissue cultures, Janet W. Hartley (now a bacteriologist). They isolated the Type 3 virus from the infected eye in each case. Also, Dr. Robert H. Parrott, a pediatrician in the N.I.H. Clinical Center, had an eye infection after an infant coughed in his face during a physical examination. His colleagues found that the baby carried the Type 3 virus.

This Type 3 kept turning up in hospital staff members and their patients. Commonly, they had a fever, inflammation in the pharynx, and an eye infection. Finally the team had a chance to study an outbreak of this feverish sort of cold in an epidemic in a Virginia summer day school as well as in other scattered groups. Often infection was traceable to swimming-pools.

The Huebner group reported their new AD viruses to the Society for Experimental Biology and Medicine. Soon they found they had competition. Their report was published in December 1953 in "Proc Soc," as the Society's *Proceedings* are called; in January 1954, Proc Soc published a report from the Walter Reed Army Institute of Research in Washington about a new virus isolated from an epidemic of feverish colds and pneumonia among recruits in an Army camp. Dr. Maurice R. Hilleman, then at Walter Reed—across town from the NIAID laboratory in Bethesda—had cultivated his virus in cultures made from human tissues taken from the placenta, or afterbirth. He called it Strain RI-67, the initials standing for respiratory infection.

Now came some trading of specimens, cross-neutralization tests, and comparison of laboratory notes. It was soon evident that the Huebner and Hilleman teams had been looking at the same virus from different sides of town. This AD or RI virus later was established as adenovirus Type 4.

Meanwhile, to complicate matters, Huebner and Rowe chose to call their find the adenoidal-pharyngeal-conjunctival group of viruses, or APC for short. It wasn't until 1956 that Enders was asked to form a committee, call a meeting, and straighten out the name business. "Adenovirus" was agreed upon. Such conflicts in terms are the rule rather than the exception in science because of original discoveries by independent researchers. Also, as Dr. Thomas Weller explained, "Virology is in a state of rapid evolution, a stage chaotic for the uninitiated and only slightly less confusing to the experienced."

Eventually the number of adenovirus types grew to eighteen from humans and six from monkeys and chimpanzees. Indeed, it was found that adenoviruses could be isolated from the adenoids or tonsils of ninety per cent of all children at some time during the year, although, strangely enough, they account for only a minor percentage of common respiratory infections including colds, except in children under six. Children have fifteen or twenty times more adenovirus infections than do adults, with the exception of those adults known in military circles as rookies or raw recruits. They, as we shall see, are in a special class.

Presumably the reason for so little infection in the adult civilian population is that most people have adenovirus antibodies in their blood and these are boosted again and again during repeated exposures. Volunteers in the laboratory at Bethesda found this to be true. They seldom manifested signs of infection after exposing themselves to adenoviruses, but showed sharp rises in antibodies.

Plainly enough, it was practicable to make a vaccine. In 1955 Huebner decided to kill the Type 3 virus with formaldehyde and try it. The Type 3 adenovirus might quite properly be described as the first virus of the cold infection complex to be isolated and successfully cultivated in tissue cultures. Likewise, it went into the first vaccine to become available experimentally and commercially.

Huebner, Bell, Rowe, and other collaborators first tested a Type 3 vaccine on eighty-three inmates of the Federal Industrial Reformatory at Chillicothe, Ohio, and the Maryland State Reformatory for Males at Breathedsville, Maryland. All were young men who volunteered to be inoculated with the vaccine and then see if they could catch a Type 3 cold. They were chosen not only for willingness but also for susceptibility, most of them. Forty-five received one to three injections of the vaccine and thirty-eight were saved for comparison.

All had antibody tests before and after vaccination, and all received challenge doses of live Type 3 virus some three weeks or so after vaccination. The virus was swabbed into one eye of each man, the other eye being swabbed with a placebo solution so that in follow-up studies neither the volunteer nor the examining doctor could know where to expect infection.

About 90 per cent of those who did not receive the vaccine developed an eye infection within seven days. In contrast, only 29 per cent who had the vaccine developed infections. This was about the same as the response in a third group that entered the study with naturally acquired antibodies. In other words, about three out of four persons appear able to develop an immunity following vaccination against this type of respiratory infection.

In this study, the over-all reduction in the chance of infection was from nine to three in every ten, or about 67 per cent.

Huebner and Bell now went ahead and requested a pharmaceutical company to prepare a vaccine containing Types 3, 4, and 7 for mass testing on new recruits at the Naval Training Center in Great Lakes, Illinois. Hilleman had found that Types 4 and 7 were those most common to military training-camps. Bell supervised administration of the vaccine injections to four thousand men between January 11 and April 19, 1956. They were then watched for respiratory illnesses in comparison with twelve thousand unvaccinated recruits throughout a nine-week training period. A sampling of vaccinated and non-vaccinated revealed that the vaccine reduced fevers of one hundred degrees or more by better than 50 per cent and cut down hospital admissions by about 65 per cent.

Hilleman got still better results with a Types 4 and 7 vaccine that he and his team of lady laboratory workers made at Walter Reed. The ladies were Mildred S. Warfield, Sally A. Anderson, and Jacqueline H. Werner—the last of whom had collaborated with him in the discovery of RI-67, or Type 4. They tested their two-way, two-shot vaccine on 311 recruits at Fort Dix, New Jersey, and compared them with 313 who received dummy injections. The tests were made over an eight-week period extending from February to April 1956.

The results were sensational. In the first place, there were no ill effects whatsoever from the vaccine. At Great Lakes the commercial vaccine had stung the sailors' arms somewhat until the residual formaldehyde was eliminated. At Fort Dix the vaccine had no effect for one week after injection and then it became about 83-per-cent effective in keeping its recipients off the list of soldiers sick with any kind of respiratory infection.

Only one of 311 vaccinated recruits required hospitalization for a lab-proved case of adenovirus infection—in startling contrast to 61 cases among 313 men from the same six companies who had received dummy shots. "This," said Hilleman, "represents a 98-per-cent reduction from the expected incidence." There also was some evidence of a reduction in the number of mild cases.

This was great news for commanding officers, who stomped and swore during World War II at the way acute respiratory infections depopulated their companies while they were trying to teach men to crawl on their bellies, shoot, and otherwise get ready to go overseas. From 1942 to 1945, more than four million soldiers went to the hospital with respiratory diseases while in training. Four of every ten men newly arrived in training-camps had feverish colds, two of the four severely enough to require hospitalization for an average of ten days. This represents a tremendous loss of time in an eight-week training program. And now it is known that adenoviruses are mainly responsible.

Following the 1956 tests, officials announced that adenovirus vaccine would become a routine requirement for recruits during peacetime, too. This plan did not materialize, however, because the pharmaceutical companies found the vaccine—made in much the same way as the Salk polio vaccine—too expensive to be feasible. The military-recruit market is presently too small to support the expense, apparently. Said Huebner, a bit sadly: "The military recruits are, therefore, still contracting acute respiratory disease at the usual rate. This is one of the discouraging things about work in the respiratory-disease field. There are many practical obstacles to prevention of non-fatal diseases, however common they may be."

Neither Huebner nor Hilleman holds an adenovirus vaccine out as the answer to colds without fever, of course. Coming somewhat closer to home, perhaps, are two new so-called "myxo," or mucus-producing viruses uncovered in small children in 1958 by Dr. Robert M. Chanock and others in Huebner's laboratory. These definitely caused typical head colds in the majority of adult volunteers exposed to them. How they figure in the total cold picture remained to be ascertained.

Others have been on the trail of other viruses held to be responsible for "the true common cold" or "cold-like infections." In the fall of 1953, Dr. Winston H. Price isolated the JH, or Johns Hopkins, common-cold virus from an outbreak of colds among Baltimore nurses. He was able to culture this virus in monkey-kidney tissue, and to make a killed-virus vaccine against it which, he reported, proved effective in tests made on one hundred boys in a training-school. The nationwide publicity following a Baltimore *Sun* scoop on his 1957 report of these preliminary results repeated the familiar refrain of good-by to colds. The *Sun* made it sound, probably quite unintentionally, as if Price were the only man who had done anything about the problem.

Among those overlooked were Drs. William J. Mogabgab and William Pelon of Tulane University School of Medicine. In the fall of 1954 they isolated a cold-like virus from recruits at the Great Lakes Naval Training Station. This virus—called "2060"—grows slowly but surely in various tissue cultures and also in hatching eggs, it appears. Mogabgab and Pelon at first were reluctant to call it a cold virus, though it produced typical head-cold symptoms.

Pelon also found that the 2060 and JH viruses were closely related and yet distinct. Occasionally, one virus would stimulate antibodies that would neutralize the other, but not all the time, as happens when the viruses are identical. Whether these viruses have continued to cause many colds has been seriously questioned. Cold viruses, like flu viruses, appear subject to continuous variation.

So we may be saying hello again not to the JH or 2060 but one of their cousins the next time we have a cold. The JH vaccine did not seem a good bet to the pharmaceutical companies, and never emerged from the experimental stage.

These days a discovery of a "new" virus must stand in line to get attention. As far as cold viruses are concerned, hopes for a preventive or cure have been dashed so many times that the general rule among virologists is that no report of another "common cold" virus shall merit serious consideration unless it first has been confirmed in somebody else's laboratory.

What virus or viruses cause the common cold?

Huebner sums up the situation thus: "Rather similar respiratory illnesses have multiple, and perhaps numerous, viral causes, and . . . the same or similar respiratory viruses can produce variable clinical manifestations."

Viruses vary and so do people. Indeed, some immunologists speculate that this is the whole explanation of what is or is not a true common cold—they refer to the argument about whether a cold ceases to be a cold when it becomes a fever. The answer—"but don't quote me," pleaded one of the country's topmost immunologists—may well be a difference in hosts rather than in parasites. In other words, the same virus, as well as different viruses, might give some persons only a running nose and others a running nose plus fever.

Whatever the case, the tissue-culture method of discovering and identifying new viruses provides a reasonable basis for renewed hope that the secret of the common cold fairly soon may be unveiled, despite all the previous disappointments. The Huebner-Hilleman work has been a fair example of the accelerated tempo of virus research following Enders's discovery. "In three years," remarks Huebner, "a new group of viruses was characterized and defined, much of its clinical importance determined, and a safe, effective commercial vaccine was made available. . . ."

In contrast, it was at least seventy-five years before smallpox vaccine, as discovered by Edward Jenner, could be regarded as reliable, in the scientific sense of safety and effectiveness. Walter Reed identified yellow fever as a virus disease in 1901, but it was 1940 before Max Theiler had a safe, effective vaccine worked out. Wilson Smith and his colleagues detected the first human, or WS, influenza virus in 1933, but it was ten years before Thomas Francis could solve the subtleties of effective vaccination against two types of flu. Karl Landsteiner isolated the polio virus in 1908, but forty years passed before John Enders and his young men found a practical way of cultivating the virus, and another seven before a safe, effective Salk polio vaccine could be offered to the public. But in three years two government laboratories solved an old wartime troop-strength problem and made at least a dent in our ignorance about the cause of the common cold.

As a means of further progress, Huebner visualizes two avenues that may be followed. One is a tailor-made vaccine against respiratory infections that may be found to beset any special group—for example, an orphanage, prep school, or summer camp. This is practicable now. The second possibility is a kind of family-size package, a vaccine with perhaps as many as twenty-five different viruses in it, all aimed to protect us against some segment of the common-cold complex. "It is time to think about it," he said. If so, we may be nearer to relief than we might think. If we could just get all these new viruses accounted for. . . .

IS THE END OF MEASLES
NOW IN SIGHT?

THE COMMONPLACE does not make much news, with the exception of the weather. Thus, the fact that 1958 set a record total for measles cases in the United States passed without alarm or general notice. Like the weather, common measles—exceeded only by the common cold and influenza as the most common of virus diseases—is always with us.

Some ninety to ninety-five per cent of us have this most usual of the "usual childhood diseases" and thenceforth are solidly immune to it in all but rare cases. For most adults, measles remains merely a dim recollection of a time when we were five or six and had to remain in bed with the window shades drawn. For parents, it is different. If measles did nothing else, it still could be regarded as ten days of misery for young mothers. It is the same for the children. But it is something more than that.

Every year, measles kills three or four hundred children and, in some degree, enfeebles the minds or permanently impairs the agility of a few thousand more. Measles is not as dramatic as polio about doing its damage; it may escape blame, but pediatricians know it does brain and other damage.

We had more than 750,000 reported cases of common measles

in 1958, compared with less than 500,000 in 1957, a more or less normal measles year. For several weeks during April and May 1958, measles rose to the proportions of a tremendous, sweeping epidemic—40,000 new cases a week. Only twice has polio topped that number in a year.

Dr. Carl C. Dauer of the National Office of Vital Statistics is of the opinion that only twenty to twenty-five per cent of measles cases are reported. Thus, in actuality, there may have been as many as 3,000,000 to 3,500,000 cases in the United States in 1958.

What happens with measles—caused by a single, stable, spherical type of virus variously estimated at from two to five millionths of an inch in diameter—is that every two or three years or so, a reservoir of susceptible children builds up. Measles epidemics empty the reservoir. Nearly all children who are exposed to measles get it.

Some ten or eleven days following exposure, generally by contact with a playmate who has or is about to have measles, the victim may have a sudden chill, or his nose may simply begin to run. He sneezes, he becomes feverish, he coughs hoarsely, and his eyes may become red and sensitive to light. The watering of the eyes, dripping of the nose, wheezing, sneezing, hacking, and all-round discomfort continue for the duration of the disease.

The first sign that distinguishes measles from other virus infections is the Koplik spots. These, appearing a day or two after the onset of other symptoms, are bluish-white specks surrounded by general redness which appear in the mouth. They are named for Dr. Henry Koplik, the New York pediatrician who described them sixty-odd years ago, though there isn't much doubt that other doctors had noted them before. Measles ranks with smallpox as one of the oldest known of virus diseases; in fact, the "Arabian Hippocrates," Rhazes (850–932), regarded it as a mild form of smallpox.

The Koplik spots climax a two-week period of virus invasion, multiplication, and circulation through the body. The spots appear two to three days ahead of a blotchy rash erupting on face and torso, often reminding one of a speckling with a brown stain. The rash is the third-act climax, for it usually portends the end of the fever.

In some few cases, complications follow. One may be caused by a bacterial infection secondary to the measles. Infections of the inner ear are common, and so is bronchopneumonia. This virus attack in the bronchial tubes is the principal killer, though a child may also die of a sort of toxic shock or from encephalitis (inflammation of the brain).

If measles encephalitis comes, it begins during the rash. It is a result of virus invasion of the brain. The rash fades, but fever continues; the child is drowsy and often rigid. There may be convulsions or coma, persisting for some weeks.

The incidence of measles encephalitis varies widely from one epidemic and one place to another. Medical authorities have reported it as occurring in anywhere from "less than one per cent" to "one in 10,000." Ten per cent of its victims can be expected to die, and sixty-five per cent will suffer permanent harm—a spastic paralysis, some loss of muscle co-ordination, behavior disorders, or a mental deterioration, in some instances so severe that the child must be put in an institution for the mentally retarded.

Measles presents no danger to the child less than six months old, because of a temporary immunity inherited from the mother, but beyond that point the maternal antibodies wear away, and up to the age of five he is in the peak danger age. Most of the deaths or other damage occur in pre-schoolers.

Measles used to be a much greater problem in the United States, and it still is a scourge in some other countries, particularly those less civilized. Among isolated, primitive peoples without a natural resistance to the disease such as we have, measles kills as savagely as smallpox, attacking old people as well as children.

Deaths and permanent disabilities from measles have decreased in the United States because of more intelligent care of children, antibiotics to control the secondary bacterial infections, and the use of gamma globulin to protect the exposed child. Home quarantine is worthless in preventing the spread of measles, for the child is infectious long before the rash raises a warning flag. On the other hand, doctors recommend keeping home for fifteen days a pre-schooler who has been directly exposed. This is to minimize complications.

The possibilities of prophylactic treatment of measles with an immune serum were recognized as early as 1918. Inasmuch as the blood of nearly all people contains measles antibodies, a transfusion to an exposed child may give him temporary aid in combating the virus infection incubating in his blood. But a whole-blood transfusion is a complicated procedure and not practical. It introduces other risks. The same effect can be accomplished by injection of an immune serum—that is, the blood of persons who have had measles, cleared of the red cells and the fibrin that causes clotting. Immune serum appeared to be useful, at least part of the time, but human serum presents some danger of toxic reactions owing to foreign proteins and, as we know from the story of the yellow-fever vaccine, a certain risk of serum hepatitis.

These dangers have been overcome in recent years by the use of gamma globulin, the purified fraction of the blood containing the antibodies and nothing else. There is good evidence now that gamma globulin, if administered after a susceptible child has been directly exposed to measles, will reduce the outcome to a mild infection with no complications in the majority of cases. It is excellent preventive medicine, especially for the most vulnerable children, those of pre-school age and those who are sick from other causes.

On the other hand, gamma globulin is expensive and not readily available to all children—many do not enjoy the constant attention of well-informed parents and expert pediatricians. Furthermore, it provides no permanent immunity. The protective effect wears off in a month or two.

What is needed, medical scientists have recognized for a long time, is a good vaccine that with one injection will provide an immunity as durable and certain as that resulting from measles itself. Such a vaccine would make it unnecessary to worry about whether measles was in the neighborhood, whether one's children had been exposed, or whether they would be susceptible to a future attack. Lives, normal brains, and able bodies would be preserved—a great many in the course of time.

A good vaccine, if universally available in 1958, could have saved our children millions of days of discomfort and time lost from school in that year alone. Inasmuch as the measles victims do not vote or pay bills, their convenience is often overlooked, but a

vaccine might be counted as worth the effort of perfecting it simply as a relief to mothers, who find that a sick child disrupts the
household and, of course, makes it more difficult to look after
his brothers and sisters.

That measles is caused by a filterable virus has been known
ever since 1911, when Dr. Joseph Goldberger, who also discovered the cause of pellagra, and an associate filtered blood from a
measles patient and produced the disease in monkeys with the
cell-free filtrate. The virus could not be persuaded to take hold
elsewhere than in man and monkey until twenty years ago, when it
appeared to physicians that a measles vaccine might be almost at
hand. In 1938 Dr. Harry Plotz, then at the Pasteur Institute in
Paris, impressively reported that he had cultivated measles virus
in tissue cultures of chick-embryo cells. The following year Drs.
Geoffrey W. Rake of the Squibb Institute for Medical Research,
New Brunswick, New Jersey, and Morris Shaffer, now professor
of biochemistry at Tulane University, grew the virus in hatching
eggs. They saw signs of attenuation, the watchword of the live-
vaccine makers.

There is now no remaining doubt that these pioneers were able
to reproduce the virus, transmit it to monkeys, and for a time
produce an immunity with an attenuated strain. But their work
was not reproducible. They lacked the techniques consistently to
detect signs of their virus while passing it from egg to monkeys
and back. At times Rake and Shaffer were able to produce a
mild sort of measles with an egg-passage virus, and do so in both
man and monkey, but after further passages of the virus they got
but slight infection or nothing at all. As Rake remarked, "There
is evidence that a too greatly modified disease will not result in
prolonged increased immunity, a result similar to that seen with
serum modification of the natural disease." [1]

Dr. John F. Enders and others tried their mettle on measles, but
produced nothing of significance prior to World War II. They
did notice one thing: monkeys were not ideal experimental animals. Sometimes the laboratory could give a monkey a definite

[1] Geoffrey Rake: "Measles," in *Viral and Rickettsial Infections of Man,*
Third Edition (New York and Philadelphia: J. B. Lippincott Company;
1959).

case of measles, but the next one might be wholly resistant to infection.

The high hopes for a vaccine gave way to a rash not of measles but of pessimism. It was the old story in virus research of trying to play the middle against both ends and failing. At one end is the virulent virus that produces disease in susceptible persons and immunity in the survivors; at the other end is an over-attenuated cousin of this virus which produces neither disease nor immunity. It is not so easy to arrive at the safe middle ground, an attenuated and stabilized virus that will not cause the disease but will produce immunity.

There measles matters stood until 1953.

It then struck Enders that the time was right for another attempt to master the measles virus. In 1948 he and Drs. Thomas H. Weller and Frederick C. Robbins had scored the great break-through of cultivating polio virus in test-tube cultures of various living human tissues. Now, through continuous and rapid culture of tissues, and through the detection of destruction of cells in the cultures by viruses, they and others were uncovering a host of new viruses, such as the adenoviruses. Why not measles?

If other viruses had these so-called cytopathogenic effects— that is, showed signs of producing sickness in the cells they invaded—then it followed that measles ought to, too. The problem would be to see the signs and read them correctly.

To Enders's laboratory at Children's Hospital in Boston came a tall, handsome young doctor named Peebles, fresh from his internship in Massachusetts General Hospital. He was then just thirty-two years old, and wanted to become a pediatrician and do research in infectious diseases of children. You might say that Thomas C. Peebles was getting a pretty late start in his career, inasmuch as he had not graduated from Harvard Medical School until 1951, but he had spent four years in the Navy, as a pilot, before going to medical school.

Many have observed that John Enders has a "green thumb" not only for virus culture but also for cultivation of young scientists such as Weller and Robbins. Peebles, now a pediatrician in Weston, near Boston, and chief of the tissue-culture laboratory at Massachusetts General Hospital, was one of the young men whose potentialities attracted Enders, or whose potentialities brought him to Enders, it is hard to say which. Dr. Charles A. Janeway sent Peebles to Enders. As part of his resident training at Children's, Peebles accepted a research fellowship in Enders's laboratory. When Enders asked him if he would like to work on measles, Peebles jumped at the chance.

The first need was for some virus to work with. Peebles searched the laboratory's deep-freeze storage cabinets for specimens from measles patients—hoping to find infected blood specimens or throat washings. But he found nothing. He then began following the Brookline and Newton Health Department reports of communicable diseases, hoping to run into a measles outbreak. The low season of the year for measles was fast approaching and he noted nothing of interest. He was able to isolate a virus from two children in one family—both had a rash. With the help of Weller and Dr. Gilbert Dalldorf, then of Albany, he established that this was one of the new Coxsackie viruses. It was simply a red herring.

Peebles looked for six months before he got what he wanted. In January 1954 he received a call from Dr. Theodore H. Ingalls, now of the University of Pennsylvania, then a Harvard epidemiologist and authority on German measles. Ingalls was school physician of the Fay School, a private boarding-school for boys in Southboro, a western suburb of Boston. He said that the school was having a measles epidemic—common measles.

Peebles went to the Fay School and sought some boys with Koplik spots, a rash, a fever, and watery eyes. He wanted blood specimens, throat washings, and a stool specimen.

To get them took a certain amount of salesmanship, for his research would be of no benefit to the boys. They would be miserable with their measles and then get well, in all probability. But the principal, Mr. Harrison Reinke, assured Peebles of his co-operation and so did the boys, once they knew the purpose.

"Now, young man," said the doctor to each one, "you are standing on the frontiers of science. We are trying to grow this virus for the first time. If we do, your name will go into the scientific report of our discovery. Now, this will hurt a little. Are you game?"

As a matter of fact, their initials did go into Peebles's report. The first one to give blood was "R.M."—"Rocky"—four years old. Rocky was not a student, but the son of one of the masters. The second was an eleven-year-old student, D.R.—David. Dr. Ingalls made the diagnosis on the morning of January 25, and Peebles was there by one p.m. for samples from these two cases.

Without delay, he took the specimens back to Enders's laboratory and injected them into roller-tube tissue cultures of infant human kidney—from surgical operations—and a variety of other human and monkey tissues.

It would take three or four days for anything to happen in the tissue cultures. On January 29 Peebles got another call from Dr. Ingalls and went back to the school to obtain similar specimens from a thirteen-year-old, H.J.—Harry. Harry looked about the same as the others—a case of measles.

On February 1 Peebles was changing the fluid in the R.M. throat-washing cultures. Eying the cells under the microscope, the doctor noticed something. Some of the cells were large and swollen—maybe from measles infection. There didn't seem to be much question that he had a virus here, and he put it down in his notebook as "measles (?) virus." He called Enders's attention to his find, and from the vantage point of years of experience the senior scientist remarked: "This looks a little like herpes, but it may be measles virus."

Rocky's contribution to science proved to be a second red herring in Peebles's quest. It took another month to clear up the confusion, but eventually from his R.M. specimens he was able to culture, in a clear-cut manner, not the measles virus but that of the much-studied herpes-simplex, the cause of cold sores and fever blisters. Apparently Rocky had a combination of measles and herpes, with one virus tending to mask the other.

Peebles had not been able to detect anything as exciting in his D.R. and H.J. tubes as yet, so he was glad to go out to the school again on February 10 when he got word that another case of measles had turned up in one of their pals. This was in D.E.— David Edmonston. thirteen. It had begun with a stomach upset two days before. When Peebles arrived at noon of the third day, this lad from Bethesda, Maryland, was in full bloom with a typical rash on his face and chest, Koplik spots, a fever of 102 degrees, a mild cough, and watering of the eyes. Peebles took a sample of this David's blood, throat washings, and stool, and went back to the laboratory, where he put them in tubes of human-kidney cells. In this case, as before, he moved his specimen all the way from boy to test tube in from two to three hours, and all within twenty-four hours of the appearance of the measles rash that indicated the virus was multiplying and on the move.

From time to time Peebles or Enders looked at the by now large variety of culture tubes representing four patients and until February 15 saw nothing except swollen cells in the R.M. tubes. On that day, however, Peebles began to see things in his microscopic examination of the D.E., or Edmonston, blood cultures in human-kidney cells.

What he saw were so-called "giant cells." Here and there in the sheet-like outgrowth of kidney cells along the test-tube wall were spots where the normal cells seemed to have run together, as if their walls had been eaten away. The conglomerate cell mass—technically known as a syncytium—often contained not one nucleus, as a normal cell does, but many nuclei apparently collected from the broken-down cells. But some others contained no nucleus. They contained areas that looked like glassy spots, or empty spaces; often many of these were packed together, producing a lacy or foam-like pattern.

Peebles didn't know what he had. There was nothing so strange about giant cells in themselves. They are well known to pathologists, who sometimes see them in the lesions of tuberculosis and also in tissue specimens from patients with other infectious diseases. There is, for example, a giant-cell pneumonia—now known to be a virus infection of the lungs caused by something indistinguishable from measles, but this was not known at the time. Peebles was sure he was looking at a "cytopathogenic effect," but he was not sure it was caused by the virus. He thought he might be witnessing the destruction of red blood cells, which have some resemblance to cell nuclei.

He showed his microscopic slides both to Enders and to Thomas Weller. In one way or another, each told him: "Well, you don't have anything there."

One way to see was to repeat the experiment. So, from the tube in which he first saw the giant cells, Peebles two days later passed some of his Edmonston blood culture to a fresh tube. The next day he noticed the same giant-cell effect that he had seen before.

A week later, on February 26, he made a second passage of this same culture line and observed the same effect when he examined the tube on March 1. He was now increasingly sure he was looking at cell nuclei in the giant cells and not red blood cells.

"I knew I had something," said Peebles, recalling how excited he was. "This was like a second honeymoon for me. Your heart sings. It is a foolhardy feeling. You need a man like Enders to prick the bubble."

From time to time Enders, in his easygoing, noncommittal way, would make a microscopic examination and say: "Thomas, I don't see this. Where is it?" Peebles confesses that Enders's role of skeptic annoyed him and made him feel rather consciously possessive about *his* discovery. Enders himself recalls: "I was loath to accept this."

A month or so later, when going to Washington to report on the discovery to the Armed Forces Epidemiological Board and the Army, which was supporting this measles research, Enders asked: "Now, Thomas, are you sure about all this?"

"Yes, sir," replied Peebles emphatically.

The intellectual baiting that Peebles underwent may try one's temper, but, for those who can give and take, it is a wonderful way to build such strong proof of a discovery that no one can assail it. That is precisely what Peebles did, under Enders's control. They stained tissue cultures of the Edmonston strain with a dye so the cultures could be clearly photographed under the microscope and shown to all doubters. Within the giant cells the many nuclei could be seen—and within the nuclei were inclusion bodies. These, as we know from the Goodpasture story, are conglomerations of viruses, thousands bound together in a package.

Everything seemed to be adding up to the conclusion that Peebles and Enders had the means of reproducing, and detecting the reproduction of, measles virus. These giant cells containing inclusion bodies were convincing. Such cells are sometimes seen in appendixes and tonsils removed from children by surgeons. So, upon examining tissue from a child's appendix, before there was

any outward sign of measles in the child, a pathologist might remark: "This fellow is going to get the measles." And, sure enough,
he would.

Enders and Peebles could not absolutely prove that the inclusion body was a package of measles-virus particles, but what else
could it be? Their first report, authored jointly by Enders and
Peebles and submitted to "Proc Soc" on May 16, 1954, called it an
"agent from patients with measles." But nobody could find fault
with their accuracy. By the end of 1954, Koch's Postulates for
proving that the agent under study is the cause of the disease
being studied were substantially fulfilled.

The laboratory was able to isolate and cultivate the measles
virus from the blood and the throat washings of three of the four
measles patients whom Ingalls referred to Peebles. Soon other
virus isolations from other measles patients were added.

But the Edmonston strain, the first to show the giant-cell effect,
remained the focus of interest. It had come from the blood of a
measles patient, it had multiplied in a tissue culture of infant human kidney, it had continued to perform when moved from one
culture to another. Peebles left little doubt that it really was a
measles virus when he and his co-workers took immune serum
from twelve measles convalescents and showed that it neutralized
the virus in the tissue cultures.

Now all that remained as a clincher was to move the virus from
tissue cultures back into humans or into monkeys and there produce an infection that behaved like measles. Enders decided to
try monkeys, though the results had been inconsistent in the
past.

Enders put Peebles and Kevin McCarthy, an Englishman then
in training in the laboratory, to work on the monkey experiments,
and soon discovered a surprising thing. Nearly all the animals sent
them by monkey collectors were immune to measles infection
and, when tested, were shown to have measles antibodies, just as
most people do.

Studying the matter, they concluded that either there was a
"monkey measles," as closely related to human measles as cowpox is to smallpox, or the monkeys coming to them had been infected with human measles at some point between the jungles

and the laboratory. "The latter explanation appears to be probably correct," said Enders. The Rhesus monkeys, from India, are customarily captured around villages; in fact, they often run wild in the streets, where they could easily pick up measles virus. The cynomolgus monkeys, flown in from the Philippine Islands and Malaya, usually are kept in animal houses or monkey farms for several weeks before being sold to laboratories. They, too, might have a chance to pick up measles virus.

Enders arranged to have twelve monkeys tested within a day after their capture on the island of Cebu. The tests bore out his hunch: not an antibody among the lot of them. They were all susceptible. He knew what to do: request the shippers to air-express monkeys to him as soon as they landed in the United States, so they would have no chance to settle down to an unnoticed case of measles and build up antibodies.

Now, with these jungle-fresh monkeys, Peebles and McCarthy were able to produce monkey measles with the human virus. Monkeys do not have Koplik spots, but they do, about half the time, have a visible rash, and the virus can be isolated from their blood. The circle of evidence was quite complete. John Enders, whose ingrained reaction to a will to believe is to disbelieve, now believed his laboratory could grow measles virus.

But infant human kidneys are a scarce item in any tissue-culture laboratory, and hence not a suitable medium for mass-production of virus for a vaccine. Besides, one could not expect to bring about an attenuation of a human virus while continuing to maintain it in human tissue. He believed, from past experience, that attenuating rather than killing the virus would be the only possible way of preserving its antibody-stimulating power.

Monkey kidneys, the source of the virus in the Salk polio vaccine, were an obvious alternative as a culture medium—but not for the fastidious. Others had found a strange "foamy" virus in cultures of monkey kidney cells—it produced a foamy appearance in the dying cells. It was a wild virus and hardly desirable in a vaccine. In the Salk vaccine its possible presence does not matter, because all virus in the vaccine is killed by formaldehyde.

Peebles—all he could see when he went to sleep were tissue cultures and stained cells, he said—now left the Enders cast of measles men. Dr. Anna Mitus, a young Polish physician, took his place. Various members of the laboratory staff tried to establish the Edmonston virus in the embryos of hatching eggs. This seemed to be an excellent place to grow and attenuate a measles virus, as the work of Rake and Shaffer indicated. None had any luck, however.

Human-amnion tissue, from the innermost membrane of the sac forming the "bag of waters" around the fetus, was coming into tissue-culture use at this time in 1955. It was in abundant supply in any hospital maternity department, and some viruses grow rapidly in human amnion. Enders suggested that Anna Mitus try it. She obtained some from the nearby Boston Lying-In Hospital.

At first she had no success with this medium either. But after the Edmonston virus had been subcultured through twenty-four tubes of human-kidney cells, one after another, she tried the virus in amnion tissue again. This time it "took," though Dr. Mitus had to be patient and watch her cultures for several weeks before she could see cytopathogenic effects. Then they appeared—the giant cells and inclusion of bodies. And here was something new: among the giant cells were "spindle cells," cells that had been stretched out into the form of a double-ended spike with a knob in the middle. This is another phenomenon in the viral destruction of living cells.

In the course of twenty-eight passages of the Edmonston virus through human-amnion cultures, she cut the cultivation time from two or three weeks to four or five days. Now Enders had an idea. Ernest Goodpasture had shown the importance of introducing the virus into an organ of the chick embryo which is compatible with the virus's habits of invasion and multiplication. If this Edmonston strain was now adapted to human amnion, would it now perhaps have a liking for chick amnion? The chick also gestates in a bag of water.

Enders put Dr. Milan Milovanovic, a Yugoslavian physician, on this experiment in August 1956. It worked. The virus grew in the chick amnion without killing the embryo or producing a rash, either one. In a nine-day period, a single infective dose of the virus multiplied 100,000 times. The multiplication could be measured by diluting the chick-embryo fluid and determining the smallest amount of virus which would infect a human-kidney culture.

This was real progress, but, it took three years for John Enders to get the Edmonston virus where he wanted it.

Attenuation was achieved not too long after young Dr. Samuel L. Katz joined the team as a research fellow at the beginning of 1957. Now chief of the pediatric service at Beth Israel Hospital, Katz was still twenty-nine when Enders put him to work with Milovanovic, who would soon be going back to Yugoslavia.

Enders was not completely satisfied with having introduced the virus into eggs once more, even after Milovanovic and he passed it six times and showed that it multiplied each time. They found it impossible to detect signs of the virus's effects on the chick-embryo cells, as Peebles had done in human-kidney tissues. Presence of the virus could be determined only by infecting something outside of the egg.

Enders remarked that if the Edmonston virus would grow in chick embryos, it should now multiply in tissue cultures of chick-embryo cells. That was the medium Plotz had used in 1938. Milovanovic and Katz in January 1957 began working side by side, the Yugoslavian seeding and harvesting the virus in eggs and the American passing the virus into test tubes containing chick cells.

The first four times Katz passed the virus, he saw no change in the infected cells. The virus seemed to be there, but did no noticeable damage, as far as he could see. Then, during the fifth passage in chick cells, he began to notice the spindle cells and small giant cells, never large ones. The virus surely had taken hold now, and Katz could detect it every time.

It was time for Enders to pose the big question: did this virus have the characteristics of the one originally found in the blood of David Edmonston, or had it changed?

Thus far there had been no opportunity to find out. But, in the past, attenuation of viruses suitable for vaccines had occurred as the result of one of two processes: removal of the virus from its normal host and cultivation in an animal strange to it; passage of the virus through a long series of a single type of experimental host or culture. These things had been done.

Now Enders and Katz—Milovanovic had gone—found that in the mere process of trying to bring the production of measles virus under complete laboratory control, they had arrived on the threshold of what promised to be a major discovery.

On May 13, 1957, Katz and Enders made new monkey tests to see what kind of virus they had after all this time—after twenty-eight passages in human-amnion cells plus six passages in chick-amnion cells plus fourteen passages in chick-cell tissue cultures. If this seems like a tremendous lot, think how many passages the measles virus has made since the beginning of its time on earth! As far as human beings are concerned, it has made all these passages without change.

Enders and Katz chose ten monkeys from Malaya, all fresh as the morning dew. These monkeys might be making history, so for the occasion the skillful, loyal laboratory technicians—Yinette Chang and Ann Holloway among them—pitched in and gave them all a clean shave—face, chest, armpits, abdomen, groin, and thighs, just as if these monkeys were going to have major surgery. They looked a little naked in the end, but a bare skin would be of great help when it was time to look for a rash.

Next the monkeys had a blood test. There wasn't a measles antibody among them. All were susceptible. Now eight received some of the Edmonston, chick-cell, fourteenth-passage virus, variously injected into their blood or under their skin and sprayed up their noses. To do all this to monkeys takes a great deal of skill, agility, and patience. Two of the monkeys were put aside for controls, receiving no virus.

It is understandable that a monkey would keep a wary eye on humans, but for the next eighteen days, man looked at monkey with peculiar intensity. Katz tested their blood every other day, putting it into human-kidney, human-amnion, and chick-cell cultures. He was watching for viremia, or virus infection of the blood. He made white-blood-cell counts on each blood specimen; a reduced white count is one of the signs of monkey measles. He took his monkeys' temperatures, carefully scrutinized them for a rash, and peeked into their throats. He made tests for the presence of measles antibodies.

Katz and Ann Holloway tested the blood of their monkeys, infected with the fourteenth-passage virus, against the virulent Edmonston strain after allowing time for antibodies to form. They were pleased to note that this blood, acting as an immune serum, neutralized the virulent virus.

But the appearance of antibodies in animals previously without them meant nothing by itself. The same thing happens with an ordinary case of measles. Did their monkeys have measles while building measles antibodies? That was the critical question.

Katz, made aware that in these great moments of discovery scientists are supposed to cry "Eureka" (I have found it) or say or do something equally dramatic, related: "We had a mild eureka when we were unable to find any rash on our monkeys. We had a second eureka when our cultures showed no virus in the monkey's blood.

"But the biggest eureka was when we found our monkeys had antibodies and these neutralized the Edmonston virus of the human kidney line. You first know they have no disease. Then later you find no virus in the blood. You have growing doubts that the virus gave your monkeys any infection whatsoever. But then you get antibodies where you had none, and your hopes rise."

The day Enders, Katz, and Holloway knew they had attenuated the Edmonston virus was June 17, 1957, when they read the results of complement-fixation tests set up the previous day.

Complement fixation is a rather intricate test for the presence of antibodies. They mixed vaccinated monkey blood with virulent measles virus and then added complement, in this instance a substance from guinea-pig blood. Complement has the peculiar capacity of combining with red blood cells in the presence of virus *and* neutralizing antibodies, but remains unchanged if virus or their antibodies are absent. The results are observed on the second day, when sheep blood cells and sheep cell antibodies are mixed with the test solution. If, for lack of antibodies in the test material, free complement remains, the sheep cells dissolve. If not, the sheep cells remain normal.

John Enders put on an old felt hat for good luck. This is an Enders joke, arising from the fact that he collects hats. For those momentous occasions which have come with marvelous frequency in his laboratory in the last ten years, he puts on the nearest hat at hand. He crossed the hall from his office, and the three of them, plus some others in the laboratory, gathered around to read "comp fixes." What this amounts to is looking at little puddles of bloody juice on a plastic grid, each puddle centered in a square. What they were looking for were intact red cells. They saw them in every square for eight monkeys—measles antibodies were there. The red cells had burst in the case of the two controls—no antibodies there.

It appeared that they had eight monkeys now immune to measles. Was this true? They found out by giving each a challenge dose of the virulent Edmonston virus, in their blood and up their noses. The monkeys didn't turn a hair, shaved or otherwise. But the virulent virus did, surprisingly enough, show up in their throats. This showed that it was in the body, and yet not strong enough to overpower the antibodies and produce a viremia or a rash.

What would you do next?

They repeated the entire experiment with twelve more monkeys, ten receiving the fourteenth-passage virus injected only under their skins. The virus hunters of Harvard got the same results as before in all but two—the unvaccinated controls. These two received no attenuated virus, and when exposed to the virulent one, they developed measles.

John Enders was pretty well satisfied that his laboratory had attenuated the measles virus. "When, precisely, attenuation occurred has not been determined," he said, "but it would seem probable that it took place during the course of passage of the virus in human amnion or chick cells."

Enders is the soul of caution, as his statement shows. Whether the change happened in one of the twenty-eight passages through human-amnion cells, one of the six passages through chick-amnion cells, or one of the fourteen passages in chick-embryo cultures cannot be determined without digging each and every one of these cultures out of the deep-freeze "file" and trying them on monkeys. Enders had neither time nor monkeys for that. It could have been that the short period the Edmonston virus spent in eggs did the trick; this was where Rake and Shaffer achieved their attenuation and finally over-attenuation of a measles virus.

In February 1958 John Enders put on his old felt hat and took the train to New York to make a report at a meeting of virologists. When he had finished, Dr. Joseph Smadel from the National Institutes of Health, the chairman at the time, turned to him and said: "John, you've done it again!"

But had he?

As Enders pointed out, the attenuated virus had not been tried in humans at all. It did appear to provide durable antibodies, as far as the observations then had extended—seven months. But would this attenuated virus cause measles in humans—or encephalitis following measles? Enders had put it in the brain of one susceptible monkey. He also put a virulent measles virus in a monkey's brain. Neither one hurt the victim's nervous system at all. On the other hand, no one ever has seen a case of measles encephalitis in monkeys anyway. The ultimate trial would have to come in humans.

Such experiments would have to be undertaken cautiously, in small numbers, with investigators at other universities making their own laboratory tests and field studies. This was the way Enders visualized it. Perhaps some country that has a major measles problem might wish to make a large-scale field test of the Edmonston virus.

One thing seems certain. Such a measles vaccine, containing a weaker virus than is found in nature, would not be likely to increase the slight risk of having encephalitis which all children face when they have measles. In fact, one would assume that a weaker virus would produce a good deal less risk, if any at all.

One other thing also seems certain. Enders has quizzed public-health officers on the subject, and many would welcome a vaccine preventing measles, measles pneumonia, and measles encephalitis provided, as he himself stipulated, that it gave lasting immunity with one shot.

Surely American mothers would welcome it. And such a vaccine would be a godsend to isolated islands and primitive countries where an epidemic of common measles (common elsewhere) has been observed to wreck the lives of expectant mothers, producing heart attacks, miscarriages, premature births, and stillbirths.

The Enders-Peebles-Mitus-Milovanovic-Katz measles vaccine is now undergoing a series of small field tests, having looked "fairly promising," as Enders put it, in its first human trials. In the fall of 1958 eleven institutionalized children in Massachusetts received the vaccine with the consent of their parents. Tests before vaccination showed that they were susceptible to measles—without antibodies. Tests from two weeks to six months later showed that they had measles antibodies.

Outwardly, the effect of the vaccine was a "modified measles." Eight of the children had a mild fever for from two to five days, and eight also had some rash, of a minor sort. As Katz and Enders reported to the American Society of Pediatric Research last May, "The most striking clinical phenomenon was the absence of any disability during the time of fever or rash. In every instance, the children went about their usual routine with normal activity and appetite."

In a collaborative field trial Dr. C. Henry Kempe, of Denver, Colorado, repeated the vaccination experiment on thirty normal children and obtained results closely paralleling those in Massachusetts.

There was some question of whether a virus that still produced some fever and rash would be publicly acceptable. One viewpoint was that, since these symptoms did not make the children sick, as ordinary measles certainly does, the symptoms were a convenient indicator of a positive take. Without some such manifest reaction, it would be difficult to tell whether a child had been immunized without engaging in the lengthy procedure of testing his blood for antibodies.

As a precautionary measure, Enders and Katz began a new series of experiments designed to promote further attenuation of the Edmonston strain. Meanwhile, further small field trials were being conducted in other communities. "The final test," remarked Enders, "is exposure to measles." In other words, will the vaccine measles protect against real measles?

Continued field tests should give the answer, for the plan was to vaccinate more children and then, in due course, expose them to children sick with measles. The natural disease is so contagious that susceptible children almost invariably catch measles when exposed to infected playmates. This infectiousness contrasts with the attenuated virus, which thus far has shown no tendency to spread from vaccinated children to others.

Other scientists' early reactions to news of the measles vaccine have been remarkable. Compared to polio and other safe, effective vaccines, this new one is quite unproved, but doctors who discuss it display an inclination to assume that because it came from John Enders's laboratory, it surely will work. Such confidence is a rather paradoxical feedback of his own scientific insistence, not on believing, but on doubting. His fellow scientists trust John Enders not to go overboard on anything.

German measles is quite a different story.

This virus complaint, also known as rubella, was recognized as a disease separate from common measles and scarlet fever in 1829. A German doctor made the distinction, hence the disease's name. Doctors continued to confuse it with measles, however, until Dr. Henry Koplik in 1896 pointed out that common measles produces spots in the mouth. German measles produces a rash but no Koplik spots. It is a mild disease, causing a slight head cold and low fever; it lasts two or three days, in contrast to the usual week or ten days for common measles.

We do not have good statistics on reported cases of German measles, as we do on common measles. About three quarters of the states require doctors to report German measles, but even in these a good many cases are either missed or reported as common measles, authorities believe. There were two hundred thousand reported cases of German measles in the United States in 1956— the latest year for which figures are available—but Dr. Carl C. Dauer of the National Office of Vital Statistics points out that this must be an underestimate. Like measles, the German-measles total fluctuates from year to year, and each year incidence will be high in some regions and low in others.

German measles is a slow spreader, unlike the highly infectious common measles. The peak incidence is in the five-to-ten age group. Apparently because of a lack of universal exposure, however, many people remain susceptible into their teens or twenties and have the disease then. This, in fact, is German measles's only arresting quality—it strikes young women in their child-bearing period.

German measles was regarded as a mere nuisance until Dr. N. McAlister Gregg, an eye specialist in Sydney, Australia, made an astonishing report in 1941. In *Transactions of the Ophthalmological Society of Australia*, Gregg wrote that German measles appeared to be responsible for an unusually large number of eye cataracts (opacity of the crystalline lens) that he and others were seeing in babies, and also for other congenital defects including other eye ailments, deafness, and heart disease.

Gregg, after noting three cases in his own practice, had written to other doctors in Australia. Among their replies he was able to count seventy-eight cases of cataract in babies, forty-four of whom had heart defects. Digging into the pre-natal background of these babies, he found that most of their mothers had had German measles early in pregnancy.

Indeed, the frequency of congenital defects followed closely on widespread epidemics of German measles in Australia in 1939 and 1940, now suspected to have been brought about by a general mingling of young men from isolated and more populated parts of this huge country as they went into military service; they, in turn, infected their susceptible wives, we may surmise. There had not been a German-measles epidemic for many years previously in Australia.

Subsequent studies in the United States and elsewhere bore out Gregg's observations and showed that the obscure virus causing this disease has an affinity for the human embryo and is quite literally teratogenic, or monster-producing, in the damage it causes.

Eventually, medical science learned that there are few freaks of gestation which may not result on occasion from a mother's infection with German measles during the first four months of pregnancy. Mongoloid features, feeble-mindedness, blindness, crosseye, cockeye, squint, unusual smallness of the head, water on the brain (hydrocephalus), and other abnormalities may be caused by this virus as well as by other conditions, such as oxygen want due to surgical anesthetics, too much X ray during pregnancy, and accident injuries. The nature of the deformity depends on the time of insult to the developing embryo. Thus has come scientific underpinning for the old wives' superstitions about "marking a baby." They were right in theory, but for entirely the wrong reasons.

When these terrible products of German measles became generally recognized, obstetricians often recommended a therapeutic abortion to terminate the pregnancy as a means of sparing the mother and her family a tragedy of birth. They could point to reports showing that German measles during the first four months of pregnancy ended in a catastrophe—miscarriage, stillbirth, or deformed baby—in 50 to 100 per cent of all cases studied.

In actual fact, as Dr. Theodore H. Ingalls points out, careful study has shown that the chance of such a disaster is 15 to 20 per cent. With an 80- to 85-per-cent chance of a normal baby despite German-measles infection of the mother, therapeutic abortion hardly seems justified, infectious disease experts now hold.

The discrepancy between figures and between the consequent courses of action demonstrates the importance of understanding scientific method. As Dr. Morris Greenberg and his New York City Department of Health associates have pointed out,[2] the high expectation of disaster resulted from retrospective studies that started with a malformed infant and then worked backwards to what the mother and the doctor said had happened at an earlier date. It had been found that most mothers of malformed infants had had the disease early in pregnancy, or so they and their doctors believed. No account was taken of German measles in the histories of mothers delivering normal children.

Remarking that "a little thought will show the inaccuracy of the cited percentages," Greenberg, like Ingalls, insisted that the only way to determine the outcome was prospectively—that is, to start with the diagnosis of German measles during pregnancy and then follow up to determine the outcome. A composite study of cases reported by this method showed about a 7-per-cent chance of the baby being stillborn and about a 12-per-cent chance of its having

[2] Morris Greenberg, Ottavio Pelliterri, and Jerome Barton: "Frequency of Defects in Infants Whose Mothers Had Rubella During Pregnancy," *Journal of the American Medical Association,* October 12, 1957.

a congenital deformity when German measles occurred in the first three months of pregnancy. There was still some risk, though a smaller one, in the second three months, but very little in the third trimester.

Ingalls, a professor of epidemiology who in 1958 moved from Harvard's School of Public Health to the University of Pennsylvania, is the leading student of German measles in the United States. In 1935, before its insidious effects were known, Mrs. Ingalls, a social worker, was placing a seven-year-old orphan girl for adoption. She and the child took a taxi. The little girl had German measles, and Mrs. Ingalls was four months pregnant. Her baby, their first, was stillborn in the sixth month. Subsequently the Ingalls had three normal children.

For a means of preventing these misfortunes, Ingalls reaches back to the days before Edward Jenner discovered smallpox vaccine. Then it was fashionable to have "smallpox parties." Under supposedly expert supervision, people—mainly children—would band together and "have the pox," presumably a small dose or a mild variety that would not kill or scar them but would leave them immune when the ordeal was over.

German measles is ordinarily such an innocent disease—its death rate is somewhere between one and three per 100,000 cases —that Ingalls advocates that mothers intentionally expose their little girls to other children who have the disease. He first suggested this approach in 1946, but as yet there is no organized effort to stage German-measles parties. The illness just does not have appeal as a party favor.

In the laboratory, the story of German measles is even more disappointing than that of virus hepatitis. Many efforts have been made, by John Enders as well as others, to culture the virus in all manner of tissue cultures including human embryo, where it should grow. All results have been negative to the date of this writing. Possibly due to its low infectivity, the virus is difficult to isolate from a patient in any certain manner, and, as yet, no one has observed any signs of its multiplication in test tubes of living cells.

Once the virus can be cultivated and produced in abundant

supply, it is doubtful that the medical profession will wait for any attempt to attenuate it or kill it for vaccine purposes. Because of its low virulence and the small risk involved, virologists and epidemiologists say the cultures of the virus probably would be used to produce the infection and thence immunity in all girls and young women, prior to marriage.

PART FIVE:
CANCER, GENES, AND THE HEART OF THE VIRUS MATTER

DO VIRUSES CAUSE
CANCER?

John Enders called the experimental impulse that resulted in the polio break-through "fishing in troubled waters." By contrast, the cancer-research people regularly fish in seas lashed by the ill wind of high mortality, constantly stirred by the rising and falling tides of fierce hope and bitter disappointment, forever breaking over dark rocks of conflicting opinion. The catch has been small and jealously counted.

A break-through in cancer may be right at hand, yet all rational cancer investigators are aware that the long history of their quest for the answer to cancer, while filled with mighty dogma and heroic deeds, has not saved 250,000 Americans from dying of cancer each year.

Scores of "cures," some helpful, some fraudulent, most of them worthless, have been publicly proclaimed in our time as well as periodically during the last two thousand years. Their net result can be measured against the yardstick of death. As our population has become larger and older, deaths from many infectious diseases have been greatly reduced, but cancer deaths have risen —up 50,000 a year in the last decade.

Cancer researchers, now well supported and working more intensively than ever, are not born pessimists. But they become so. What troubles them is that their own contributions may be cast aside as of no final importance, or may give rise to another false hope. In one direction, the scientist risks oblivion; in the other, quackery.

One thing that sensational headlines do not tell us, but the experienced know full well, is that any bold, unqualified announcement of a "new cure" for cancer is a good sign that the source may be a charlatan, a crank, or a fool. It hardly matters which—the statistics are all against the claim proving true. Somewhat the same thing applies to assertions about the exact cause or causes of cancer, but in a lesser degree.

Thus, the basic scientist in this field is all too prone to stick with his mice, make timid reports, and avoid criticism. As we shall presently recognize in greater detail, the man or woman who one day truly finds a cause or a cure of cancer—a medical or chemical approach beyond what is presently known or is possible through surgery or radiation therapy—will find himself hard pressed for unassailable proof.

The cancer people know this, or find it out and are sadder and wiser for the experience. Some at first have been unable to restrain their natural enthusiasm over a new find, but then have been seen to recoil and retreat into their laboratories when they found some colleagues catching fire about their work. They could hear other colleagues speaking harshly of their "unwarranted" and "premature" optimism.

So, when the real answer comes, it may at first be heard only as a reluctant whisper about "a finding of possible interest," or may pass almost unnoticed as the addition of an obscure but essential bit of evidence proving something we thought we already knew. In fact, the observation may already have been made and may be only awaiting re-discovery before it falls into place in the visible body of useful knowledge.

Work in the field of cancer research affects the lives of those who try to solve the cancer problem, and almost certainly affects the kinds of solutions they seek. Dr. Wendell M. Stanley, who himself has done no cancer research, appeared to sense this

when he spoke at a joint conference of the National Cancer Institute and American Cancer Society in Detroit in 1956. Reviewing fifty years of observations of virus tumors in animals, Stanley
said:

> Evidence for the virus etiology of cancer has come
> from so many different laboratories and has been of such
> good quality and quantity that I find it very difficult to
> understand why so many investigators have continued to
> have such a firm blind spot with respect to the virus cau-
> sation of cancer. . . . I continue to be amazed at the
> willingness of so many investigators to accept viruses as
> etiological agents for animal cancers and their unwilling-
> ness to consider them . . . in cancers of man. . . .
>
> The experimental evidence now available is consistent
> with the idea that viruses are the etiological agents of
> most, if not all, cancer, including cancer in man. Ac-
> ceptance of this idea as a working hypothesis is urged
> because it will result in the doing of experiments that
> might otherwise be left undone. . . .

Stanley, an old hand at fanning the flames of scientific controversy and hence stimulating progress, has spoken in this vein
repeatedly over the past six years. He has been widely quoted,
and a change of attitude definitely has been taking place. So
Stanley either started an important trend or at least verbally pin-
pointed it. But the reaction of some insiders was characteristic.
"What right has Stanley to talk?" said some, plainly offended. "He
has done no work in this field." This statement was true, but it
missed Stanley's point.

The point is, as he put it elsewhere, "What we do depends in
large measure on what we think." If the most influential cancer
authorities are not curious about why many cancer viruses can
be readily found in animals but not in man, they will not do, or
spur others to do, research that in time may explain the reason.

In cancer research, one sees more clearly than in other scientific pursuits that skepticism is to the scientist what faith is to the
religious person, the source of his strength to believe that he will
know the truth. We speak of honest, competent scientists.

Strangely, in this field, where so much is at stake and the odds are so long, one hears the words "dishonest" and "incompetent" tossed about often enough to make us appreciate the injunction of Dr. Thomas M. Rivers: "Young man, if you are going to write about virus hunters, you are going to have to learn that there are as many crooks, liars and thieves among us as any other class of human beings." This is really a statistical question—we cannot particularize it—but it could be that Dr. Rivers is out of touch with other classes of humans.

His point, as far as it relates to cancer research, on the other hand, possibly refers only to the rash, intemperate estimates that scientists who are basically competitors may make of one another during the trying process of determining whether cigarette smoke, air pollution, radioactive dust, tars and oils, sex hormones, defective genes, rogue enzymes, or perhaps the perfect parasites —viruses—figure most importantly in the cause or causes of cancer. These scientists are human. Dr. Rivers made his point.

'Such is the approximate state of human affairs in cancer research today. Unless one understands this at the outset—that cancer sometimes may toxify the outlook of the man who would cure it as well as of the man who will die of it—then one cannot fully appreciate what the tiny band of tumor-virus workers have been through in the last fifty years—or how far they have come. Until recent years they have been treated as an oddity, a kind of two-headed scientific calf, born of pathology and bacteriology but claimed by neither.

Dark, quick-witted, fast-talking Dr. Joseph W. Beard of Duke University, a Georgia-born surgeon and authority on chicken leukemia, is one of their most aggressive spokesmen. Beard appears to believe that Stanley went too far in his "most, if not all" hypothesis of viruses as a cause of human cancer, and himself seems to prefer "some, but not all." "This field," he remarked, "has been cursed by too many hypotheses—a lot of complicated hot air." Yet he quite agrees in his summing up of the plight of his people, the tumor-virus workers:

"Until two years ago, we were as welcome as a bachelor at a family reunion. The virologists were not interested in tumors, and the animal cancer workers were not interested in viruses."

The proponents of the virus theory of cancer, unable as yet to prove a virus link to human cancer, have developed a sort of inferiority complex, judging from some indications. For example, the New York Academy of Sciences in 1956 held a "Conference on Subcellular Particles in the Neoplastic Process." The disguise fooled no one; the meeting was about viruses in tumors, some of them cancerous, but the purity of the terminology avoided any question of whether the particles really were viruses or something else, and whether the neoplasm, or new growth, was a cancerous one.

Today some people claim to have seen viruses in human cancers. There is research into the possibility of developing vaccines or immune serums to prevent cancers. Indeed, press releases and newspaper reports about cancer vaccines have become as common as "cancer cures" in former times. But vaccines are, as yet, equally far away from effective application in the control of cancer.

How goes the battle?

THE MAJESTY OF
THE CELL

THE SCIENTIFIC study of cancer began nearly a century ago, as microscopic observation and systematic description of the structure of diseased tissues and cells.

The leaders were two brilliant, strong-minded disciplinarians of the authoritarian German imperial school of medicine, Dr. Johannes Muller and his student Dr. Rudolph Virchow, respectively the father-king and even more eminent crown prince of the science of cellular pathology. The kind of people who first made medicine a science, Muller, Virchow, and the pathologists who followed them elaborated the infinite details of *what* cancers are. These early pathologists of the nineteenth century gave medicine its general understanding of malignant growth. They put information about cancer on a solid footing that, in its broadest dimensions, will surely stand.

Cancer is the bitter fruit of the most stimulating part of life— growth. We love to grow, make things grow, see things grow. Cancer excepted. It is a frightful, shocking case of life turning against itself. This form of growth is wholly abnormal, aggressive, and destructive. It mocks the creative process. We might call it one of nature's crudities, a biological spite trick, a form of biochemical second childhood. The great majority of cancers occur as a growth of young, immature tissue in old age. The destruction is in surrounding normal flesh.

The chief characteristic of cancer is uncontrolled growth. In contrast, the chief characteristic of normal growth is that it continues to a point and stops. A baby becoming a man proceeds from small to big under the strictest kind of cellular discipline. The rules are laid down through heredity and expressed in biology's own peculiar kind of multiplication table, a table based on a system of division. Scientists call the process *mitosis*. Through mitosis—the phenomenon can be noted under the microscope—the single living cell multiplies its kind by swelling and dividing. Biologists term this form of non-sexual reproduction a mother-and-daughter relationship. The cell grows and forms two daughter cells, and these in turn grow and divide.

This vital process fits well in Bertrand Russell's concept of "molecular imperialism" as the supreme law of the universe. But over the empire that each cell sets out to build stands some kind of master controller that tells cells how far they can go in their imperialism. It may be a molecule of special protein or a special kind of acid found in the cell nucleus, but many now believe that this dictator resides in our genes. "In our genes" means in the units of heredity that make up the chromosome threads visible in the nuclei of all living cells.

As we mature, something inhibits further growth, except for replacement and repair. Inhibition is essential to normal biological behavior. Down to the last living cell in the body state, we must control ourselves in order to survive and reproduce, in good genetic health. Such mature restraint might even be construed as the price of the pleasure of early freedom of growth. Cancer eludes this growth inhibitor, whatever it is. Cancer tends to grow, to move and go on growing and moving until it has crowded out normal cells and choked out all life. Only then will it die—together with its host.

The Virchow school of pathology looked upon malignant growth as of three general kinds: carcinomas, sarcomas, and leukemias—that is, tumors of surface tissues, of connective tissues, and of the white blood cells. Cancer originally meant only a malignant tumor of skin cells, but, in the manner of the disease itself, the word has spread to cover all types of malignant growth in modern usage.

"Malignant," meaning little more than "bad" in its Latin origin, has acquired a rather narrow definition in medicine. It has come to mean "going from bad to worse" or "ending in death." The pathologist thinks of a malignant cell as being a "neoplasm," a cover word meaning a new growth of any kind, and being a "tumor," or morbid swelling, and as having a distinctive characteristic, "anaplasia," or loss of individuality and regression to more primitive forms.

The normal cell consists of nucleus, cytoplasm, and membrane. In character, it is a virtual Daughter of the American Revolution, imitative, conventional, slavishly loyal to its own kind, in both structure and function. When this same cell becomes malignant, whether it comes from the liver, the lip, or elsewhere, its daughter cells gradually cease to resemble liver or lip cells. What they most resemble, when malignancy is unmistakable, is the "young" cells of tissues in the embryonic stage of life. They are now complete strangers to their mother cells.

Thus, the experienced pathologist can peer through his microscope at a thin shaving of tumor and, at a glance in most cases, say whether it is malignant or benign.

A benign tumor, such as a wart, mole, cyst, or polyp, is also a form of neoplasm and abnormal growth. It tends to reproduce normal cells of the kind it started with, simply producing too many. The benign tumor has another characteristic, usually: there is some sort of wall or capsule around it. It grows as does a football when inflated, and may stop at some point. Its main threat is in the pressure it may exert on surrounding organs.

The true cancer, as the classic pathologist would insist, is invasive, autonomous, recurrent, and irreversible. It grows as do the roots of a tree, at first merely causing a lumpy or crusty break-down of tissue in its own locality, then invading near-by blood vessels, nerves, and the lymph-gland drainage system of the body, and finally spreading by metastasis (meaning "new stands"). The tumor transplants its destructive cells in other parts of the body. For example, a cancer may start in the prostate gland of a man, just below his bladder, and end by producing a hemorrhage in his brain. Runaway prostate cells can actually be found in his brain, together with purely malignant ones that have lost all identity with their source.

Most pathologists also emphasize the irreversibility of the process. Except in rare cases, an untreated malignant cell will not stop reproducing itself until it and its host are dead. This is a rather horrible idea, but, to date, medical science recognizes no cure for a malignant tumor except total extirpation by a surgeon or total destruction by X rays or radium therapy. The new chemical treatments one hears of, such as nitrogen mustard, and also sex-hormones, are mainly useful in relieving the patient's pain and in slowing down the cancer's growth and spread. For some patients, such treatments prolong life. But no drug thus far has met the test of having cured cancer, though a tremendous all-out effort is being made to find a chemical that will do so.

All this is essentially descriptive—the *what* and not the *why* of cancer. There is a rather majestic finality about studying the structure of cells killed by disease, and this, in the long run, seems to have structured the thinking of many a hospital pathologist, who commonly looks over the surgeon's shoulder at the tumor to be removed and himself presides at the autopsy, if any. Traditionally, he has the last word on what is and what is not cancer.

This studious, little-known, noble breed of doctor is frequently heard to insist—indeed, to rise at meetings of cancer-virus hunters and insist—that a cancer is not a cancer and a tumor is not malignant if it stops growing or does not show clear signs of a throwback to more primitive cell structure. Indeed, a few pathologists maintain that a cancer cannot be a cancer if the patient survives, even with radical surgery. They hold that the true cancer cannot be overtaken, and therefore those patients who are cured must have had a more or less benign, host-dependent tumor not yet transformed into cancer. This is rather fatalistic thinking, and reminiscent of the German psychiatrist Dr. Emil Kraepelin, who defined dementia praecox as an incurable mental disorder; when a patient recovered, he changed the diagnosis instead of his mind! It is a rather neat way of keeping one's terminology pure and intact, but it does not make room for fresh slants. This kind of resistance to new thought becomes important when viruses come into the cancer picture.

Progress in science depends on man's daring to take a new and fresh look and upset old conceptions if need be. Today, thanks to the virus hunters—and to the geneticists, to the biochemists, and to *avant-garde* pathologists and surgeons who are moving right along with them—the old line of strict definition in cancer seems to be crumbling.

In actual fact, "cancer" never has been as exact in marginal cases as the strict definitionists might lead one to think. Textbooks sometimes divide the malignancy of a carcinoma, for instance, into four grades. The basis for distinction is the extent to which the cells show normal differentiation in keeping with their type.

Only the most malignant tumors lose all identity with the normal. The older view that benign is benign and malignant is malignant and never the twain shall meet softens in the face of the fact that, between the two extremes, these intermediate grades "render a hard and fast line of demarcation impossible," as Dr. William Boyd of the University of Toronto points out. "It is not possible at present," he said, "to say whether an innocent tumor ever becomes converted into a malignant one. Certainly the clinical evidence points that way. . . ."[1]

As a matter of fact, there is more and more reason to believe that transformation is possible and does take place under some ill-defined circumstances. Even the cherished laws of cancer autonomy and irreversibility have been challenged. As Drs. Tilden C. Everson and Warren H. Cole of the University of Illinois have reported, many doctors have seen a pathologically proved cancer spontaneously reverse itself and disappear for good. This happens only rarely, yet it is a microscopic crack in the adamant rock of the negative outlook on cancer; it is enough to admit the probing questions of scientists whose minds are still young and flexible.

This one little fact and all these adumbrations become of great significance when we turn to the *why* of cancer, and presently to the virus theory of cancer. As much as the pathologists have

[1] *Surgical Pathology* (Philadelphia: W. B. Saunders Company; 1948).

learned, the explanation of cancer has eluded them during the same period when their laboratory neighbors, the bacteriologists and later the virologists, were finding one microbe or millimicrobe cause of infectious disease after another and *proving* it. The Microbe Age shattered the ancient morbid-humors theory —that is, that diseases have vague, multiple causes—with the newer concept that a specific disease has a single, specific cause. The pathologists thoroughly agreed with this idea of specificity, because various types of cancer were specific too, in the cells and organs where they originated. On the other hand, cancer obviously was not an infectious disease, obviously not contagious, and thus could not possibly be caused by a bacterium or a virus.

Or could it? With the addition of another fifty or seventy-five years' worth of knowledge in genetics and biochemistry, the limitations on such a possibility melt away. The cancer researchers talk of such things as enzymes and nucleic acids, antigens and antibodies, virus activity and virus latency, and a complex of factors that add up to a resurgence of the belief in multiple causes. But this time it is not just a belief in the morbid juices of the body, the humors, as causes of disease, but a belief in *multiple specific* causes.

Why does a living cell suddenly go wild?

"Theory after theory has come up as a flower, only to be cut down like the grass," commented Boyd.

Certainly a large number of theories of cancer etiology have risen, but, strictly speaking, we cannot say that they have fallen. The important ones have remained in the foreground and, in fact, have become more and more integrated. It is really a fascinating story—if one does not insist on a successful outcome. It is the story of the evolution of thought on one of the most complicated subjects known to man: abnormal growth. It makes one feel optimistic that the scientific approach will yield the final solution, but this is the optimism of the man who *knows* that *someday* a long shot *will* come in.

The oldest theory, held by Virchow himself, is that a chemical or mechanical irritation of the tissues disturbs the cells and brings about cancerous growth. The irritation may be a constant rubbing, a sudden blow, or a bruise. This is the theory of carcinogens, or cancer inducers. Many of the carcinogens are chemical compounds, particularly hydrocarbons such as coal tar and mineral oil. Soot was the first known; as the result of many years of pursuing this subject from Virchow on, a long line of chemical carcinogens has been discovered. Curiously, the obvious irritants such as acids and alkalis do not figure in cancer production, as far as is known. It is an odd fact that soothing substances are often implicated.

As everybody knows, one of the latest carcinogens under scrutiny is cigarette smoke. Unless one has stock in the tobacco industry or is on its payroll, there is little good reason now to discount the ponderous evidence that smoking a lot of cigarettes for a long time will increase the statistical chance of having lung cancer. People who look at the facts and still disagree appear mainly to be exercising their right to be stubborn. As physicians point out, smoke itself is finely divided particles of carbon, and inhaling them across the mucous membranes that line our bronchial tubes and lungs cannot help but irritate (possibly excepting our nerves). But people who do not smoke also get lung cancer, though the incidence is much lower, so smoking is not the sole explanation of lung cancer.

This is the trouble with the carcinogen theory. It will not stand alone. There has been a long, long line of experiments of inducing cancers in mice and rabbits by painting their ears with coal tar or by injecting various chemicals under their skins. There has been an equally long line of experiments with the transplantation of these induced cancers from animal to animal, originally suggested by the fact that cancer cells transplant themselves within the victim's body. In general, it was found that cancers would take in animals closely related to the original host, but not in others. Here we see dim beginnings of cancer as a problem in immunology and in biochemistry, but the early transplantation line of attack did not bring the science of cancer very far. These were artificial cancers, started and transmitted under precise laboratory conditions and little resembling anything seen in nature. Edward C. Dodds, British biochemist, one of the first to show that sex hormones were also involved in the stimulation of malignant growth, observed: "When one considers the vast amount of labor expended during the last fifty years to gain this meager knowledge, one wonders how much more will have to be done before the cancer problem is solved." [2]

We can avoid some cancers by avoiding certain known carcinogens, but this fact really offers little hope. On this basis, we would have to avoid all bumps and bruises, sunlight, tobacco smoke, mineral oils, X rays, atomic rays, and all the tar on our pavements and roofs, among other things.

Dr. Maud Slye introduced another line of attack. She said cancer was a hereditary disease. She proved it—in mice. Leading pathologists, surgeons, and more sophisticated geneticists ridiculed her.

Maud Slye was a little old maid with tousled gray hair and black eyebrows who lived for a half-century on the Midway campus of the University of Chicago, in a musty-smelling, three-story house full of mice. They were very special mice, and all in cages. Few knew Dr. Slye; those who did were moved by her dedication to the conquest of cancer; but some thought of her simply as the "mouse woman."

She was the first cancer geneticist, and her story is a poignant one. The three things the researcher longs for, most of all, are satisfaction of his curiosity, recognition for his work, and the possibility that it will make a difference in the sum of knowledge and hence may benefit humanity. Persons trained in the profit motive and material gain may not appreciate how highly the scientist values these goals.

Dr. Slye's curiosity about cancer was awakened around 1905, when she began working on her doctoral thesis, a study of genetics in mice. Tumors appeared in some of her mice, and what began as a short investigation became her life's work. She forgot aspirations for a Ph.D. degree (thus remaining academically a "Miss," though much later she received an honorary degree as a Doctor of Science). She went on to build up one of the greatest genealogies in history—certainly the greatest in mouse history, the brilliant and more widely recognized mouse-breeding work at the Jackson Memorial Laboratory in Bar Harbor, Maine, not-

[2] *Medical Research: A Midcentury Survey*, II, 82 (Boston: published for the American Foundation by Little, Brown & Company; 1955).

withstanding. The usual life expectancy of a mouse, barring cats, cancer, or other acts of nature, is about two years. Maud Slye, when she retired forty years later, had raised 150,000 mice and recorded their lives and their deaths—30,000 of verified cancer.

Dr. Slye began on solid ground. She took her cue, when she began more than fifty years ago, from the Austrian monk Gregor Mendel (1822–1884), who discovered genes. These units of heredity, as they link together in the fertilization of female cell by male cell and as they separate in the reproduction of the cells, determine the transmission and assignment of characteristics inherited from the mother and father.

The role of genes in cell reproduction has been simply and aptly described by Dr. O. Malcolm Ray:

> Body cells multiply by increase in size followed by division. The daughter cells are faithful reproductions of the parent so that growth may be described as a process of self-duplication of cells. Cell division appears to be initiated by a complex series of changes in the nucleus. In the course of these, a bundle of filamentous structures —the chromatin network—separates into individual filaments, called chromosomes, which proceed to split lengthwise. The duplicate halves separate and reassemble to form two new chromatin bundles at opposite ends of the cell. The cell as a whole then divides to form two new cells; each . . . carries a nucleus which, by inference, contains a complete replica of the chromosomes of the parent. Thus the nucleus and the individual chromosomes as well as the cell as a whole have this unique property of self-duplication.

> All this can be seen under the microscope. Where vision ends the eye of the scientific mind takes over to project events into the invisible. Current ideas in genetics rest upon one of those magnificent flights of imagination that change the face of thought and create new worlds. The basic idea is the concept of the gene. Genes are conceived to be the ultimate units of heredity. They are assembled in the nucleus like strings of beads to form

the chromosomes. Each gene differs from its neighbours
and each occupies its own particular place in the chromosome. . . . Genes are . . . recognizable only by their
effects. . . . Each heritable characteristic of the cell is
assumed to be determined by the character of a single
gene or of a group of genes acting together. . . .
    Occasionally the machinery of ordered duplication
goes wrong. This is inferred from the observation that
the progeny of a particular cell differ in some characteristic way from the parent and continue to produce
offspring with the same modified character. A heritable
variation—a mutation—has occurred. It follows, from
the basic premise of the gene, that, sometimes in the life
of the parent cell, some physical or chemical change in
one or more genes, or some change in the relative positions of the genes in the chromosomes has occurred. . . .
    In recent years new horizons have been opened up by
the demonstration that a mutation in a single gene may
result in a single metabolic disability. That is to say, a
particular gene is responsible for the control of one specific chemical reaction within the cell. . . .[3]

Dr. Slye did not concern herself with mutations or metabolism
—this part of the long and complicated story was to come from
the work of other geneticists and biochemists. What concerned
Dr. Slye was that a gene for cancer—she did not go into the
nature of it—could be bred into and out of her precious mice.
    A virtuoso of cancer genetics, Maud Slye could breed a
hundred-per-cent prospect of dying from spontaneous cancers—
breast cancers or leukemias, for example—and almost hundred-
per-cent immunity to cancers into the chromosomes of her long
lines of inbred mice—mice bred brother to sister.
    She held that a tendency toward or away from cancer worked
according to Mendelian law, susceptibility to cancer being a
recessive gene and resistance being a dominant one. She also
held that the cancer gene was type- and site-specific—that the

[3] Committee on Growth of the National Research Council: *Sixth Annual
Report to American Cancer Society*, July 1950–June 1951, pp. 15–16.

type of cancer it would cause (carcinoma, sarcoma, leukemia) and the body site or organ where the cancer would appear were predetermined.

Thus, it would follow that when two human parents each carried the recessive gene of a certain type of malignant tumor—say, stomach cancer—their child was destined to have stomach cancer. On the other hand, if one parent had the gene for susceptibility and the other had the gene for resistance, then the child would not have stomach cancer because resistance would be dominant, but the susceptibility gene could be passed on to another generation. If two parents with the dominant gene for resistance reproduced, then the child could neither have stomach cancer nor pass it on.

When Miss Slye, a timid woman of thirty-seven, presented her theory in 1916 at a meeting of cancer researchers, big-name authorities—pathologists and surgeons—jumped on her in untender fashion. "Cancer a hereditary disease?" they asked. "Would you end all hope for the families of our cancer patients?" She proceeded through the years to pile up evidence showing that all types of cancer were gene-controlled diseases in mice.

And out of her original discovery came the "pure cancer" strains of laboratory mice which are the tools, as much as test tubes and microscopes, of every modern cancer-research laboratory—mice that are born and have one cancer or another; their death is almost as predictable as growth itself. It fell to other cancer geneticists, such as Dr. Clarence Cook Little, one of the critics of Miss Slye's theory, to mass-produce the cancer-susceptible and cancer-immune mouse lines that came into world-wide use.

But the original discovery was Maud Slye's, and she made herself rather unpopular with it. She replied to her tormentors that her theory was not the end of all hope, but the beginning. She proposed to breed cancer out of the human race, by establishing state bureaus of human genetics which would keep records of every cancer in every family and, through the accumulated information, discourage cancer susceptibles from marrying one another. A maiden lady, perhaps she did not reckon with the problems involved. Certainly she forgot the great Robert Koch's injunction to his students: "Gentlemen, never forget that mice are not human beings."

Other cancer researchers shook their heads at Maud Slye's arguments and smiled none the less when she behaved like a woman scorned. They pointed out that, to produce cancer resistance and hence prevention of cancer, she had to breed brother mouse to sister mouse for many generations. This scarcely appeared possible with humans, who not only are hopelessly, endlessly out-bred and cross-bred, but also, laws and morals aside, in their exercise of free choice are wayward, unscientific souls at best.

Dr. Slye's genetic theory of cancer, true for mice, fell by the wayside because, for one reason, there was no way of testing it in humans, much less any practicability in manipulation of the laws of heredity in human cancer control. But we should mark Maud Slye well, because she is a perfect example of the pained determination that a cancer researcher often exhibits in hoeing his own row to its narrow, uncertain end.

Maud Slye died in 1954, at seventy-five, not of cancer, but of heart disease. She was a full ten years older than she had expected to be; she had been so certain, as she repeatedly told friends, that the Slye family was genetically short-lived. The recognition and the impact that she craved had eluded her, and in the end even her own genes seemed to mock her. She had expressed herself so bitterly and angrily so many times—she regarded Dr. Little as an archenemy—that her colleagues avoided her. The late Dr. Ludwig Hektoen, himself an eminent cancer pathologist, once likened her torrential, tormented outpourings to James Joyce's "stream of consciousness." But she did find expression and release as a poet, in *Songs and Solaces* and *I in the Wind*, and ultimately became reconciled, as her later publications showed, to the fact that the cause and control of cancer were more complicated than she had originally thought.

Surely cancer as a hereditary disease is a repelling thought. Yet from time to time some human data turns up which seemingly corroborates Maud Slye. Various physicians have described "cancer families"—for example, a mother and father who both died of cancer had six children and they all died of cancer, as did the single grandchild. In one instance, four brothers died of cancer of the lip.

Only in the last year or so, Dr. Clarence P. Oliver, University of Texas geneticist, reported that a study of 312 comparable women with, and 134 without, breast cancer showed this: if a daughter had breast cancer, there was a one-in-fourteen chance that her mother also had had it, whereas if the daughter had no breast cancer the chance of her mother having had it was one in forty-four.

Nevertheless, the Slye theory was too narrow to encompass the cause or causes of cancer by itself. This fact became evident as early as 1936 when Dr. John J. Bittner made another important discovery involving mice. He was then at the Jackson laboratory in Maine, and is now at the University of Minnesota. Dr. Bittner found something in the milk of mother mice from a cancer-susceptible strain which transmitted breast cancers directly to their daughters or through males to the males' daughters. He called it the milk-borne mammary-tumor agent, or MTA for short.

His experiments were some of the prettiest in mouse-cancer research—pretty to the technician. He found that if the babies of a cancer-susceptible mouse were taken from her and suckled by a female of a cancer-resistant strain, they did not develop breast cancer when they reached maturity. He also showed the reverse. When he made high-cancer mothers the wet nurses for low-cancer offspring, he found that many of these offspring would develop breast cancer despite their hereditary cancer resistance. Even some males developed mammary tumors. (This also happens, rarely, in human males.)

These findings appeared to fly in the face of the Slye theory, and were most upsetting to Dr. Slye. To her friends, she expressed herself as horrified that anybody would suggest that cancer might be an *infectious* disease that any baby girl might acquire from nursing at her mother's breast.

On the other hand, it became increasingly evident as time went on that the Bittner agent transmitted through mouse milk was a *virus*. Bittner also demonstrated within the next few years that mouse mammary cancer was not simply a matter of virus infection.

As a matter of fact, he and others who confirmed and extended his observations disclosed that the development of a breast cancer in mice depended on an interplay of three factors: susceptibility to the disease inherited through genes, a particular pattern of sex-hormone stimulation, itself probably inherited, and the virus. Without the defective gene or stimulation of hormone activity or the virus, no cancer resulted. The evidence involved a staggering variety of experiments with breeding females, virgin females, females with their ovaries removed, and females with one ovary removed.

And yet men are not mice. No virus has been found, though some virologists point out that the experiments that would most likely disclose such a virus have not been done. So the Bittner virus has not advanced our knowledge of the cause of human cancer, though his work has aided in the understanding of the role of hormone stimulation of cancer growth in the breasts of women and men's prostate glands.

It must be, we imagine, a source of inner regret to Dr. Bittner, as it was to Dr. Slye and to a host of other cancer researchers, that his excellent work has not as yet resulted in a break-through against human cancer. As one tumor-virus man, also hemmed in by working with animals, remarked, "You can see how it is. Who cares whether mice get breast cancer?"

To account here for all the cancer theories and whence they came would take us too far afield. One other general theory needs to be sketched in, however, because it has dominated modern cancer thought and later seems to converge with the virus hypothesis. We speak of the theory of somatic mutation—the theory that for some reason or combination of reasons, the soma, or structure, of the living cell undergoes a change from its normal self and the cell thenceforth transmits this change each time it divides. The theory was originated in 1919 by Dr. Ross C. Whitman, then of the University of Colorado.

Presumably, the change involves the genetic structure of the cell nucleus, although this is not always clear in statements about somatic mutation. In any event, there is a cell change, it is seemingly irreversible, and it results in runaway growth. The idea originated with the classic work of Hugo De Vries, Dutch botanist, and his discovery, in the early 1900's, of spontaneous mutations in plant life. It obtained verification in the equally classic work of Dr. Hermann J. Muller, the Nobel Prize-winning student of the Nobel Prize-winning geneticist Thomas Hunt Morgan. Morgan had spelled out the genetic structure of chromosomes in fruit flies. These insects sometimes undergo spontaneous mutations and produce a gene that foretells the cause of the fly's eventual death. Muller, in 1927, found that these mutations could be speeded up by bombarding the fruit fly with X rays. He was the first to suggest a relationship between mutation and cancer-inducing agents.

This was the basic-science backdrop for a multitude of experiments by Dr. Leonell C. Strong, then of Yale University, and others, all suggesting that the probable effect of various physical and chemical carcinogens was to produce a cell mutation, as Hermann Muller had postulated. Nonetheless, because of its generality and lack of essential, intricate details, the somatic-mutation theory has produced the kind of intellectual storm which inevitably develops around any new explanation of cancer; critics have been thoughtfully hacking away at it with sincere vigor for years. One question is whether the mutation arises only in a single cell. Another involves the apparent fact that there is a pre-cancerous stage of relatively benign overgrowth of cells—only in its final stages is cancer apt to meet the rigid diagnostic definitions of the pathologists.

But radiation does produce leukemia in humans and animals exposed to excessive doses of X rays or atomic rays. Patients undergoing X-ray treatment of high dosage in attempts to save their lives from other diseases occasionally develop leukemia (the incidence appears to be about one half of one per cent). So do radiologists (X-ray specialists), who have more leukemia than other physicians, according to Dr. Shields Warren. But the most ghastly confirmation came from Hiroshima and Nagasaki in 1945. Some of the Japanese who did not receive an immediately lethal dose of atomic radiation when the A-bombs were dropped to end the war, went on to develop a fatal leukemia apparently caused by a mutation in their white blood cells.

No theory of cancer inducers or heredity changers brings us down to the operational details of the changes in cell chemistry, and neither does any combination of such theories. What happens to the cell?

One of the best explanations comes from Dr. Otto Warburg, the German who won the 1931 Nobel Prize in chemistry for discovering an enzyme that controls cell respiration—that is, its use of oxygen. He holds that malignant growth—cancer—may arise from a hereditary injury to the cell's breathing-system, so to speak.

In 1926 Warburg detected (and others since have verified) that cancer cells do not have the same need for oxygen as normal cells. Louis Pasteur had discovered that the normal cell splits the simple sugar glucose, taken in as food, into lactic-acid molecules, oxidizing or "burning up" some lactic acid as energy and resynthesizing some back into glucose for further use as food. Warburg observed that when the normal cell lacks sufficient oxygen, completion of the process is blocked and lactic acid accumulates. In the malignant cell, and also in the embryonic cell to some extent, this principle of glucose resynthesis operates only in a limited way, even when oxygen is present.

Thus, it appears the defect in malignant cells is in oxygen utilization. As a result, they split more and more glucose to obtain their energy, without using much oxygen. The process is uneconomical, but when the supply of oxygenated blood is poor, as it may be in the vicinity of a tumor, the malignant cell has a great advantage over the normal one. The defect of cell respiration is passed on from one cell to the next, in hereditary fashion. Warburg regards benign tumors as an intermediate cell condition between normal and malignant. Here, of course, he runs into Old Guard pathologists who draw a sharp line between benign tumors and malignant.

In sum, what Warburg seems to tell us is that oxygen reaching the cell through the blood may control growth. Yet even the Warburg theory has its limitations in solving the mystery of cancer, inasmuch as it begs the question of what factor causes the defect in oxygen utilization. Furthermore, the question of whether the growth defect lies in the genes is a hard one to test.

The proliferation of cancer cells is asexual, involving the growth of an organism rather than the perpetuation of a species. Dr. John G. Kidd maintains: "No final proof of gene effects in production of cancer is possible, since tissue cells are vegetative and not sexual, and since chromosome changes are not regularly demonstrable." That, of course, is the next step—to demonstrate regular changes in the chromosomes, made up of protein and nucleic-acid molecules. Biochemists are now working intensely to discover how normal cells and malignant cells differ in nucleic-acid structure. This could be the final step.

BUT WHERE IS
THE VIRUS
IN HUMAN CANCER?

IN CANCER, something destroys the adult living cell's growth inhibitions without killing the cell. Now, as if some infantile wish for omnipotence had been granted to a biological Sorcerer's Apprentice, the cell is free to multiply. The result is a tumor, benign or malignant. But what is this something? Could it be a virus?

In their attempts to explain cancer as an infectious but not contagious process, the tumor virologists have had as much of an uphill struggle as the geneticists have had in explaining it as a hereditary phenomenon, or the chemists, as a problem in cell metabolism.

For a half-century, as Joseph Beard indicated, it has been even harder to get an audience for the accumulating evidence that viruses belong in the picture.

The imaginative Frenchman and pioneer virologist Amédée Borrel, of "Borrel body" fame, was apparently the first man to suggest viruses as a cause of cancer. He did so in 1903. Beijerinck had discovered a filterable virus five years before; subsequently, animal and human diseases had been shown to be the result of viruses—foot-and-mouth disease, yellow fever, rabies, and some of the poxes. Why not cancer? Borrel noticed that virus infection sometimes caused a rapid proliferation of cells. But these were normal cells. Nobody took him seriously.

The first virus-caused tumor to be discovered was a fatal leukemia in chickens. Two Danes, Wilhelm Ellerman and Oluf Bang, reported in 1908 that they had transmitted fowl leukosis by means of cell-free filtrates. The disease, involving an overwhelming multiplication of the type of white blood cells known as lymphocytes, was not thought of as cancerous at that time, so the significance of their discovery was overlooked.

The chicken-leukemia story was completed about a half-century later, in 1956, when Dr. Ben R. Burmester of the United States Department of Agriculture poultry-research laboratory in East Lansing, Michigan, made an effective vaccine against the epidemic form of chicken leukemia—the first vaccine ever made against one of the so-called cancer viruses.

This should prove a great blessing to chicken farmers, who suffer a reported annual loss of more than $60,000,000 from leukemia in their chickens. The disease has become more prevalent since the mass production of chickens in battery brooders. It does not infect humans, so it presents no problem in chicken as food.

The virus—Dr. Joseph Beard and his wife, Dorothy, were the first to report isolation of it in a pure state—is highly infectious. They have found some forms of it—there are three or four types —in concentrations of as many as two trillion particles per cubic centimeter of infected chicken blood. A "c.c." is the amount one could put in a two-fifths-inch cube.

Burmester found that some hens were immune and that they transmitted this immunity (antibodies) through their eggs to their chicks. He then made a vaccine from cell-free extracts of leukemia cells that operate by the same route. The veterinarian vaccinates the hens to protect their chicks!

The various chicken-leukemia viruses have been the cause of

some hot disputes as to whether they produce true cancers or not. The white cells grow wildly but appear normal otherwise, Dr. Jacob Furth points out.

It was Dr. Peyton Rous of the Rockefeller Institute for Medical Research who really put tumor viruses on the map. A Baltimore-born, Johns Hopkins-trained, "Popsy" Welch-inspired pathologist, Rous made a surprising observation in 1909, a few months after he came to the then new Institute as a research assistant and was still casting about for something to do.

Today everybody in cancer research has heard of the Rous chicken-sarcoma virus, or Chicken Tumor No. 1, just as every middle-aged layman has heard of Halley's Comet or every child, of Sputnik I. Rous discovered the virus when he was thirty years old. He is now eighty.

He has spent a good part of the intervening half-century cautiously extending and elaborating the significance of this discovery in his youth. However, it would be a mistake to think of him as a one-discovery man, as observers tend to do. It would be more accurate to regard Rous as an excellent example from science of a man born a bit ahead of his time. As indicated earlier, Rous anticipated the Goodpasture chick-embryo technique of virus cultivation by growing his tumor virus in hatching eggs a good twenty years or more before the chick-vaccine breakthrough. He likewise anticipated single-cell tissue culture by about thirty-six years. In 1916 he used the enzyme trypsin to break down tissue fragments into single living cells, which he cultured on plates, in layers one cell deep. In 1952, as we also have seen, Renato Dulbecco wrapped the Rous and Enders tissue-culture methods together in a new technique for cultivating single virus particles in single monkey-kidney cells. Thus, Rous's discoveries have figured in the background of three important fields of virus research, both in chick-embryo and test-tube cultivation of viruses and in cancer viruses.

His career took its curious turn down the narrow, thorny path of cancer research when a poultry breeder came into the Institute carrying a Plymouth Rock hen with a big tumor in her breast. He said she was the only one in his flock which had the disease, whatever it was, so apparently it was not contagious.

Rous was a pathologist, and could tell malignant cells when he saw them. When the chicken died, he excised the tumor and inspected it in the most minute detail. It was a sarcoma, a malignant tumor of connective tissues, the fibers that bind the various parts of the body together. He saw the characteristic "spindle cells" of a sarcoma. A pathologist can go wrong in differentiating some sarcomas from innocent fibrous tumors, but not on Rous's. The chicken's tumor was solid, it had invaded other tissues, it had spread widely into lungs, heart, and liver, and it had killed in four to five weeks. All this was apparent upon autopsy. It certainly was a sarcoma, one of the most malignant of tumors. His associates agreed with Rous, and nobody ever has proved otherwise. This point is important, for some pathologists wave aside virus tumors as not being true cancers.

It was already well known that cancer cells can be transplanted from animal to animal, if one has the right animals with the right degree of relationship. To determine if a virus was involved, Rous decided to try an experiment without cells. He ground and mashed a bit of the tumor, added water, made a sort of soup out of it, and pushed it through a bacteria-tight filter—one that certainly would not pass a single cell through its pores.

He obtained some young Plymouth Rock chickens and injected the cell-free juice into their breasts. By the end of 1910 he had used up nearly one hundred chickens. In some, he got takes. A simple little injection of clear juice containing no bacteria and no apparent organic material produced solid tumors and metastases—new stands in other parts of the body—just as he had seen occur in the one chicken sarcoma found in nature. Not all chickens in any series developed tumors, only a few. But he got more takes with a filtrate passed through a Berkefeld No. 2 (coarse) filter than with a No. 5 (medium), with which he had no luck at all. This strongly suggested not the living contagious fluid that Beijerinck talked about, but a midget microbe of a certain size, along the lines visualized by Pasteur.

It was an exciting, dramatic discovery—and it filled young Rous with alarm. As he reminisced many years later, "I used to quake in the night for fear that I had made an error." He had made no error, but he was a well-trained pathologist and there was no question that he had committed an act of heresy. Virchow, the crown prince of pathology, and all his followers, including Welch, had taught their students that living cells were the citadels of disease and cancer was a disease of the cells. There were normal cells, tumor cells, neoplastic cells, malignant cells. The cause lay within, in their growth mechanism. So the pathologists were convinced.

One almost needs to be a pathologist to appreciate how firmly this disease-cell relationship had become fixed. It was like a Fundamentalist's interpretation of Genesis, but with somewhat more scientific basis.

Now this young rascal named Rous suggested that cancer was merely a virus infection. Well, it was possible to ignore him, and this the heavyweights of cancer research did for many years to come. Yes, he got a report into the *Journal of the American Medical Association:* "Transmission of a Malignant New Growth by Means of a Cell-Free Filtrate."

Young Rous wanted to call it a virus, but an older man warned him against sticking his neck out. Nowhere in that report, published on January 21, 1911, did Rous use the word "virus," and not for the next twenty years did he desecrate the majestic science of cancer with that word, although the evidence that it was a virus piled up and up. Ultimately it became possible to take a picture of a Rous virus with an electron microscope and measure its size as eighty-nine millimicrons—a little less than four millionths of an inch in diameter. Rous, the personification of scientific conservatism, always called it a "tumor agent."

It was just as well, for the Rous virus remained one of the isolated facts of science for many years. It did not fit anywhere. But Rous and others have kept the virus from the one he saw in 1909 alive ever since. It is almost as much a fixture of a cancer biological laboratory as a cancer-susceptible mouse.

Nothing like a Rous virus ever turned up in a human sarcoma, as far as anybody could tell. But, one cannot take a tumor from a human being, make a cell-free filtrate of it, and inject it into other humans. The fact that a human filtrate won't "go" in this laboratory animal or that means little. It remained obvious to the clinicians in the big teaching-hospitals, where patients with cancer came in every day, that human cancer was not an infectious disease—and, as some told Maud Slye, not a hereditary one.

Nothing exciting occurred on the tumor-virus front for another twenty-five years. There was one event of some slight interest. In 1919, again in the A. M. A. *Journal,* Udo J. Wile and Lyle B. Kingery reported from the University of Michigan good evidence that common warts were caused by a virus, and hence added these minor blemishes of man to the list of infectious diseases in humans. The discovery seemed of no consequence, and was readily accepted. It had been known for some years that the many types of warts—conical, flat, folded, thread-like, rough, tumorous—and also a nodule known as molluscum contagiosum are transmissible.

The wart virus is a slow spreader and slow grower—it may take anywhere from one to twenty months for a wart to appear following infection. The virus—all human warts are believed to be caused by one type of virus—stimulates cell growth, apparently as a means of reproducing itself. The common wart is simply a horny outgrowth of skin cells. In it are the inclusion bodies and crystals so characteristic of viruses. The single virus can be seen under the electron microscope.

Warts go away in time. If one's fellow man attempts some magical incantation or manipulation at the right time, he is sure to work a cure—or at least take credit for it. Mankind has generated a wonderful lot of nonsense about the cause and cure of warts.

Virologists got their toe a little more firmly in the door in the early 1930's. Dr. Richard E. Shope, at the Rockefeller Institute's now defunct Princeton laboratory, put aside his pigs and swine influenza long enough to make two chance observations of some importance. In wild rabbits he found a virus that caused a fibroma, or tumor made up of connective tissue, the benign opposite of sarcoma, so to speak. Next he found a virus that produced "horns"—warts—on wild rabbits. It became the virologically famous Shope rabbit-papilloma virus.

He made his discoveries in typical Shopian fashion—as a "meat hunter." He had hunted cottontails in Iowa with ferret and rifle and sold them at the meat market for twenty cents each. He had heard that some rabbits had huge warts, but he never had seen one. After he went to the Rockefeller Institute, he made a field trip to Iowa. A hunter remarked: "Warts in rabbits? Man, I can show you some that grow horns!"

Shope told the man he would give him five dollars if he shot a rabbit with "horns" and twice that if he would send it to the laboratory in Princeton. The man did, but from this first rabbit Shope could produce no virus. He had better luck when he went hunting with a New Jersey friend who shot a rabbit in its burrow. Shope did not think it much of a shot, but was interested in the rabbit because it contained a large tumor. This was a fibroma. He transmitted the disease to other rabbits in a cell-free filtrate. Subsequently Shope acquired more "horned" rabbits and now was successful in transmitting the virus that produces rabbit papilloma.

None of this mattered much—the discovery that rabbits have virus warts and benign tumors, as humans do—until some of Shope's colleagues got to work on the problem. Rous, joined by the friendly, argumentative young Georgian Joe Beard, found that sometimes the warts progressed into cancer in wild rabbits. Also, when they injected the wart virus from wild rabbits into domestic rabbits, occasionally it produced *not warts but cancer.* This was carcinoma, a type of malignant growth in the skin.

This made cancer appear to be an infectious disease! To be sure, this was only in rabbits, but the rabbit, being a mammal, is closer to humans than the chicken, though we use the words almost interchangeably to describe some human behavior.

A little later Dr. George P. Berry and Helen M. Dedrick, then at the University of Rochester, enlivened and confused the picture still more by taking the Shope fibroma virus and mixing it with a virus that gives rabbits a benign mucous tumor, myxoma. They produced a transformed virus that behaved as a cause not of isolated tumors but of a highly infectious, fatal outbreak involving fever, multiple tumors, and general swelling.

Out of all this work came several knotty facts. One was that a virus could cause a benign tumor and another was that this tumor could progress into a malignant one. It was interesting that, whereas the virus could be found in the benign one, it somehow disappeared from the malignant tumor. Also there was the alarming evidence that the same virus could produce an infectious, communicable disease under some circumstances and a malignant growth under others.

It was all very unsettling. When times are unsettled, the orthodox cling tightly to their old beliefs.

As we have pointed out before, the 1930's was a great period of virus discovery; in truth, virology came of age in that decade. Further discoveries in the mid-thirties strengthened the case for virus cancers.

Dr. Balduin Lucké, University of Pennsylvania pathologist, found a virus that caused carcinoma of the kidney in leopard frogs hopping around in a New England swamp, and John Bittner, already described, rocked the world of mouse cancer (and of Maud Slye) with his discovery of a virus transmitting breast cancer in mice.

Bittner, like Rous, was cautious and called it a "factor" or "agent" rather than a virus. Nonetheless, it was a virus, and eventually others reported viewing it under the electron microscope as a sphere about four millionths of an inch in diameter. This is about the same size as the Rous virus.

Now the evidence for a virus relationship to cancer in various animal hosts read: chickens, rabbits, frogs, mice; leukemia, sarcoma, carcinoma. It was impressive, but it did not extend to humans, and therefore nobody really was impressed, even when Rous passed his chicken sarcoma to ducks, turkeys, and pigeons.

The tumor-virus front was quiet during World War II, by and large, with one exception. He was Dr. Francisco Duran-Reynals, a Yale University microbiologist who served the tumor-virus workers as a kind of Moses during their wilderness years. Duran-Reynals, who was born in Barcelona, Spain, and came to America in his youth, had a patrician profile and was sweet and soft-spoken, reasonable and insistent. He did a variety of experiments fitting parts of the puzzle together. He extended the earlier findings of others to prove, in a variety of circumstances, mainly involving chickens and mice, that neither chemical carcinogen nor virus would produce a tumor alone, but that the two would do so when working together. In some cases a hormone injection was also required. Out of his experiments came the theory of co-carcinogens as the cause of cancer. Simply put, the chemical carcinogen—he used methylcholanthrene—prepares the cell soil and the virus capitalizes on the situation, producing not merely infection but also malignant growth.

Duran-Reynals's experiments were pretty, as the technicians use the term, but they did not precisely revolutionize pathological thought. For example, we can cite the remark attributed to a witty Yale professor of pathology, Dr. Harry S. N. Greene, who does not necessarily spare his fellow pathologists in his sharp comments either. Upon finishing a lecture to his students, Dr. Greene is supposed to have said: "And now, if you are interested in viruses as a cause of cancer, you can go upstairs and listen to Hans Christian Andersen tell you a fairy story."

He referred, of course, to Duran-Reynals. He was simply making a joke, of course, but also made it clear that he thought the virus theory to be something of a joke. This did not bother the old Spaniard greatly. As Duran-Reynals said, the "stormy course" of the virus theory of cancer did not surprise him, nor did the fact that "the great majority of workers have refused even to consider it a possibility." As he pointed out, "many experiments designed to disclose the presence of viruses in tumors have been negative."

Duran-Reynals was greatly loved by his tumor-virus colleagues. Not all of them agreed with him either, but they stuck closely together in a defensive stance, and sometimes with a certain amount of truculence, like African oxen grouped rump to rump, presenting a circle of horns against any lion that would pull one down. There are a few pathologist lions left, but they are becoming weaker and one day they all may be gone. Dr. Duran-Reynals did not live to see this. He died in 1958, before he was sixty, of cancer.

In 1952, it is worth noting, Drs. Alfred G. Karlson and Frank C. Mann of the Mayo Foundation brought the idea of cancer as an infectious disease a little closer to man, via his best friend, the dog. Karlson and Mann reported that kennels are sometimes swept by epidemics of venereal sarcoma, a disease spread by intercourse. The tumor grows malignantly, invasively, and metastatically, and eventually kills the animal. The cause is unknown, but a virus is suspected.

In the last five years or so, excitement has mounted in the virus-cancer field as in virus hunting in general. In fact, the 1950's have looked like the 1930's all over again, but magnified.

As far as cancer is concerned, there have been four major focuses recently in research related to viruses. One has been on leukemia—in chickens, mice, and men. A second has concerned the chemical similarities of viruses and genes. A third has involved the immunity mechanism in cancer. A fourth, an outcome of the mastering of the technique of tissue culture, involves cultivation of live cancer cells in test tubes.

One might speculate that tissue culture will tell the story finally; as we already have seen, it is the ideal device for unmasking, or uncovering, viruses that hitherto have hid themselves beyond any hope of detection. Also, growing living cells and viruses in tissue cultures puts them beyond reach of the body's general defense mechanisms, such as antibodies. Curious things sometime happen in tissue cultures, Dr. Wilton R. Earle of the National Cancer Institute in Bethesda first noted and many others have reported.

Sometimes cells that appeared perfectly normal when they were put into a test tube display, after prolonged cultivation, a runaway growth very much like cancer, though nobody seems prepared to claim that it is true cancer. Furthermore, nobody at this writing seems to have detected a virus as the *agent provocateur* in this amazing phenomenon. This appears about all there is to be said, right now, on this issue. As for the others, let us take leukemia first.

Leukemia, as we have indicated, is a malignant growth of various types of white blood cells. These cells, normally in the first line of defense against disease, grow wildly and crowd out the red blood cells in the bones, spleen, and lymph glands. As leukemia progresses, severe anemia sets in and the multidunous white cells cease to look—to the trained eye of the pathologist—like normal cells. They become embryonic or primitive in appearance —anaplastic.

Leukemia generally follows two courses, one short and devastating—acute leukemia—and the other slow and insidious— chronic leukemia. Acute leukemia behaves like an infectious disease, often starting with a cold or sore throat, fever, and chills. The chronic form has a virtually painless beginning, with swollen lymph glands in the neck, armpits, and groin, paleness, weakness, fatigue, and a tendency to bleed easily. The victim may live two or three years, sometimes much longer, whereas acute leukemia usually kills in a month or two. Either type is regarded as invariably fatal, no matter what treatment is attempted.

Leukemia is often called the cancer of childhood, but actually affects two disparate classes of people in the main—young children, around five, and old people, sixty to seventy. Leukemia deaths total more than ten thousand a year now.

A study by the National Cancer Institute epidemiologists showed that the leukemia death rate in the United States tripled between 1921 and 1955, largely as the result of a greatly increased rate in age groups over fifty-five. Since 1940 the increase in the leukemia death rate has been less, year by year, leading the N.C.I. epidemiologists to conclude:

> The trends presently evident provide no support whatsoever for a theory which postulates a sharp increase within the last 15 years in leukemogenic factors affecting the environment of Americans in general. On the contrary, the data suggest that such exposure has either become stabilized or has actually decreased during this period, if exposure to environmental factors is in fact responsible for the disease.[1]

In short, neither radioactive fall-out from nuclear bomb tests nor excessive exposure to X rays or other forms of radiation is apparently responsible for the sharp increase in leukemia deaths. All the nuclear explosions have occurred since the upward trend began leveling off.

What about viruses? Recent American discoveries of viruses that cause leukemia and other classic cancers in mice were waved aside in a 1958 Harvard lecture by Sir Macfarlane Burnet of Australia, who said they have "more the flavor of a laboratory curi-

---

[1] Alexander G. Gilliam and William A. Walter: "Trends in Mortality from Leukemia in the United States, 1921–1955," *Public Health Reports*, September 1958.

osity." This caused Dr. Wendell Stanley to charge Burnet with being "most unbiological."

We mention this to illustrate that resistance to the virus theory of cancer is stubborn even though, as Dr. Jacob Furth of the Harvard Medical School Department of Pathology points out, it is perfectly sound to reason from mammals to man in fundamental biological phenomena. Anyone who has kept a running score, as has Furth,[2] can see where the bridge from mammal to man probably lies, in theory at least. Before trying to cross it ourselves, let us get up to date on recent events.

A new era of tumor-virus knowledge has come about from laboratory curiosities such as the discovery that some cancer viruses will take hold in newborn mice, whereas ordinarily they disturb adult mice not at all. This approach has progressed with the additional discovery that similar viruses acquire some sort of boost, or increased malignance, from passage through tissue cultures, so that they will kill mice previously impervious to them. And, in one case, a leukemia virus has turned up which attacks adult mice directly.

Dr. Ludwik Gross raised the curtain on this new series of discoveries. A refugee physician from Poland in 1940, a medical officer in the American Army during World War II, Gross became chief of research at the Bronx Veterans Administration Hospital in New York after the war and turned his attention to the strain of laboratory mice known as AK. Eighty per cent of these purebred mice die of a natural inherited leukemia between the ages of two and a half and eight months.

Gross wondered whether these mice were passing a virus on to their young and, if so, whether he could isolate it. In 1950 he reported success. He extracted a cell-free filtrate from AK mice dying of leukemia and injected it into C3H baby mice but a few hours old. The C3H is a strain of laboratory mice that rarely has leukemia. But after he inoculated these normally leukemia-free mice with his extract shortly after birth, better than one in every four developed leukemia one to two years later.

Of course, following the usual pattern, nobody believed Gross

[2] Jacob Furth and Donald Metcalf: "An Appraisal of Tumor-Virus Problems," *Journal of Chronic Diseases,* July 1958.

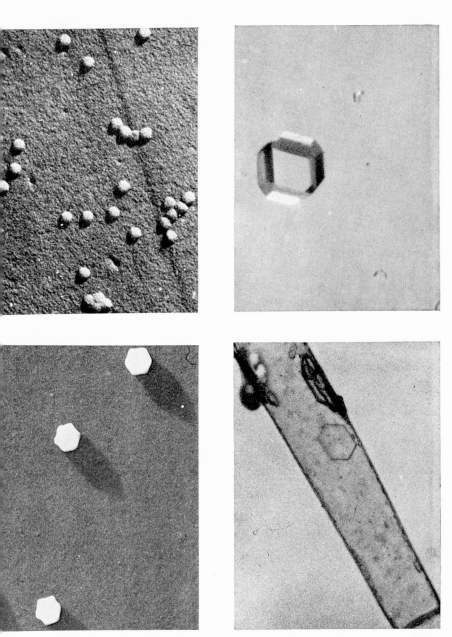

Upper left: The Shope papilloma virus, cause of warts and sometimes cancer in rabbits. *Upper right:* A unique micrograph of a single crystal of Mahoney (Type I) polio virus. Magnified only 80 times, this crystal contains an estimated one billion virus particles. *Lower left:* This astounding virus from a crane fly has twenty sides, each an equilateral triangle. *Lower right:* A natural crystal of tobacco-mosaic virus particles, or inclusion body, magnified 500 times in an ultra-thin section of hair cell of a Turkish tobacco plant.

PLATE 13

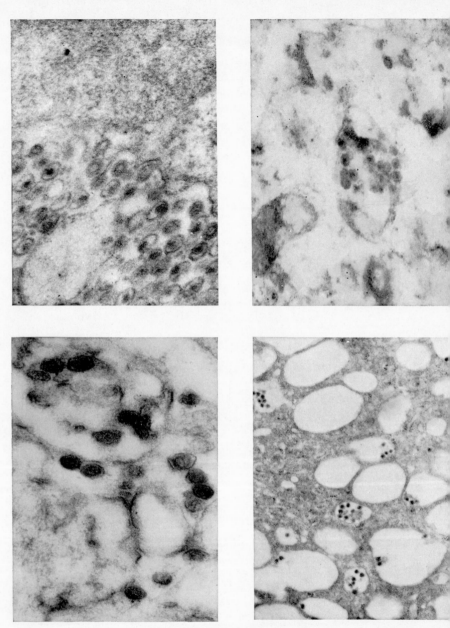

What the electron microscope shows when infected tissues are sliced in ultra-thin sections. *Upper left:* Virus particles in the protoplasm of a cell from breast cancer in a mouse. *Upper right:* What appear to be virus particles in cell from lymph glands in the neck of a human patient with acute leukemia, magnified 63,000 times. *Lower left:* Virus particles in cell of mouse leukemia, a virus disease discovered by Charlotte Friend. *Lower right:* These black dots in air spaces within the protoplasm of a chicken-sarcoma cell are the virus of Rous chicken tumor no. 1, multiplied 43,000 times in size.

PLATE 14

at first. He said he produced tumors of the salivary glands, too, and suggested that he might be dealing with two different viruses. He was right. Eventually he made his case for a leukemia virus stick. Eventually, too, he received some general support from some lady cancer scientists on the question of a second virus.

The first lady was Dr. Sarah E. Stewart, a National Cancer Institute bacteriologist with both a Ph.D and an M.D. Dr. Stewart is tall, well groomed, with a touch of gray in her hair and a warm, frank, friendly manner. One could not imagine her behaving in an arrogant fashion; in fact, she speaks in a rather timid, tremulous voice that one guesses may be the result of some years in the pathologist lions' den. But she, more than anyone else, has had the tumor-virus field jumping with excitement in the last year or two.

Dr. Stewart set out to see if she could confirm Gross's find. As she was to report in 1953, when she injected a C3H baby mouse with a cell-free extract from a leukemic AK mouse, she got no leukemia at all but tumors of the salivary glands, of the same order as Gross had noted. When her mice grew up they looked as if they had mumps, itself an infection of the salivary glands.

Dr. Stewart and a colleague, Dr. Bernice E. Eddy, from the N.I.H. Division of Biologic Standards, decided to see if a cell-free extract of this salivary-gland tumor would grow in monkey-kidney tissue culture. It did, part of the time. They passed the agent—they were not calling it a virus yet—back to mice. And now they hit a jackpot. To summarize a great many experiments, the mice—no matter what kind now—nearly all got malignant tumors. Of forty-one different kinds! Solid tumors. Fast-growing tumors. Some of the cells closely resembled the malignant changes one sees in human-cancer tissues.

It was a startling experience, even for blasé visitors, to have Dr. Stewart enthusiastically point out an array of tumors scattered throughout the body of an autopsied mouse pinned to a board. It was as if tumors had been fired at the animal from a shotgun.

Dr. Stewart now set out to prove that what she had was a virus. It behaved like one, in every respect.

Dr. Eddy was able to transmit tumors to the rodent known as a hamster and also to rats and in rabbits. All developed multiple tumors at some time during maturity if they were inoculated at a very young age.

In biological circles, the discovery of what was soon called the polyoma—many-tumor—virus was a sensational event by any definition. This was a virus, beyond any doubt. It produced malignant tumors not only in susceptible mice but also in supposedly resistant mice of several types. And, laboratory curiosity and tissue-culture product or not, it was the first tumor virus to cross the so-called species barrier and produce tumors in more than one kind of animal. In fact, it crossed the barrier three times, from mice to hamsters, to rats, and to rabbits.

Others in the many-mansioned National Institutes of Health, including Drs. Wallace P. Rowe and Robert J. Huebner, now joined the ladies in the tissue-culture study of the polyoma virus, a fellow traveler of the Gross leukemia virus and not the same at all, evidently. The virus thrives in the test tube and, what is most striking, behaves in animals in the same manner as any ordinary infectious virus. It can be found in nose, throat, and urinary secretions. Like the influenza virus, it can infect through the mucous membranes of the respiratory tract, and, like polio, it produces only inapparent infections most of the time. And it causes specific antibodies in the blood. "Wouldn't it be interesting if more tumor viruses turned out to be similar to and spread like the 'common cold'?" asked Huebner, rhetorically voicing a most dreadful thought. We may still admonish him, in the manner of Robert Koch, that mice are not humans (and meanwhile remind ourselves that we know full well that man may behave like a mouse). But mice's viruses behave remarkably like man's. Interestingly, the polyoma virus is about the same size as the Rous-and-Bittner tumor viruses—fourth millionths of an inch.

The two ladies went on to prepare a vaccine against the virus which, according to a report in October 1958, prevented the development of tumors in ninety-seven per cent of the hamsters inoculated with it. The hamsters received the immunizing agent —Stewart and Eddy shied away from calling it a killed-virus vaccine—at the age of two days and again at eight days and then were given challenge doses of live virus at the age of two weeks.

Two out of three control animals that received the live virus but no previous vaccine developed tumors and died within five months. But ninety-seven per cent of the vaccinated ones withstood the live virus just fine.

Making a vaccine to protect hamsters from an artificially induced virus tumor does sound a little like a laboratory trick. It is —except that it proves a point of fundamental interest: this tumor virus produces antibodies, and hence conforms to the well-established laws of immunization.

As a matter of fact, the tumor-virus-vaccine stunt had been worked before by Dr. Charlotte Friend, a demure little lady from the Sloan Kettering Division of Cornell Medical College in New York. Dr. Friend is the discoverer of another mouse-leukemia virus. In 1956 she reported that she had extracted a virus from the spleens of leukemic mice; it transmitted leukemia not only to baby mice but rather quickly to adult mice normally resistant to leukemia. This discovery, like Gross's but involving a different virus, also has stood up.

"Until recently," Dr. Friend remarked, "anyone who claimed he had a cell-free filtrate that caused cancer and said this filtrate was a virus was regarded as falling in one of two classes: either he (1) had holes in his head or (2) had holes in his filter."

She made a killed-virus vaccine that produced antibodies and prevented mouse leukemia about 80 per cent of the time. Dr. Rous, in accordance with some general reservations about the new mouse-tumor viruses, chided Dr. Friend for calling her preparation a vaccine. Hence, when Drs. Stewart and Eddy made a hamster vaccine, they avoided criticism and called it an "immunizing agent."

But there is no reason why we cannot call it a vaccine here if we remain fully aware, as Dr. Stewart said, that "at present, we have no evidence to show the implications of this work in the prevention of human cancer."

In Chicago is a man who does suggest some implications. He puts human leukemia in mice and transmits it from mouse to mouse, presumably in the form of a virus. A layman would think that when Dr. Stephen O. Schwartz first reported this—at the same 1956 meeting in Detroit where Stanley said it was high time to get busy on viruses as a cause of human cancer—the tumor-virus workers would have hoisted him to their shoulders and marched around the room just for the pure joy of releasing their prolonged, pent-up tension. Instead, they turned a cold, suspicious eye on this man who had the nerve to mix humans into the discussion of chickens and mice. In the beginning, Dr. Schwartz even had trouble getting his findings published, though he was obeying the frequent injunction of the tumor-virus spokesman, Beard: "It's time we got this stuff out of animals and into humans."

Technically, what Schwartz and his Chicago group did was just the reverse. They had found something in the brains of humans dying of leukemia which produced leukemia in mice. As we have seen, such an event is a matter of great importance in the prevention of most virus diseases: the finding of a test animal in which the human disease can be studied. But, as we also have seen, cancer is a different kind of story. One complicating factor is that the Schwartz group found the "something" in the brains of leukemic mice as well as in leukemic humans.

Dr. Schwartz is an internist, a specialist in internal medicine, and also director of the hematology department of the Hektoen Institute for Medical Research at the world's largest hospital, Cook County Hospital, where the poor of Chicago bring their many miseries. The Institute bears the name of the eminent cancer pathologist Dr. Ludvig Hektoen.

Schwartz—tall, lean, dark, semi-bald, with hawk-like features and a smooth, imperturbable manner—has the viewpoint of a clinician. This is to say, he is primarily interested in doing something for patients.

"I'm a doctor," he remarked by way of background. "I see patients. And you can't see patients for twenty years without becoming convinced certain things are so. Leukemia looks like an infectious disease. If the laboratory findings do not confirm clinical impressions, then the laboratory findings are wrong—if these impressions are right."

In other words, here was a man ready and willing to adopt Stanley's working hypothesis and assume that a virus caused human leukemia. Nearly ten years ago Schwartz and his associates, Dr. Harold Schoolman, Dr. Paul B. Szanto, and Wilma Spurrier, found a new lead in their studies of the immunity mechanism in leukemia. Stripped to its bare essence, it was that brain tissue of both leukemic mice and men behaved as if it might contain a leukemic agent and yet never seemed to contain the wild-growing white blood cells that characterize leukemia and can be found in most other parts of the body.

This suggested one of the oldest and most reliable maneuvers known to man: when you cannot solve a problem from one direction, try to turn it around and get a fresh slant on it, even if that means going at it from the opposite direction.

Everybody, it seemed to Schwartz, had been trying to get the leukemia virus, if there was one, out of the tumor, or malignant white cells. But these white cells—what are they for, if not to dispose of foreign invaders and infectious agents in the body's first line of defense? The tumor cell might well be the last place one should look for active virus.

"We are taught that leukemia is a lawless overgrowth of white cells," Schwartz explained. "But if you say that this is a violent reaction of the body to an infectious agent, then you see the body is in a last-ditch fight and saying, like Winston Churchill, we will fight the invader in our streets and in our houses. In so doing, the tumor finally can contain the organism locally, perhaps. But the brain does not show this quality of leukemic infiltration."

So that is where Schwartz decided to look for a leukemia virus —in an organ so highly specialized that its tissues apparently rejected white cells in the passing blood and refused to become a last-ditch battleground.

Their findings can be summarized thus:

First finding: Take the brain of an AKR mouse dying of leukemia and make a cell-free filtrate. (Ninety per cent of these AKR mice regularly die of spontaneous leukemia in from twenty-four to fifty-two weeks.) Inject the filtrate into six-weeks-old AKR mice. Most of them die within the month, so it is apparent that something in the filtrate at least accelerates the onset of leukemia in leukemia-susceptible mice.

Second finding: Take the brains of six patients, aged from two to fifty-seven, who died of acute leukemia and again make a cell-free filtrate. Inject this filtrate into young AKR mice. Filtrates from three of the patients bring about leukemia in 71 of the 326 animals in from two to twelve weeks—in all cases, before the natural onset would begin. By way of comparison, normal human brain tissue or leukemic brain tissue heated to virus-killing temperatures has no effect whatsoever on control mice.

This finding, the Schwartz group said, did not answer the question of whether the human-brain filtrate initiated the leukemia or merely accelerated it; but, they said, there could be no doubt the filtrate contained an accelerating agent.

Third finding: Now take white Swiss and DBA mice, only rarely victims of leukemia, and test them with a brain filtrate from a thirty-three-week-old Swiss female that happened to die of leukemia after being caged with leukemia-susceptible AKR males. Leukemia develops in the majority (87 of 161) of leukemia-resistant Swiss mice in from one to three weeks!

The Schwartz group first took this as proof that the brain agent induced leukemia, rather than merely accelerating its arrival. Less than one per cent of these Swiss mice have spontaneous leukemia, and the rate in the DBA type is less than two per cent. This was a good experiment, but somebody said that perhaps a leukemia cell or two had slipped through the filter; that would be enough, probably, to transmit the disease.

Fourth finding: By now the Schwartz group has been able to isolate a leukemia agent from eight of eighteen leukemic human brains. To prove that their cell-free filtrate is indeed cell-free, the Schwartz group now engages in the passage of the agent from human brains through the brains of five consecutive, resistant Swiss mice and then into AKR mice. Nineteen of twenty AKR's develop leukemia well before their time. Next, the group injects Swiss leukemic-mouse brain into C3H mice, used as a "bird of passage." When the agent is now passed to Swiss mice, eight of twenty develop leukemia. When the route of transmission was abdominal injection, sixteen of twenty Swiss mice got leukemia.

These experiments cleared up the holes-in-the-filter question because in the course of five passages from animal to animal, the researchers diluted the original amount of brain filtrate 100,000,-000,000,000 times. Infection after this degree of dilution had to depend on multiplication of the leukemia agent. Hence, it seemed reasonable to Schwartz to call the agent a virus. These, after all, are the classic tests for a virus in a fluid that contains no cells or living matter: Does it infect? Does this infectivity multiply?

Schwartz appeared satisfied that the answer was probably "Yes" in each case. But there—rather surprisingly, but perhaps shrewdly —he let the matter rest, without further attempts to claim or prove he had cornered the cause of human leukemia.

Furth, who furnished some of Schwartz's mice, observed: "Schwartz postulates that it is a virus. This far-reaching conclusion calls for stronger evidence than presented thus far." Another observer remarked: "Some have failed to confirm him; a couple of others say they've done so in a rather roundabout way. Schwartz's stuff is worth watching, but I'm not completely sold on it." One leading virologist, who tried to get the same results in his own laboratory and failed, said: "Schwartz has something there, but what?"

Plainly, cancer research is a terribly unrewarding way of life. The wise man in this field does not press his luck, if any, too far. He could easily knock himself out, spiritually and professionally, against the Great Wall of Cancer Mystery. Schwartz evinced some recognition of this when he said in 1956:

> Those who object to the virus etiology of leukemia believe that even though the leukemic cells may harbor a virus, this virus is not in itself an etiologic agent, but simply . . . hastens the animal's death . . . by altering the antigenicity (antibody-producing capacity) of the cells or the immune reactions of the host. This is a delicate point which will undoubtedly take a long time to resolve and which must be recognized as crucial.[3]

More recently he has attempted to turn the problem around again and come at it from the opposite direction: antibodies and the possibility of inducing immunity. According to a 1958 report in "Proc Soc," his group had some success in immunizing mice against leukemia as previously produced with cell-free leukemic-

[3] "Blood," *The Journal of Hematology*, November 1956, p. 1045.

brain filtrates. What they did was expose the filtrate to ultra-violet light to make a "vaccine."

The story is far from finished.

At the University of Texas in Houston, Dr. Leon Dmochowski has taken some marvelously good electron-microscope photographs of white cells from human leukemia victims, containing "virus particles," or "V.P.'s," as he labeled them. He accomplished this through a technique of slicing the diseased cell in cross-section. He found the same sort of particles in mouse and chicken leukemia, too. Dr. Dmochowski was naturally enthusiastic about this observation when he first reported it in 1957, and said that it placed a virus "at the scene of the crime."

Then the skeptics went to work on *him*. Stanley, for one, said it would be better to call Dmochowski's particles not V.P.'s but V.I.P.'s—"very important particles." In short, how did he know they were viruses? And how did he know they weren't some other virus, herpes or mumps maybe? asked others. He did not know, of course, and said so. There is no direct method of applying the acid test of infectivity to the virus depicted under the electron microscope because it is necessary to kill both cell and virus to take their picture. The only other convincing way would be to induce leukemia in an experimental host with a cell-free filtrate of the same white-cell sample. Such evidence has not been reported.

So it goes. Others have taken pictures of virus-like particles in various malignant cells. It is exciting business for everybody but such professional skeptics as Dr. Robley C. Williams, the most expert of them all. Aware that the body abounds in viruses and virus-like objects, he says: "Prove that the particle under study is the cause of the disease under study."

Unhappily, scientific skepticism requires that the man with a hot, new lead be greeted with a wet blanket in place of a welcome mat.

There is a growing belief that cancer results from a defect—natural or acquired—in the body's immunity mechanisms, irrespective of whether a virus or something else acts as the trigger. This has been difficult to substantiate in classic fashion because cancer, or what causes it, does not always induce its host to manufacture good, strong antibodies. Even when such antibodies appear, they do not necessarily arrest the cancer.

But the immunity mechanisms involve certain non-specific and perhaps even local, cellular forms of resistance as well as the well-known specific antibodies in the blood. There are, in fact, some rather formidable theories regarding the protein chemistry of this immunity defect. Dr. H. N. Green, the philosopher-pathologist of the University of Leeds in England, holds one. Simply, perhaps over-simply, it is that all types of normal cells, as part of their protein-building systems, contain particular molecules that give them individual identity and inhibit uncontrolled growth by causing the body to make some antibodies against these molecules —enough to maintain organic balance.

Through somatic mutation, Green believes, the cell loses its identity, the body can no longer make antibodies against it, and the power to inhibit abnormal growth disappears. The theory arises from mouse-tumor experiments showing that coal tar, a hydrocarbon, not only contains a carcinogen that induces cancer—as everybody since Virchow has said—but also contains an anti-carcinogen that can inhibit the growth of cancer started by the carcinogen in the first place. The idea seems consistent with nature when one thinks of the parallel in X rays. Overdoses can cause cancer, and still greater doses destroy cancer.

Truly, it must be for our cells as Thomas Carlyle put it in *Past and Present:* "Bobus, you are in a vicious circle, rounder than one of your own sausages." Circles, sausages or cell growth, normal or abnormal, all this is highly theoretical. We can find more practical implications, closer to home.

Some daring human experiments carried out by the Sloan-Kettering Institute in New York, the world's largest cancer-research center, give further evidence of the above fact. They established, quite definitely, that human cancer, in its causes and in our defenses against it, is a problem of immunity—and also that antibodies are not the whole answer.

Drs. Chester M. Southam and Alice E. Moore conducted the study in 1957, with the aid of human volunteers—patients who were dying of cancer and had nothing to gain, and prisoners in the Ohio State Penitentiary who likewise had little to gain. The scientists inoculated these individuals with cancer cells that had been removed from patients and then cultured in test tubes and dishes, in many instances using pure colonies grown from a single cancer cell, according to the Dulbecco plating technique described in Chapter 26.

It would be difficult to narrate the course and outcome of these experiments more vividly than was done in a Sloan-Kettering progress report:

> Why will cancer strike one American in four—and why will the other three *not* get cancer? What are the differences between the cancer-prone and the cancer-free? Why does a tumor smolder in one human, grow slowly but steadily in another, flame wildly through the body of a third? Why does a cancer—very rarely, but demonstrably—stop growing, melt, disappear in some patients? Why does cancer growth, in other patients, seem at times temporarily checked, and then why does it accelerate again?
>
> There are exciting—and practical—questions underlying these puzzles. Is there immunity to cancer? If so, is it something that exists in the cancer-free but is lacking—or lost, or destroyed—in the cancer victim? Are there at least partial natural defenses against cancer? Can they be identified, studied, stimulated, increased, created artificially or borrowed to protect the potential cancer victim—or rescue those already attacked? . . .
>
> To begin with, the [Sloan Kettering group] transplanted cancer to volunteers who already had cancer.
>
> There was logic in this seemingly senseless experiment. We knew that the transplantation of any living tissue into a normal human body—unless it comes from an identical twin—causes an inflammatory response that swiftly destroys the transplant. White cells rush from the bloodstream to the transplantation site to begin one kind of chemical warfare against the transplanted cells. Elsewhere in the body, a chemical assembly line begins to

pour out antibodies—proteins specifically designed and shaped to recognize the invading or "foreign" tissue, grapple with it, neutralize it. Scar tissue grows to wall off the invader. In a week or two, the transplanted cells are dead.

Many animal experiments indicated that this effective defense system worked even if the transplant consisted of invasive, malignant cancer cells.

But would it work in humans who already had cancer —had cancer, perhaps, because they lacked some defense mechanism? To find out, fifteen patients with far-advanced, inoperable cancer were asked if they would accept transplants of fresh bits of different types of human cancers removed from other patients. . . . They agreed.

The fifteen patients received a total of twenty-three such implants. In thirteen of the patients—and twenty-one of the transplants—there was no inflammatory response. The cancer cells, implanted under the skin of the forearms of the volunteers, "took," grew vigorously, and spread, for periods ranging from six weeks to six months, before they were surgically removed. If defenses against transplanted cancer exist, the cancer patients lacked them. And this was not because they were too disease-riddled to muster any defenses at all. When these patients were challenged with inoculations of bacteria or viruses, it was shown they produced antibodies and fought back. When they were inoculated with normal human tissue cells, these cells did not grow.

There were two possible interpretations of these results. One was that something was wrong with the cancer patients—a defect in their defense systems that made them specifically vulnerable to the growth of cancer cells. The other possibility was that something was wrong with the transplanted cancer cells—that they had changed, in the test tube, in some way that made them unsusceptible to body defenses.

There was only one certain way to find out: by injecting these cells into normal, healthy, cancer-free volunteers.

The Sloan-Kettering team found such volunteers at the Ohio State Penitentiary. They were men who bore some of society's ugliest labels: murderer, rapist, swindler, thug. Unlike the cancer patients, who were already doomed, they had a great deal to lose. Yet—in response to a single call in the prison newspaper—more than 100 volunteered.

From this group, fourteen were selected. They represented different age groups. Half had family histories of cancer, half did not. Each received injections of the same stock of cancer cells that had flourished in the bodies of the cancer patients.

But this time there *was* a defense. There was some initial growth—the cancer cells were, indeed, struggling for a foothold—and then, in every case, there was an overwhelming inflammatory reaction, and within four weeks almost all the cancer tissue had been destroyed.

Three months later, the Sloan-Kettering researchers returned for a crucial follow-up test. Each convict-volunteer was inoculated with cancer cells of the same type he had received before. Again there was a defensive response—but this time it was in high gear. The reaction was swifter and more intense, and it killed all the cancer cells in a week.

When a few of the original cancer patient-volunteers—those who had shown some slight ability to fight off transplants—were similarly re-inoculated, they too showed an enhanced defense and a more vigorous response.

What did all this mean? It looked as if we were dealing with two types of response, two different lines of defense against cancer. The first one, we thought, was a general, nonspecific kind. The normal volunteers had it —but most of the cancer victims didn't. The second line of defense was the one that appeared on re-inoculation, as if something had been triggered into action, or in-

creased, by the first transplant and was just waiting for
another challenge.

We wondered what that first, nonspecific cancer defense might be. We wondered about the second response, too. Had we created an immunity to cancer by
inoculating humans with cancer cells, in the same way
that we can create immunity to polio or diphtheria or
typhoid fever with appropriate inoculations? Did this
induced immunity similarly depend on the production
of antibodies? And we had another big question. There
are many kinds of cancer. Would immunity to one give
protection against any of the others?

Once again, the researchers journeyed to Ohio. This
time they had cells from seven different kinds of human
cancers—tediously grown in test-tube tissue cultures, in
chicken eggs, in rats and hamsters, by hard-won techniques that did not even exist ten years ago. This time
there were fifty-three volunteer subjects, including
twenty-six who had had previous inoculations. Some received cancer transplants for the first time. Some received another inoculation of the same cell type they
had received previously. And some veterans of the previous studies were given cells of a different cancer strain
than the one they had received before.

Would these last volunteers show an enhanced immunity or defense against these new cancer transplants?
They did. It was not as great as the response of those receiving a second injection of the same cancer cell type,
but it was measurably greater and faster than the response of those fighting cancer transplants for the first
time. There seemed to be at least a partial cross-over of
immunity from one cell type to another.

This . . . suggested that different kinds of cancer
may stimulate a common cancer-resistance factor—or
that different kinds of cancer have something in common that stimulates bodily resistance.

Now there was a new question to answer. Were these
defenses aroused only by living cancer cells—by some

chemical, perhaps, that only living cancers produce? Or would dead cancer cells prove just as effective in causing an immune response?

Six prisoners were inoculated with killed cancer cells. Nothing happened. There was no inflammatory response. It was as if their bodies saw no immediate threat.

Yet somehow, subtly, the killed cells were causing a change. For when these convicts were challenged with inoculations of living cancer cells a few weeks later, they were just as immune—their local inflammatory responses were just as rapid and as great—as if living cancers had previously been injected into their bodies. This was not true of a few subjects who had previously been inoculated or "primed" with normal cells.

What had happened, in fact, for the first time in a controlled medical experiment, was that human beings had been successfully, safely immunized with dead cells against an implanted cancer.

The story, of course, does not end here. What part of the killed cancer cell had this immunizing power? What is the immunizing substance? If it is identified and extracted, could it be used in larger-scale immunizations? Would it protect as well against "real," spontaneous cancer as it does against transplanted cancers?

One way to find out was to split the killed cancer cell into fractions and inject these fragments separately into groups of volunteers. This is being done at the present time. In one experiment, cancer cells have split, crudely, into two fractions corresponding roughly to the nucleus or core of the cell and to the cytoplasm or "meat" of the cell. In another study, cells have been divided into five fractions. It is too soon to know the results. But if just one of these fragments of the cancer cell proves to have immunizing power, then the search for the immunizer would be vastly narrowed. . . .

But—as the Ohio prison experiments further show— there is another approach that pays at least as much attention to the man surrounding the cancer as it does to the cancer itself. It is this approach that compares the cancer patient—unable to resist implanted cancer cells —with the healthy individual able to destroy them, and asks, "How do these men differ?"

One by one, the defense mechanisms of the cancer patients and the convicts were compared. They did not differ in the ability to produce white blood cells, the swarming foot-soldiers and scavengers of the blood-stream. They did not differ in the power to manufacture antibodies—the paratroops of bodily defense, designed to descend specifically and accurately on foreign invaders (bacteria and viruses). They did not differ in any of the several known specific reserves usually called up when the body is attacked by infection or other disease.

Then a difference did turn up—in a bloodstream substance so recently discovered that its function in the body's defense is still only dimly understood. The substance is called "properdin." The prisoners had it—in normal amounts. The cancer victims with advanced disease lacked it—or, at best, had abnormally low levels of it.

What is properdin? No one knows its chemical make-up as yet. But the late Dr. Louis Pillemer and his associates at Western Reserve University, who first discovered it in animal and human blood, sparked world-wide studies that have disclosed a great deal about its action and its powers. Properdin, these studies suggest, is the first line of body defenses—a nonspecific, wide-ranging barrier to disease (particularly infectious disease) that is present in normal bodies at all times. Unlike antibodies, which are found specifically in response to particular invaders after an attack is launched, the properdin system is there to start with. It can destroy a wide range of bacteria, stun many viruses into submission, kill abnormal blood cells. Is it a defense against cancer?

A study of thirty-eight of the healthy Ohio convicts

showed that they had an average properdin level of seven units; none was below two units. The fifteen advanced cancer patients averaged less than two units and six had almost no properdin at all.

This is circumstantial evidence. While it is possible that some human beings have cancer because they lack properdin, the reverse is also possible: perhaps they lack properdin simply because they have cancer, and the growth has destroyed or blocked properdin formation. . . .[4]

None of this work, of course, placed a virus at the scene of the crime in human cancer. On the other hand, human cancer has become a problem involving immunology, in the past more largely concerned with infectious diseases.

It seems necessary to consider the virus, if not as the villain in chief, at least as a chief accomplice, or one possible cause of human cancer. Clearly, opposition to the virus hypothesis of cancer causation has weakened, especially among American scientists. The skepticism regarding viruses as a cause of human cancer has been based on a long, long series of failures (1) to find a virus in the cancer, or (2) where virus-like particles have been seen in a cancer, prove that they are its cause. However, as a matter of logic, negative evidence can work two ways, as Dr. Gilbert Dalldorf has pointed out:

The virus theory of cancer . . . remains a theory, so far as human cancer goes, because no one has found convincing evidence of a causal relationship between a virus and a malignant tumor of man. Proof of such a relationship for any one of our human cancers would have a tremendous impact on cancer research, but the obverse, the absence of proof, does not justify us in denying that viruses may be responsible. The failure to find a virus does not mean that one is not there. For one thing, we don't experiment with man as with animals.

[4] Sloan-Kettering Institute for Cancer Research: *Progress Report* (June 1958). The report was prepared by Dr. H. Jack Geiger, a physician who can write well by virtue of having been a science writer before becoming a scientist.

There are still difficulties, furthermore, in explaining how a virus produces a malignant growth of the cell it infects even in animal-tumor viruses, where there is no question of the cause-and-effect order of events.

Jacob Furth has said: "It also remains to be proved that host cells multiply following any virus infection." The more common effect of a virus is sooner or later to kill the cell, not make it grow. As far as he has been able to determine, Furth says, there is no definite structural difference between the classic viruses and tumor viruses. The tumor viruses are round and range from about three to five millionths of an inch in diameter, for the most part. Like the pox viruses, they have a complex internal structure, and contain fat and at least one enzyme.

There is some evidence that tumor viruses can behave as infectious diseases in a variety of cells but act as a cause of cancerous growth in just one cell type—they are that specific. There is also some evidence that a malignant cell produced by a virus will support infection by other viruses.

Furth, reviewing the present state of knowledge, discusses three possible ways that a virus might cause cancer: conditioning, mutation, and transduction.

By conditioning, he means that the cancer virus would parasitize the cell without destroying it and induce a rapid reproduction of new cells and viruses without causing a mutation in the gene structure. In brief, the virus would seize control of the cell's growth-regulating mechanism and tell the cell: "Make more cells for my sake." This might explain why in some virus tumors, such as chicken leukemia, the cells appear normal although there is great proliferation of new cells.

We are already familiar with the theory of mutation, involving a change in the genes. In this case, the virus would behave as any other carcinogen, whether a chemical or radiation. This might explain how the Shope rabbit wart progresses to a true cancer, manifesting the presence of virus in the wart stage but disclosing no virus after it turns to cancer.

Transduction means that the virus takes the place of a gene in the transmission of hereditary characteristics—an impostor on the throne of life, as it were. In the phrase of Dr. Salvador E. Luria,

University of Illinois virus geneticist, the virus can behave as "an infectious bit of heredity," as a means of securing its own perpetuation as well as making the cell grow abnormally. There is, as a matter of fact, some evidence that the Rous virus reproduces by dividing in two like the cell itself, rather than using the cell as a nesting and feeding place while making several hundred copies of its virus self. Also, it has been observed that viruses and genes are remarkably alike in size and chemical structure. In the transduction theory, the virus acts:

1. As cell passenger—the virus is its usual parasitic self at the outset.

2. As a cancer gene—the virus passes on the messages of heredity, but now they are mistaken messages as far as cell integrity is concerned.

3. As an *agent provocateur*, inducing the cell to go on its malignant way, rapidly reproducing itself, so that the virus can reproduce with it—*and never leave the cell.*

Consistent with this theory is the commonly observed fact that, upon entering a susceptible cell, a tumor virus (as well as some others, such as herpes) goes through a masked or latent period —also known as an "eclipse stage." This may happen, for example, in the young host infected with the virus. Subsequently nothing may happen until the host reaches at least middle age. After that, a tumor may begin to grow. There is a general parallel here to what occurs in old age, except for certain malignancies of childhood, such as acute leukemia, which behave more like the short, swift, and especially virulent infectious diseases.

Thanks principally to virus geneticists and virus chemists, undoubtedly this is the most popular theory of cancer in America today: that viruses behave as cancer genes. At least, it is at this writing. Dr. Rous observed: "In dealing with cancer, genes and nucleic acids, you are dealing with subjects which have a relationship to one another that shifts almost month by month nowadays, at least in men's minds."

It may turn out that there is no conflict among major theories —that in time they all will fit together.

A simple summing up of the relationship has been provided by Dr. Harry Rubin. He is a young doctor of veterinary medicine at the California Institute of Technology who has accomplished the feat of getting a single Rous sarcoma virus started in a single normal chicken cell and hence showing how, in two days, the cell becomes malignant. This cell then goes on to produce cancerous daughter cells, hundreds of them in a week's time. Dr. Rubin remarked:

> These studies indicate that tumor viruses must be incorporated into the genetic material of the cell. In doing so, they introduce a piece of misinformation in the hereditary information of the cell. This piece of genetic misinformation is duplicated just as any normal part of the cell when it divides, and the mistake is thus perpetuated in all the daughter cells. This finding shows that there is no area of fundamental disagreement between the two major theories of cancer causation which have been in conflict for many years. The somatic mutation theory asserts that cancer is due to a permanent change in the hereditary apparatus of the cell while the virus theory attributes it to infection by a special agent. These theories become reconciled when it is seen that the virus itself is an efficient agent for introducing change in the hereditary apparatus, and that the basic mechanism in both theories is the same.

This sense-making statement, exuding a feeling of progress in the theoretical understanding of cancer, would not have been possible without a long and recently breathtakingly rapid chain of discoveries involving the virus heart of the matter: nucleic acid. In this strange, complex substance the story lines of cancer, genes, and viruses can be seen to converge, as we may gather from the apt way Dr. Thomas M. Rivers has added up the various lines of attack:

"If nucleic acid is the business end of a virus, if nucleic acid is the business end of heredity, and if nucleic acid is the business end of cancer, then anyone who is working in one field is working in all three."

We might also add one other *if*: if all this is true about nucleic acid, we also are somewhere in the vicinity of the secret of life.

Let us see for ourselves.

32

AND NOW,
NUCLEAR CHEMISTRY

CERTAIN virologists like to point out that Wendell Stanley missed a trick in 1935 when he crystallized the tobacco-mosaic virus. They are human beings, of course; thus, it may be that in indulging themselves in all the privileges and pleasures of the second guess, from the vantage point of what we now know about viruses, some may suffer from a mild infection of malice. No one denies, of course, that Stanley's purification of the virus in crystalline form was a remarkable feat, that it shook the microbiological earth, or that, in the ensuing organule-versus-molechism controversy, Stanley catalyzed one of the most fruitful disputes in the history of basic science.

But the fact is that Stanley first said that his pure virus was a protein molecule. And two years later two English biochemists, Bawden and Pirie, showed that there was also some nucleic acid in the virus, in addition to the proteins. Stanley repeated the experiment and confirmed them, as they had confirmed him on the matter of crystallization. Eventually, he and his colleagues established that the TMV rod is 94 per cent proteins and 6 per cent ribonucleic acid (RNA). He still likes to speak of TMV as a single nucleoprotein molecule made up of about fifty million atoms, but says he has no real objection if people want to call the virus a micro-organism, implying that it is alive and contains more than one molecule.

When the probing question of how he came to miss the RNA in 1935 was put to him recently, Stanley did not fall silent, refuse comment, or try to ignore the question—common procedures among medical scientists, many of whom are notorious for not answering pertinent inquiries.

Stanley promptly replied that the missed trick "still remains somewhat of a mystery." He does not know whether the procedure he followed washed away the telltale phosphorous of the nucleic acid or whether the chemical analyst who helped him simply failed to find the small amount present. In either event, he remarked, "it is not necessary for any one individual to discover everything there is to know about a particular material." As a matter of fact, it is not possible; as we have seen so many times in the virus hunt, the next man adds something to what the last man found. And, though their opinions sometimes may differ, each man has some reason to congratulate the other.

In any event, snide critics now have little cause to complain about some overlooked phosphorous of a quarter-century ago. In 1952, Stanley opened a new Virus Laboratory at the University of California which, with him as its director, has replaced his old employer, the Rockefeller Institute for Medical Research, as the concentration point for the largest single group of virus researchers in the world. His laboratory has done as much as any research center—more than most—to put nucleic acid on the biological map and develop a new field that might be called, quite properly, nuclear chemistry. In this case, the "nuclear" refers to the nucleus of the living cell rather than to the nucleus of the atom, as in nuclear physics. By the strangest sort of paradox, Stanley's laboratory has proved quite the opposite of what he originally thought was true. He has presided over this curious train of events with all the delight we might attribute to a man about to win a second Nobel Prize, something that has happened to no man and only one woman (Marie Curie).

The laboratory came about as the result of a chance encounter a few months before Stanley won the Nobel Prize in chemistry for his 1935 discovery. In the late spring of 1946 he was flying out to the University of California to collect one of his eight honorary degrees, in this instance an LL.D., when he was set down for three hours in the Cheyenne, Wyoming, airport because of engine trouble. Among the grounded passengers was a tall man with a deep voice, who introduced himself as Robert Gordon Sproul, president of the University of California.

"We'll meet officially when I hand you that degree," said Dr. Sproul, "but we won't have much chance to visit then. Let's sit down here and talk."

It's not a matter of record what was in Sproul's mind when he spied Stanley's Anglo-Saxon face. Because he was president of a university (the nation's largest), because part of the business of a university president is to scout talent, and because 1946 was a time of change, we can rightfully suspect that recruitment may have crossed Sproul's mind.

Stanley chattted with Sproul about his conviction that the multiplication and mutation of viruses in the cells of their hosts was accompanied by measurable chemical changes. As a matter of fact, he said, what he would like to do, now that the war was over, would be to assemble a staff of first-class biochemists and biophysicists and to engage in a concentrated effort to spot those changes.

Couldn't he do that at the Rockefeller Institute? It did not seem possible. Several wartime developments had demonstrated what group efforts could do in research with a specified goal and large financial resources. The Institute's budget appeared fairly well fixed. It seemed to Stanley that if he were to ask for a lot more money, he would be asking somebody else to take less. This was hardly fair. No, he said, what was really needed was a new institute devoted to virus chemistry alone. As they prepared to emplane again, Sproul told Stanley: "You've got some exciting plans. Maybe we can help you do something about them."

It took another year for this airport dream castle to materialize. The fact that Stanley meanwhile won the Prize, with Sumner and Northrup, surely did not deter this materialization. It also furnished another example of Stanley's good fortune and "knack for getting results."

In the fall of 1948, Sproul announced that Stanley would come on as professor of biochemistry, chairman of the department, and director of the Virus Laboratory. Some $2,000,000 still had to be raised and the laboratory had to be built, of course. This required another four years.

The Biochemistry and Virus Laboratory building is situated on the side of the Berkeley hills, overlooking the campus, the city of Berkeley, Oakland Bay, San Francisco, and the Golden Gate.

Research in infectious diseases is restricted to the fifth floor of the laboratory, isolated from the rest of the building and under a slightly negative air pressure, so that air moves into it from the rest of the building. Exhaust air from laboratory workrooms is sucked into hoods and sterilized by electric heaters and banks of ultra-violet lamps before passing outdoors.

There are several other safety features, but even without them the danger of infection would not be great with ordinary precautions. Probably the most dangerous virus that the staff works with is polio. Those who have not acquired a natural immunity to this disease, as most adults have, get vaccinated if they so desire. It is possibly a bigger problem to see that the many plant viruses don't get loose and mottle or stunt the University's shrubs and grasses.

Visitors to Stanley's laboratory are amazed at the speed with which major discoveries have been made there; after all, the Virus Laboratory is still only seven years old.

At Princeton, a long succession of investigators who have since made names for themselves came to work with him. Now, men of like stature come to Berkeley to work under him. His main responsibility is to create an atmosphere in which the research mind can pursue its thoughts, unworried about security and under no pressure to produce at any given moment. This means getting his people permanent faculty appointments—there are only half enough, he says—and also securing a $500,000 annual budget. That much is required to keep his thirty doctors of science and medicine, twelve graduate students, and forty technicians and helpers busy learning, as he puts it, the "intimate details" of viruses.

The typical researcher, picking away perhaps at a tiny peptide chain in the long double spiral of the molecule of acid which transmits life, is not apt to understand fully the research administrator's problems in meeting the payroll of science. This is evidently true even when the administrator is a Nobel laureate such as Stanley, who hands every scientist in the building a key to the supply room, leaves the scientist at work alone, installs no time-clock, and fastidiously refrains from putting his own name on the scientist's papers either as senior author or co-author, as some research directors consider it their right to do.

The close observer notes that Stanley's own name tails off in the literature of original virus research about the time he went to California. This is no small loss. He still has a small laboratory of his own, across from his busy fifth-floor office, and often goes there to talk to staff members. Rarely, however, does he find occasion to cross the hall to work with his own hands, as he did in Princeton. The distance to the other side of the hall, we can guess, is a cause for inner sadness. It is the gulf between an administrator and a scientific worker.

Few employees of superior competence, probably, are ever completely satisfied with their boss. There are some on Stanley's staff who make no bones about complaining: "He talks too much." This view is unquestionably short-sighted, ignoring the need to interpret science to the public as a means of securing greater financial support. In any event, the opinion is not universally shared, inasmuch as Stanley writes and speaks with imagination as well as a kind of chemical purity.

For example, Stanley summed up his changed views about the nature of viruses, cancer, genes, and life in a 1957 lecture before the American Philosophical Society. It has been widely acclaimed by other scientists and, digested, masterfully leads us to the heart of the virus matter:

> One would think that the nature of life would be easy to define since we are all experiencing it. However, . . . we find that in reality it becomes extremely difficult to define just what we mean. . . .
>
> There is no difficulty in recognizing an agent as living or non-living so long as we contemplate structures such as man, cats and dogs or even small organisms such as

bacteria, or, at the other extreme, . . . iron or glass, an atom of hydrogen or a molecule of water, sugar or . . . blood. . . .

But what is the true nature of the difference between a man and a piece of iron? . . . The ability to grow or reproduce and to change or mutate have long been regarded as special properties characteristic of living agents. Certainly mankind and bacteria have the ability to assimilate and metabolize food, respond to external stimuli and to reproduce their kind, properties not shared by molecules of iron or hemoglobin.

Now if viruses had not been discovered, all would have been well. The organisms of the biologist would have ranged from . . . whales and elephants . . . down to the smallest of the bacteria, which are about 200 millimicrons in diameter. There would have been a definite break with respect to size since the largest molecules known to the chemist were only about 20 millimicrons in size.

Life . . . would have been represented solely by those structures [with] the ability to reproduce themselves . . . and all of these were [at least] ten times larger than the largest known molecule. This would have provided a comfortable area of separation . . . between living and non-living things and would have provided ample justification for considering life as . . . unapproachable and unexplainable by science.

Then . . . came the discovery of the viruses. . . . Here . . . was a molecule that possessed the ability to reproduce and to mutate. . . . The distinction between living and non-living . . . seemed to be tottering and soon a full scale intellectual revolution was in progress.

Today the revolution is past and we know that the gap between 20 and 200 millimicrons is filled in completely by the viruses—so much so that there is actually an overlapping with respect to size at both ends. Some large viruses are larger than certain well accepted living organisms whereas some small viruses are actually smaller than certain protein molecules. We have, therefore, a continuity with respect to size as we go from the mesons, electrons, atoms and molecules of the physicist and the chemist, to the organisms of the biologist and on, if you please, to the world and the universe.

Nowhere is it possible to draw a line in this continuity of structures and say all above this size are living and all below are non-living. . . . One is reminded of the quotation attributed to . . . Aristotle over 2,000 years ago . . . that Nature makes so gradual a transition from the animate to the inanimate that the boundary line between the two is doubtful and perhaps non-existent. . . . The essence of his statement is as true today as . . . when he made it. . . .

The discovery of viruses has permitted us to contemplate the nature of life with new understanding. It has enabled us to appreciate in a new light the inherent potentialities of chemical structure. . . . Viruses were discovered by virtue of their ability to replicate. . . .[1]

Now I am only too fully aware of objections that some may have to considering a crystallizable nucleoprotein molecule as a living agent. Some may feel that life is a mystery which is and must remain beyond the comprehension of the human mind. With these I must disagree. . . .

The logical reasoning provided in schemes . . . by means of which relatively complex organic substances could have risen from inorganic matter provides justification for assuming that a chemical structure, perhaps something like nucleic acid, which possessed the ability to replicate, did come into being once upon a time. It needed to have happened only once. . . .

However, Nature has provided a built-in error so that the replication process is not perfect and about one in every million or so replicates is slightly different. This change . . . we now recognize as mutation and as these . . . differences were accumulated . . . it be-

[1] To make replicas; reproduce.

came necessary to make formal recognition of them.
These differences or markers we now call genes. We do
not recognize genes directly but only by differences.
Needless to say, some physical structure had to be responsible. . . .

Now let us consider for a moment the relationships
between genes and viruses since we see that both are related to life. Muller's estimate of the maximum size of a
gene would place it . . . near the middle of the viruses.
Both genes and viruses seem to be nucleoproteins and
both reproduce only within specific living cells. Both
possess the ability to mutate. . . . Actually the similarities between genes and viruses are so remarkable that
viruses very early were referred to as "naked genes" or
"genes on the loose. . . ."

Viruses have been implicated in animal cancers. . . .
Even if eventually one should find no cancer viruses
among the large number of human viruses, the fact that
man carries so many viruses within his cells and that
these are continually passing from person to person
means that we should be ever alert to the possibility of
transduction [2] by these viruses. Of course, there is no confirmed case of transduction in higher organisms as yet.
However, human cancer is a fact and there is certainly
something within every human cell that insures its reproduction whether we call it a gene or a chromosomal
fragment, and so long as human viruses are so abundant
we certainly have the possibility of transduction. . . .

I hope that by this time it is obvious that viruses, cancer, genes and life are tied together . . . that viruses
can act as genes . . . that viruses can cause cancer and
that viruses are structures at the twilight zone of life par-
taking both of living and of molecular properties. Let
us see if there is a common thread of understanding per-
meating all of these relationships. . . . Until recently
no gene or chromosome or any of the ordinary viruses
had been isolated as such in the form of nucleic acid,

[2] Transfer of genes from cell to cell.

hence the "stuff of life," as well as the viruses, had been considered to be nucleoprotein in nature with considerable doubt as to whether the protein or the nucleic acid or the combination of the two was really the biologically active structure.

A recent very important discovery made in our laboratory by Dr. Fraenkel-Conrat has changed the situation considerably and now makes it seem certain that nucleic acid is the all-important structure. . . .

I believe that the elucidation of the structure of nucleic acid in all of its aspects is the most important scientific problem we face today. It is vastly more important than any of the problems associated with the structure of the atom for in nucleic acid structure we are dealing with life itself. . . .

Here, in one of the finest scientific orations of the Virus Age, we have seen Stanley convert what some would see as a retreat from his original position as a protein chemist into a triumphant forward march of knowledge.

In the old question of the virus as "organule or molechism," the virus unequivocally meets only two of the four tests for "life," if we accept the definition of the world in Webster's unabridged dictionary. The definition occupies an entire column, but the special characteristics of life appear to boil down to these four capacities: reproduction, metabolism, growth, and internal adaptation to environment.

Unquestionably, virus particles can reproduce, or multiply, as Stanley has emphasized. If unchecked, they could populate the earth—that is, the living creatures of the earth, inasmuch as they require a living host cell and its protoplasm to feed, clothe, shelter, and, in fact, mother them.

This dependency on the host cell stems out of the virus's almost complete lack of protoplasm and hence metabolism. Metabolism means, in effect, the capacity to eat and use what is eaten. The organism assimilates food unlike itself and chemically changes it into energy and substances identical with its own composition. This process depends to a great extent on a variety of enzymes. Some viruses, such as that of influenza, can synthesize one or two enzymes, and thus technically perform a metabolic process, but only, it appears, to produce substances enabling them to cut holes into the walls of the cells that they invade.

Viruses, on the other hand, are quite lacking in capacity for true growth (though virologists commonly speak of them as growing when they multiply in a culture). As far as is known, viruses do not grow from babies to adults, and do not grow larger during reproduction, something organisms as low as bacteria and as high as woman definitely do. Generally speaking, the higher the order of life, the longer it takes to reach maturity following birth. Viruses presumably come into existence full-grown—about as low as one can get in the scheme of life. But this view, it must be recognized, is that of slow-growing man and not that of the more efficient virus.

The fourth characteristic of life, says the dictionary, is internal powers of adaptation to environment. This power viruses certainly have—they adapt to changing circumstances with remarkable ease. Many virologists would agree with Stanley that viruses are capable of true mutation, or permanent hereditary change in characteristics, but some duck the mutation idea or seek another explanation. One is that the variations are little more than chemical accidents owing to circumstances of the cells infected, plus natural selection of the fittest to survive. Obviously, those fittest to survive are those which can circumvent host antibodies and other forms of resistance to infection. As viruses are continually mixing their vital ingredients with those of the cells they inhabit, there do seem to be endless possibilities for different mixtures of nucleic acid and protein.

A virus, we can now see, leads a kind of half-life—a "borrowed life," in the phrase of Sir Patrick Laidlaw—dependent on the finding of a willing host cell. It appears more analogous to the nucleus of a one-celled organism than to the organism itself. This is virus life, as virologists surmise it.

It is the kind of life that the chemists and physicists have been taking apart in Stanley's laboratory.

33

FRÁENKEL-CONRÁT
ÁND THE ÁCID OF LIFE

THE TWO brightest stars in the galaxy of talent which Stanley has assembled in the Virus Laboratory at the University of California are the biophysicist Robley C. Williams, whom we already know as the astronomer who looks at viruses, and the biochemist Heinz Fraenkel-Conrat, who reached his zenith in 1956 as the first man to take viruses apart, locate their vital ingredient, and then put them back together. Williams and Fraenkel-Conrat, who frequently collaborate in experiments, are both tough-minded investigators and they are quite in agreement that "all this talk about the creation of life doesn't get us anywhere." At least, it doesn't get the working scientist where he wants to be—mainly at his laboratory bench figuring out ways of cracking the nucleic-acid molecule.

Dr. Fraenkel-Conrat has expressly disavowed that he is working on the secret of life in his studies of TMV, or tobacco-mosaic virus. It is quite evident that he doesn't want other biochemists —scores of whom are now analyzing cell nuclei, viruses, and genes—to think he is so pretentious or ambitious. There is also a great difference of opinion as to where the virus fits into the evolution of living cells.

Stanley's view is well known. Viruses, he feels, could have been the first type of life on earth. They now exist, he suggests, as an intermediate form between the inanimate and the animate, between the molecule—a combination of atomic elements—and the organism—a system of life. Other biological thinkers are just as certain that viruses cannot be regarded as the prototype, or original form, of life because they can multiply only as parasites within living cells; hence, the living cells must have come first. Some regard viruses as evidence of an evolutionary slip-up resulting in a backward movement from a higher to a lower form of life. This line of thought holds that the original life models were, and still are, giant protein molecules that have the capacity to cause lesser molecules to rearrange themselves in patterns identical with the protein molecules.

The trouble is that the idea of proteins building proteins does not, of itself, account for the role of nucleic acid in the cell nucleus, a subject of compelling interest only in the last dozen years —of almost feverish interest in the last two or three years. We can say *feverish* because, behind the scenes and behind the visible face of sincere effort to give credit where credit is due, as part of the ethics of science, placing honesty above all else, there is also a tremendous competitive drive and desire to be first, even though, as Dr. Joseph Beard once commented, "Being first can ruin a man." By this he meant that support of an original claim may throw the scientist on the defensive when others proceed to analyze his findings, accept or reject his interpretations, and then add new findings or new interpretations of their own.

What is nucleic acid? This question needs to be answered before we attempt to sketch in the rather random gathering of information that eventually has brought the virus hunt into the midst of our new science, nuclear chemistry.

In the first place, the word is pronounced "new-clee-ic." All it means, in bare essence, is something found in the nucleus of a living cell. The cell normally is made up of nucleus, cytoplasm, and a containing membrane. The cytoplasm, earlier described as the "meat," is also the "potatoes" and, indeed, everything from soup to dessert.

In the cytoplasm, one will find sugars, starches, and fats as well as proteins, all in a chemical factory that has as its chief function the utilization of energy to tear down old materials and build up the new. In this enterprise of cell metabolism, the proteins are the building-blocks. They are made from smaller building-blocks, amino acids, with the aid of enzymes, themselves usually proteins, acting as machine tools. Naturally, in manufacturing America, everyone knows that machine tools are machines that make other machines—cutting, milling, boring, and shaping other metals, for example, without changing themselves.

Every factory worker knows this. He also knows that you have to have designers to furnish the blueprints and behind them engineers to create workable, copyable models in the first place. Protein molecules have been regarded as blueprints for other proteins, and quite probably *are* in some instances. But, according to the more up-to-the-minute theory, the nucleic acids act as "templates," or patterns, for proteins. We might regard them as the master designers of proteins and also capable of engineering their own duplication. In this latter process, they function as genes and transmit hereditary characteristics. The geneticists think of them as messengers, carrying messages to every newborn cell as to what it must be like and how it must behave. But the nucleic acids should be dignified as something more than messenger boys. They are messengers who have risen to become presidents of companies, the top executives who see that policy is carried out and the job gets done. The policy seems to be to seek immortality by perpetuation of the species—"molecular imperialism" again.

There are two definite kinds of nucleic acids; deoxyribonucleic acid (DNA) and ribonucleic acid (RNA). DNA is much better understood, owing to its having been discovered earlier and studied more prior to the last three years.

In their elements, the nucleic acids sound simple enough, since they contain the old standbys of organic life: carbon, hydrogen, and oxygen, plus nitrogen—ordinarily the hallmark of proteins—and phosphorous, in the form of an acid.

Francis H. C. Crick, who describes himself as a molecular biologist, is principally responsible for the most widely accepted theory of DNA structure, based on X-ray studies and experiments largely carried out by others. Crick, of the University of Cam-

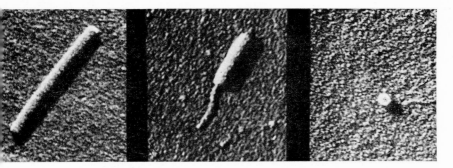

oger G. Hart of the Virus Laboratory, University of California, made these unusual serial ʜotos in a magnification of 150,000. Left, the intact tobacco-mosaic virus rod. Center, the ʜus with its protein tubing partly removed and its nucleic-acid core protruding from both ends. Right, a short cross-section of the protein tube, showing a central hole.

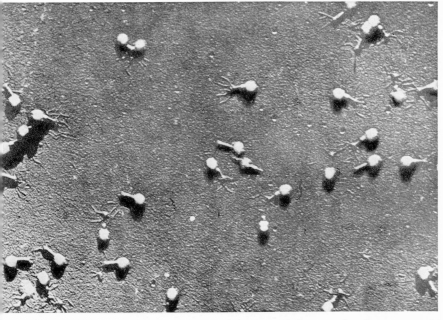

ʜe T-2 bacteriophage particles with their tail fibers unraveled to attack a bacterium and ʜerce the bacterial cell wall. The phage squirts its nucleic-acid content into the cell, and virus multiplication follows.

PLATE 15

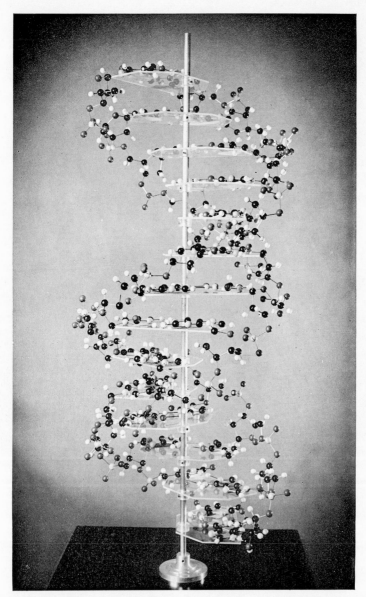

Scientists at the Sloan-Kettering Institute built this strange, complicated structure as their conception of how the atoms in a short section of the long, thread-like molecule of deoxyribose nucleic acid must be put together, according to the theory of Crick. Each ball is an atom of carbon, hydrogen, oxygen, nitrogen, or phosphorus. The atoms are connected in two chains, twisted around each other. Somewhere within this chemical juggling act, involving 300,000 atom balls per single whole molecule of DNA, lies the scientific secret of life—virus life, at any rate.

PLATE 16

bridge, is an amiable, rusty-complexioned Britisher with stupendous eyebrows and a puckish air about him. During World War II he designed mines for the British Admirality. Now he thinks hard, in his laboratory, about what he speaks of simply and colorfully as the "mucky mess" which is the structure of DNA.

Structurally, the DNA molecule is tremendous, though not as big as some protein molecules. A DNA molecule contains as many as 300,000 atoms, perhaps more in some cases. It consists, in well-supported theory, of two chains twisted around each other. Each contains a phosphate and a simple sugar—deoxyribose sugar. Attached to these chains are four nucleotides, or sub-molecules. These sub-molecules are known as bases—something that combines with acids to form salts. In DNA, the bases are guanine, adenine, cytosine, and thymine. The only difference in RNA, other than the fact that the sugar molecule is a slightly simpler ribose, is the fact that RNA contains uracil in place of DNA's thymine.

The sugar, by the way, is not sweet. So we must avoid any fanciful flights about "Ah, sweet mystery of life." With this kind of sugar, life has an acid flavor.

Inspection of a DNA molecule with the electron microscope has revealed it to be a long, thin, wire-like structure, about 2 millimicrons wide and 3,000 millimicrons long. If all the DNA in a single chromosone were laid end to end, it would be an inch and a half long, but only $\frac{2}{25,000,000}$ of an inch thick!

From what he has seen of the DNA molecule through X-ray photography, Crick believes that its structure "consists of two helical [spiral] chains wound around a common axis and held together by hydrogen bonds between specific pairs of bases."

The idea here is somewhat the same as if a football team dropped into formation so that, across the line of scrimmage, eleven opposing players took the same positions, center to center, guard to guard, and so on. In this case, however, instead of playing football, the players just tackle each other. And instead of eleven players on each side, we have several hundred thousand. Crick theorizes that this two-stranded chain reproduces itself by unwinding, permitting each chain to become the pattern for building a replica of itself from materials in the cell.

Not every DNA expert agrees with Crick, and he finds some difficulty in explaining the function of nucleic acids even to his own satisfaction, he says. "If we ever achieve a complete understanding of their construction and behavior, we shall probably have the answer to how nature goes about forming each living organism," remarked Crick, lending Stanley some moral support.[1]

Knowledge of the nucleic acids evolved rather slowly at first. DNA was first discovered in 1869, in the sperm of salmon. RNA (also called pentose nucleic acid [PNA]) was differentiated from DNA some years later, after its discovery in yeast. Historically, DNA overshadowed RNA; it seemed more important to life. The impression grew that RNA was a kind of second-class nucleic acid, since it was first found in a plant organism and then later in tobacco-mosaic and other plant viruses, whereas DNA repeatedly showed up in animal cells. However, in human-virus research, RNA now seems vastly more important.

A German biologist named Joachim Hammerling linked the transmission of hereditary characteristics with the nucleus of living cells in 1931. Another German, the biochemist Robert Feulgen, developed a dye test that turns DNA crimson wherever it is found. This showed that it is always in the nucleus and not the cytoplasm of the cell. In fact, it is always found in the chromosomes of the nucleus, making DNA sound almost synonymous with heredity. The only time DNA appears elsewhere in the cell is when it is in transit to another nucleus.

A young German biochemist in apparent self-exile, Dr. Max Schlesinger, was the first man to find a nucleic acid in a virus. He did this in 1933, while working at the National Institute for Medical Research in Great Britain. The virus was one of several types parasitizing the bacteria normally found in the human intestines, and called a bacterial virus, or bacteriophage. With the help of the centrifuge, Schlesinger reduced his virus to a remarkable state of purity and observed that it contained proteins and a nucleic acid of the DNA type. This feat, as generally overlooked as it was stupendous, was not as exacting as Bawden and Pirie's finding of

[1] F. H. C. Crick: "Nucleic Acids," *Scientific American,* September 1957.

the 6 per cent RNA in tobacco-mosaic virus, however, inasmuch as DNA makes up nearly half of the typical bacterial virus.

Schlesinger did not crystallize his virus, as Stanley did with TMV two years later, nor did his DNA discovery attract as much attention as did Bawden's and Pirie's finding of RNA in TMV in 1937. The excitement and subsequent debate took place on another stage with another cast, and somehow fame passed Schlesinger by. Little is known about him except for his short report on his 1933 discovery, in *Nature,* and his final act: a few years later he shot and killed himself, we are told.

A strong research interest in bacteriophage developed in the next few years, in direct competition with the findings regarding tobacco-mosaic virus. The bacterial viruses—"Every bacterium you look at has dozens of them," says Luria—have been a great source of information about how viruses behave. In fact, in the search for means of preventing virus diseases in humans, the bacteriophage has been a thrilling sideshow, perpetually threatening to take over the main tent, but never behaving quite as ordinary viruses do.

The bacteriophages were discovered by an Englishman and a Frenchman, F. W. Twort, and Félix D. d'Hérelle, in 1915 and 1917, respectively. For some years to come, the subject was mainly characterized by the quarrels over who made the discovery first. D'Hérelle called them "bacteriophages," or bacteria-eaters—phages for short—because he saw that they commonly destroyed the bacteria by dissolving them. This, however, proved to be only one phase of the bacterial virus's activity, occurring when it was reproducing. So there was much argument about the name, too. It appeared that the phage people were behaving disgracefully; at least, other scientists were paying them no attention.

Around 1940, under the leadership of Dr. Max Delbruck of the California Institute of Technology, described by some of his colleagues as "The Pope," the phage researchers agreed to work together in close harmony and try to get their story across. The "cardinals" in this effort included Drs. Alfred D. Hershey, a shy genius of the Carnegie Institution in Cold Spring Harbor, New York; Salvador E. Luria, an Italian-born radiologist, now professor of bacteriology at the University of Illinois in Urbana, who says he got interested in phages while talking to a friend on a Turin trolley car; Renato Dulbecco, also at Cal Tech in Pasadena; Seymour S. Cohen of the University of Pennsylvania; and Gunther Stent, now with Stanley in Berkeley. The chief overseas delegate was Dr. André Lwoff of the Pasteur Institute in Paris.

In the bacterial-virus field, everybody seems to do everything, so it is difficult to assign priorities in the dramatic discoveries. Everything about phages is dramatic, incidentally. The virus is tadpole-shaped, with a "head" and a "tail." To invade the colon bacterium, the virus sticks its tail—some insist it is really a beak—into the microbe. Through this tiny "hypodermic needle," the virus injects its "naked body" of nucleic acid into the cell. In the process, it leaves behind its protein covering. In other words, it "loses its head" and sheds its "overcoat" in the first step toward reproduction.

Last year Dr. Lloyd M. Kozloff of the University of Chicago reported experiments indicating that the phage's tail fibers may be covered with a protein that has an ability to contract—myosin. This would relate it to higher animals, whose muscles are made of myosin. The tail fibers also contain two nucleotides, as extensions of the phage's DNA core, and these interact with the host-cell wall on contact. The muscle now contracts, blows out the plug of fibers, and causes the DNA to squirt through the now open hollow needle.

It is easy to understand why the phage virus always fascinates investigators. One of three things may happen when a phage attacks a bacterium in this manner.

From fifteen to thirty minutes later, the bacterium may burst, releasing anywhere from fifty to two hundred exact copies of the single virus that injected its nucleic juice into the cell.

Or, secondly, the bacterium itself may go on living, as if nothing had happened, growing and dividing and producing more germs. Then, twenty or thirty or even forty or fifty generations later, one of its descendants may explode and release the new crop of viruses!

As Luria points out, this could be one way of explaining how a cancer virus could infect a young host and then not reappear until the host is mature. During this eclipse stage—first recognized by Lwoff—it is impossible to detect the midget microbe that has infected the microbe, since it exists only in the form of DNA. But this has been experimentally demonstrated only with bacterial and not with cancer viruses.

There is a third possibility—transduction. It is illustrated in the case of a phage inhabiting the strain of bacteria causing diphtheria. It long has been known that the troublemaker in diphtheria is not the bacteria per se, but the toxin it produces. But it has not been known why some strains of diphtheria bacteria produce a toxin and why others do not.

Toxins are non-living poisonous chemicals given off by certain germs—such as those of tetanus, botulism, and diphtheria—and are themselves responsible for the illness, in many instances a critical one. Toxins are cell-free, readily passing through bacteria-tight filters like viruses, and, like viruses, having the capacity to produce antibodies—in this case, called antitoxins. The one big difference is that toxins will cause disease but do not multiply in the victim and hence transmit the disease further, whereas a virus will both cause and transmit disease.

In 1951, Dr. Victor J. Freeman of the University of Washington in Seattle—and, later, other researchers—succeeded in changing non-toxic diphtheria bacteria into toxin-producing ones simply by exposing them to viruses that were descendants of those inhabiting virulent strains.

One is immediately apt to think of the virus, riding inside the bacterium, as being the cause of the disease, and therefore of diphtheria as a viral rather than a bacterial disease. But this does not seem to be the case, although the possibility of a virus inducing a bacterium to cause disease is an intriguing speculation. Rather, the observers interpret the diphtheria-virus discovery as an example of transduction, a virus behaving as a gene and carrying hereditary characteristics from one germ to another—in this case, apparently by lugging some of the toxin-producing bacterium's nucleic acid with it.

This amazing process of transduction was first discovered by Dr. Oswald T. Avery of the Rockefeller Institute. In 1944, Avery showed that DNA was the gene material in pneumonia bacteria, and that the characteristics of various types of pneumonia could be changed by transferring molecules of purified DNA from one strain to another. Specifically, the characteristic transmitted via the DNA genes was the presence or absence of a "rough" or "smooth" coat—that is, a capsule around one germ and lack of a capsule around the other.

This had nothing to do with viruses. It remained to be shown that both virus and free DNA would at times behave as the gene. That this was a reasonable presumption was implied from the use of radioactive phosphorous as food for colon bacteria and, hence, for the bacterial viruses living with them. A Geiger counter detected where the phosphorus went.

Dr. Seymour S. Cohen, in 1946, was the first to use radioactive tracers in this way. He and, subsequently, Gunther Stent and Ole Maaloe of Denmark definitely showed that the radioactive phosphorous went into DNA, and that the DNA was what the virus squirted into the bacterium. Inside the cell, the virus DNA then got busy and, utilizing proteins and DNA from the cell, manufactured virus particles of its own kind, all with new protein coats.

The process of building phosphorous into DNA in the bacterium took about twelve minutes. In another twelve minutes the viruses were completed, and then burst the cell. The offspring were radioactive, too, but to a lesser extent in each successive generation.

These experiments provided the first evidence, as far as bacteriophages were concerned, that the agent of heredity is in the nucleic-acid core and not the protein jacket left behind, and also confirmed Schlesinger on the fact that the phage nucleic acid is DNA.

Another brilliant study, reported in 1952, showed that what Avery said about transfer of genetic characteristics via free DNA in pneumonia microbes was also true when a bacterial virus and another bacterium were substituted. Dr. Norton D. Zinder, now of the Rockefeller Institute, and Joshua Lederberg of the University of Wisconsin, made the decisive experiment in Madison. Zinder was then only twenty-three, and Lederberg about five five years his senior. Lederberg, at thirty-three, won the 1958 Nobel Prize in medicine and physiology (with Drs. George W.

Beadle and Edward L. Tatum) for "genetic recombination" discoveries, including the experiments that he and Zinder did together.[2] Lederberg since has accepted an appointment at Stanford.

What they set out to do was to see if they could mix and hence "mate" two strains of *Salmonella* bacteria that cause typhoid fever in mice. Each of the strains they selected lacked a capacity possessed by the other to synthesize a certain amino acid needed for its growth. The acid needed was a different one in each case. Ordinarily, of course, bacteria reproduce like cells by division and proliferation without fertilization. If mating took place, by recombination of genes, Lederberg and Zinder agreed, then some of the offspring ought to be able to grow normally in cultures not fortified with either amino acid. This, in fact, was the case.

But when Lederberg and Zinder experimented to see if their creation of a genetic swap shop would work with still other traits of these choosy bacteria—and it should if a general recombination of genes took place—they found that it did not work. They struggled with various hypotheses to explain this baffling discrepancy. Mutation was ruled out. They eliminated the possibility that free DNA was involved by introducing a DNA-destroying enzyme.

They put their two strains of bacteria in a U-tube, each fluid specimen walled from the other by a filter that would permit fluid to pass but no cells. Transduction of a single trait still took place.

Now they were struck with the idea that they must be dealing with a virus as the genetic messenger, for it could pass through the filter. They were now "getting warmer." When they looked for virus particles, they found them in their donor bacteria. The viruses, they found, were carrying the genes from one strain of bacteria to another, and behaving as genes. They were not acting as infectious agents because they did not kill the one-celled organisms they invaded. Occasionally a virus did become infective, explode a cell, and release new viruses. When these were tested, it was found some had cores of virus DNA, synthesized from the bacterial cells, and some had cores of *Salmonella* DNA, unchanged.

[2] Norton D. Zinder: "Transduction in Bacteria," *Scientific American*, November 1958.

They had disclosed virus transduction of hereditary traits. "A very important discovery," commented Stanley.

There is one trouble with the sensational discoveries involving these tadpole-shaped viruses that live in the bacteria that live in us: they don't look or behave quite like any virus of plant, animal, or human, and they are of no practical use to us in killing disease bacteria. They have furnished a tremendous amount of information about life in the microscopic and ultra-microscopic worlds, but every good biologist knows, however tempting and however often he may be right, that there is risk in reasoning from one living thing to another. To repeat John Enders's sage conclusion, all we are finally sure of in biology is individual variation.

The story of the tobacco-mosaic virus is quite different and, as a source of information on pure virus antigens, of vast potential importance in vaccine making. These two viruses, TMV and phage, have been the greatest rivals in fundamental research into the nature of midget microbes.

For some years Stanley and associates—such as Drs. Hubert S. Loring, Claude A. Knight, and Howard K. Schachman—pondered TMV, trying in every way they could think of to analyze what was in it and whence came its infectivity. They measured the RNA and counted twenty amino acids in the protein coat of the virus rod. The make-up of the nucleic acid in the TMV core seemed to be constant, whereas the percentages of amino acids varied a good deal, no matter which of the many strains of this virus was analyzed.

Hence, Stanley assumed that the proteins probably were the active part causing infection and multiplication. Amino-acid variation, it appeared to him, could account for the different effects produced in different plants. But he was not dogmatic about it; any man could see that phage-and-DNA ran counter to the TMV-and-RNA story. For one thing, DNA made up such a large part of the phage and RNA such a tiny part of TMV.

So we see that at least two schools of thought developed regarding the chemistry of heredity. One group found DNA in bacterial viruses, in pneumococci, and in the nuclei of living cells, and believed that this was the stuff of life. They found some RNA, too, but usually it was in the cytoplasm of the cell, outside the nucleus. They figured that it was primarily a protein builder, not a gene transportation agent at all.

This deduction, however, failed to account for the fact that TMV contains RNA and no DNA. The plant viruses seemed to be in quite a different biological boat from animal viruses, and provided some phage people with an opportunity to look down on TMV people as working with an inferior product of nature. Or so it seemed.

When Heinz Fraenkel-Conrat joined Stanley in the new Virus Laboratory, he, too, was of the protein school of thought. It fell to him, for one, to try to resolve the stuff-of-life issue and, in so doing, to score a victory for *both* sides.

Fraenkel-Conrat is a medium-sized, black-haired, square-jawed, sharp-nosed, and sharp-tongued Prussian forty-nine years old. He has fine, delicate hands—of as much importance in a biochemist's work as in a surgeon's. While he manifests the basic civility that obliges a man to answer questions about his work, he is not a cordial handshaker, but rather indicates a wish that all publicity people would leave him alone. At first he strikes the visitor to his laboratory as an aloof esthete, but his tanned skin betrays an amazingly robust side of his nature. Fraenkel-Conrat—a naturalized American, married, with two children in their teens— is also a thoroughgoing Californian and skis proficiently, both on snow and on water. He questions, rather acidly, whether such facts are of importance in public understanding of science. Let us say that they are of some importance to human understanding of scientists.

Fraenkel-Conrat was born in Breslau when Germany was the world center of chemical research. He became a doctor of medicine in 1933, the year Hitler came into power. Fraenkel-Conrat recoiled from the Nazi order by leaving the country the next year.

Thence he wandered far—to Scotland, where he obtained a Ph.D. degree in biochemistry; to the Rockefeller Institute in New York, at the time when Stanley was first telling the Old Bacteriologists that viruses were protein molecules; to São Paulo, Brazil;

to the University of California for four years; and to the Western Regional Research Laboratory of the Department of Agriculture in Albany, California, where he remained from 1942 to 1950.

In Albany, Fraenkel-Conrat did what he wanted—basic research in protein chemistry—under a budget for wheat research and a research director who gave him his head. But the director was replaced with a more efficient one, who said: "We have spent $100,000 for research on wheat. What are the results?"

This, we can now appreciate, is not a proper question to ask a basic scientist. It was a happy day, therefore, when Stanley visited Fraenkel-Conrat and invited him to join his staff and do biochemical research. He accepted the invitation and went to Berkeley in 1952, after a year's study in England and Denmark. He was happy to find that his new boss leaves him alone to do just as he pleases, as he himself points out.

The thing Fraenkel-Conrat did not like was the publicity that came to him in 1956. What he did of lasting consequence in improving man's understanding of virus diseases all the way from tobacco leaf to tobacco auctioneer was to show that infectivity arises not in TMV's protein coat but in its RNA core. This confirmed the phage-DNA story and seemed to be the end of the protein school of thought. Fraenkel-Conrat was frank about it: "I'm a protein chemist. I hoped protein was the determining factor. It was against my personal inclinations to have a greater interest in nucleic acid."

There could be no doubt about his conclusion, however. Almost at the same time, and quite independently, Drs. Von Alfred Gierer and Gerhard Schramm at the Max Planck Institute for Virus Research in Tübingen, Germany, discovered the same thing.

Schramm's laboratory, much older than Stanley's, was one of the first to get interested in the problem of taking the 300-by-15-millimicron TMV rod apart and putting it back together, but Stanley's caught up, four years after it opened.

"The reconstitution of virus from its constituents and building blocks is an idea which has had us fascinated for a long time," said Schramm. "I think we did the first experiment about fifteen years ago. At that time we found that we could separate the protein from the nucleic acid and that from this protein we could again prepare the virus rods. At that very early time, the role of nucleic acids in the biosynthesis of proteins was not known to us. . . . We were disappointed that we had no activity in this reconstructed rod. Naturally this was because there was no nucleic acid inside the rods."

Fraenkel-Conrat had to work his way through this same problem of reconstitution, and well beyond it. In so doing, he first "discovered" an artifact that attracted a great deal of attention—and taught a lesson. Artifacts are products of human workmanship—that is, facts not in the nature of the thing studied but resulting from man's manipulation of it. Whether he is observing a natural phenomenon or merely the effects of his own technique is a real problem to a virologist because his subject is so tiny. If publicity comes too soon, before he has exhausted all possible sources of error, it can put him on an embarrassing spot.

We remember that in the early 1950's Robley Williams and others had had some success as virus smashers. They found several rough-and-ready ways of leaving the TMV but a hollow, broken shell of its former self. They tore off its protein casing and left it floating around in its nucleic acid birthday suit as "naked genes," to borrow a Stanley allusion.

In March 1955, Fraenkel-Conrat elected to see if he could gentle down these techniques of removing the protein "lock washers" from the nucleic-acid "twisted cable" so that he might have some undamaged parts to put back together. The idea was to see if he could disassemble and then reconstitute a virus with some "life" in it.[3]

With a common household detergent called sodium lauryl sulfate, he delicately removed the protein hides off one group of viruses, dissolved in solution. Then he treated another group with an alkali, sodium carbonate; this pulled out their nucleic-acid cores. The entire process was a meticulous one, full of ticklish details and minute maneuvers, involving correct temperature and timing, among other things. Fraenkel-Conrat's fine hands and capacity for concentration were essential here.

[3] Heinz Fraenkel-Conrat: "Rebuilding a Virus," *Scientific American,* June 1956.

Williams's electron microscope showed Fraenkel-Conrat that he had what he wanted, some intact hollow cylinders of protein on one hand and some long strands of nucleic acid on the other. There was no sign of a whole virus in either solution.

Now the dark-haired, slender chemist took his two specimens from his fifth-floor laboratory up to the greenhouse on the roof and rubbed a little of each on the leaves of tobacco plants, being careful to keep them separate. As we already know, potent TMV will cause a young tobacco plant to break out with a rash overnight. Nothing happened. Therefore, it appeared to Fraenkel-Conrat that neither the protein shell nor the RNA core contained any infectivity by itself. It did seem that he had taken life apart.

Now, freely predicting that nothing would come of the experiment he was about to try, he took some more of the two solutions and mixed them together. A few minutes later an assistant noted an opalescent sheen forming in the solution. It was reminiscent of Stanley's 1935 tobacco-juice filtrate when the TMV crystals were beginning to form.

Fraenkel-Conrat and Williams examined the combined solution under the electron microscope and saw perfectly formed TMV rods! It was as if a peck of oysters had been shucked from their shells and then had crawled back in—but not into the same shells. In effect, these were "synthetic viruses."

The next question was whether this reconstituted virus had the old TMV punch. On a Friday morning Fraenkel-Conrat applied some to the leaves of fresh tobacco plants on the roof. Returning on Monday morning, he found the plants covered with hundreds of spots of infection. He noted that the synthetic virus was not nearly as infectious as the natural kind. Neverthelesss, what had appeared lifeless in its component parts did show signs of life again.

What a great day in the life of a scientist—and in the life of a research director like Stanley!

There was no unseemly rush to spread the news. Not until the following October did the *Proceedings of the National Academy of Sciences* publish the Fraenkel-Conrat–Williams report of the discovery, and not until then did Dan Wilkes, the University of California's public-information director, get out a release.

Now came the headlines. Science writers decided that this was "creation of life in a test tube." It did sound like it, if you stretched the facts some. *Collier's* entitled it: "Now—MAN-MADE VIRUS—First Step in Controlling Heredity."

In further experiments, however, Fraenkel-Conrat found that the naked nucleic acid was extremely unstable and rapidly lost its infectivity when deprived of its protein life-jacket. It appeared that what the protein did was to provide some padding and protection to keep these delicate strands alive.

The first sample of RNA Fraenkel-Conrat had taken up to the roof had died en route, apparently. Perhaps he had tarried too long in the hall, talking to a fellow biochemist. Further work showed that when he exercised tender care, the stuff remained alive. It did cause infection by itself, though it was far weaker than when packaged with protein.

So Fraenkel-Conrat had not exactly taken life apart and put it back together again, as the headlines proclaimed, even though, by the oddest freak of circumstance and enthusiasm, another researcher repeated the error and confirmed the artifact!

The second discovery was of greater ultimate significance, of course, though now somewhat anticlimatic. It narrowed the search for the virus heart of the matter, rather than broadening it. Fraenkel-Conrat showed that the vital part could be separated from the non-vital part and examined by itself, and that the two parts could then be repackaged with only a certain amount of post-surgical shock and tendency toward fainting spells. As he got better at it, he was able to reconstitute TMV rods that looked, under Williams's electron microscope, exactly like natural ones, and he showed that they were from 70 to 100 per cent as infective as the original rods.

By 1958 he had gone further still, and had begun the breakdown of the nucleic acid itself in an attempt to find in what fraction of it lies its infectivity, or "life." This is a fantastically complicated business, judging from DNA. The DNA molecule consists, as we said, of two chains twisting around a common axis and held together by chemical bonds along the way.

Fraenkel-Conrat has found some evidence suggesting that he has narrowed the infective, or vital, fraction down to a piece of the RNA core called a polynucleotide chain, meaning that "life" might be found in one nucleotide or another.

Visualize this: the intact TMV rod with a molecular weight of 40,000,000 to 50,000,000 atoms contains an RNA core weighing about 2,400,000, all the rest being the protein coat. From the core, the scientist has broken off some pieces that show signs of life, but, as he reported in 1958, there are some question marks about it. "All we know definitely," he said with utter scientific honesty, "is that the question marks are right."

As for man-made viruses, he wrote: "We can now gracefully retreat from a position which we have never held or expressed. Life was not here created in test tubes, since the nucleic acid alone shows 'signs of life' similar to those of the original virus."

Stanley's laboratory had not achieved his cherished hope, despite a little premature celebration at the crossroads of life. It was a crossroads, apparently, for now it appeared possible to leave the protein theory behind in plant as well as animal viruses and pursue the acid of life.

Although this might be read as a defeat for protein protagonists, such as Stanley and Fraenkel-Conrat themselves, there was an unqualified victory in another respect. RNA has been shown to be the equal of DNA as a vital life force, and here's the best part of it:

Not long ago, Stanley's laboratory found that polio virus contains RNA—not DNA. Meanwhile Burnet's laboratory in Melbourne found that influenza virus is also a member of the RNA clan. Polio and flu are not merely animal but also human viruses, so it now has become apparent that the viruses within us are not essentially different, as far as we know, from those in plants.

Events in the nucleic-acid story change from one meeting of scientists to the next. For example, Drs. Frederick L. Schaffer and Carl F. T. Mattern made a joint report in April 1959 before the Federation of American Societies for Experimental Biology. Schaffer, we may recall, had crystallized polio virus, and Mattern—then at the National Institutes of Health, but now, like Schaffer, at the University of California in Berkeley—had crystallized Coxsackie virus. Now they were able to state that they had refined RNA from these viruses and, with the nucleic acids alone, had produced polio and Coxsackie infections in tissue cultures and paralysis and death in young mice.

All told, virus researchers have found RNA to be the infectious element, or "active ingredient," in about a dozen different animal and human viruses, including some of the ECHO's, foot-and-mouth disease, encephalitis, and one of the mouse leukemia viruses. DNA, in the field of virus disease, appeared definitely to be taking a back seat.

Whether this narrowing of the gap between plant and animal virus life will ultimately make any difference in disease prevention is a question we must leave to the future. As this is written, one thing seems fairly sure: doctors can no longer kid Stanley about wasting time and money on the lowly plant viruses. As one great, medically oriented microbiologist recently acknowledged, "He's better than I thought."

That is about all we can say for a laboratory creator of life at the moment, except that, if one ever does show up, there is this chance that he may be in virus chemistry, and, if this happens, then the scientific bibliography will have the name of Stanley somewhere near the beginning and the name of Fraenkel-Conrat somewhere not far from the climax.

Yet one great characteristic of fundamental research is its unpredictability, and therefore no one dares predict whom science will endow with immortality.

As we bring this book to a conclusion, DNA appears to bid for the center of the stage again and, by a paradoxical twist, to have brought with it an old friend of protein chemistry, an enzyme. Many different laboratories are making artifical DNA or DNA-like substances; likewise, RNA.

Dr. Arthur Kornberg, formerly of Washington University in St. Louis and now of Stanford in Palo Alto, reported at the 1958 annual meeting of the American Chemical Society that he and his associates in St. Louis had, in original work first reported two years before, virtually solved the problem of synthesizing molecules of DNA—in a different approach to the problem of laboratory "creation of life."

The Kornberg group started with one hundred pounds of colon bacteria, called *Escherichia coli*. This is one kind commonly inhabited by bacteriophages. One hundred pounds is equal to an estimated twenty quadrillion individual germs. From these bacteria they extracted a powerful new enzyme that seems to hold the key to life in *E. coli.*

With this enzyme and a small amount of DNA from any source —for example, a bacterial virus or the thymus gland of a calf— Kornberg can build an unlimited amount of new DNA by adding the proper building-materials. These are four nucleotides or submolecules of nucleic acid—namely, the triphosphate combinations of thymine, adenine, guanine, and cytosine. The final product meets every test for DNA.

The tiny amount of DNA used as a primer acts as the template, or pattern, that the enzyme follows in working on the building-materials as a catalyst. The curious thing about this whole operation is that an enzyme is itself a true protein or a protein conjugated, or chemically coupled, with something else. This discovery, in the DNA camp, puts the earlier pro-protein views of Stanley, Fraenkel-Conrat, and others back in the picture, for the relationship between the nucleic acid and protein enzyme in the St. Louis experiment seemed to be more that of active partners than master and servant.

Kornberg points out that the discovery bears out the Crick theory of the double spiral structure of the DNA molecule very nicely. He also points out an unexpected turn of events. In his mixtures he detected a peculiar template substance containing not four but only two of the DNA bases—adenine and thymine. This substance, labeled AT, behaves like DNA in stimulating production of replicas of itself. Regretting that it was too early for any conclusions, Kornberg commented:

"Nevertheless, at the risk of being highly speculative and perhaps even somewhat facetious, the possibility can be pointed out that this 'peculiar monster' is actually a genetic template more primitive than DNA and perhaps even more closely related to the origin of life."

WHAT'S NEXT?

WHAT'S NEXT?

The virus hunt has brought us a long way and has illustrated, with each forward step, that it still has a long way to go. What can we hope for next? A cold vaccine? A cancer vaccine? Family-size packages of antibody-producing, purified antigens? Super-vaccines? Drugs that will block out or blot out the virus in the cell it infects? Some kind of molecular medicine, or cell resistance builder, that may render us, the imperfect host, impervious to the perfect parasite?

The hope within us for longer, healthier life compels us to expect great things of medical science; it has produced great things. We can expect even greater, most of all perhaps from biochemistry and biophysics.

The nuclear chemists, such as Dr. Alfred E. Mirsky of the Rockefeller Institute, one of the original DNA experts, are now finding that the course of life is not only determined by atoms of a molecule bonded together in chain-like formations but by electrical charges playing along this chain. So, to the contest of gene and virus for mastery of the cell race, and to the concept of chemically counterfeit molecules as a cause of disease or of resistance to it, we must add the expectation that electrochemistry, electronics, and even nuclear physics conceivably will take their places beside microbiology, immunology, genetics, and endocrinology as new avenues to the study and possible control of diseases in the cell. Perhaps someday science will fight disease with some sort of electrochemical shock therapy that will untwist defective molecules.

When we turn an eye to the future, this is the way our imaginations carry us forward, in non-stop, high-altitude flights of fancy that can easily overshoot the evidence and overlook the valleys between the mountain peaks. It is stimulating and inspiring, and scientists themselves engage in such speculations from time to time, in their own brand of cracker-barrel mental relaxation.

But they are always aware, the good ones, of the risk they take in predicting the future, especially in the biological sciences. The Cal Tech prophet of molecular medicine, Dr. Linus Pauling, likes to point out: "We do not know the molecular structure of liquid water, although it makes up seventy per cent of our bodies!" Everybody knows the chemical formula of water, of course, but we do not know how the two atoms of hydrogen and one of oxygen, endlessly repeated, hang together to form a fluid.

Occasionally, strong-minded scientists crawl out on a limb and find no way back from their unfulfilled prophecies. They are not as lucky as Sir Macfarlane Burnet, a case in point. In his well-written little Penguin book, *Viruses and Man,* he said of polio in 1950 that he could see "no immediately visible way" of producing a killed-virus vaccine in quantity, and he was "chary" of a live-virus vaccine. "Given a continuation of peace and prosperity," Burnet commented, "I should prophesy that within twenty-five years poliomyelitis immunization will be a general policy in at least a few American states." Except for the fact it was *five* years and *forty-eight* American states, his was an accurate statement. Fortunately, in a postscript at the end of the book, dated 1953, Burnet had an opportunity to crawl back, take the Enders tissue-culture break-through into account, and correct his timetable to take care of the Salk vaccine. But he remained dubious about live-virus vaccines, such as those since developed by Koprowski and Sabin. These now show great promise.

Taking full advantage of hindsight, we can appreciate the perils of attempting to divine the future, either too optimistically or too pessimistically. The dangers need not deter us, if we simply remember what the virus hunt has taught us about medical research. As indicated before, the scientist himself knows this dictum full well: basic research ultimately produces results of benefit to us all, but we cannot predict when a given result will come or even that it will be the one that the scientist was looking for.

Knowledge of cause does not necessarily mean prevention or cure is at hand. It was forty years from the time that Karl Landsteiner found the cause of polio until the requisite knowledge for making a vaccine was assembled. Nor does the finding of a preventive or cure necessarily wait on fundamental knowledge. Jenner gave the world a vaccine against smallpox nearly one hundred years before cause (virus) and effect (antibodies) were understood.

Notwithstanding, we should like the answers to at least three questions:

1. What more can we expect from the viruses within us?
2. Will we ever have cures for some of the more common virus diseases—that is, treatment effective after infection begins—something like penicillin or a sulfa drug?
3. What improvements can we look for in vaccines?

First, we can easily see from the discovery of the Coxsackie viruses, adenoviruses, enteroviruses, mucus viruses, and others—close to one hundred in the last ten years—that we can expect more new virus diseases. They really will not be new diseases, to be sure; they will be old diseases linked with viruses identified for the first time.

We scrutinized the virus theory of cancer in some of the last chapters.

Viruses are also suspected in Hodgkin's disease, a malignancy of the lymph glands.

Some have thought multiple sclerosis to be of virus origin, and also, recently, ulcerative colitis.

Mongolism, a form of congenital idiocy, has been considered in association with both leukemia and German measles, one a suspected and the other a known virus offender.

Arithritis often has been branded as a virus disease, but apparently without good evidence.

One even hears talk about schizophrenia, the number-one major mental illness, as a virus disease.

We have no credible documentation in the case of schizophrenia, and very litttle more than circumstantial evidence in the case of such diseases as ulcerative colitis, a chronic ulceration of the colon that some psychiatrists regard as psychosomatic and surgeons know is sometimes pre-cancerous. Yet we now know how virus nucleic acid can injure cell metabolism and habits and patterns of cell reproduction without manifesting the usual signs of infectious disease.

As virus researchers have come to appreciate the capacity of viruses to hide out in the cells for years, suspicion has grown—and has been voiced by such people as Huebner and Salk—that some of the chronic degenerative diseases of old age are the eventual result of virus damage. Huebner speaks of "human erosion," or tissue aging and breakdown, as the result of floods of virus infections over the years. Salk comments on the possible damage done to brain and spinal-cord cells by a multitude of minor virus infections in childhood. He thinks perhaps the weak backs, abdominal-muscle weakness, high blood pressure, and stomach ulcers, as well as various aches and pains that beset us, may be the consequence of viruses that invade our central nervous systems when we are children and—normally held in check by antibodies—produce organic disease when we are under emotional stress or are weakened by fatigue or by age. Salk labeled his speculations "flights of fancy," meaning that he wished to raise the intriguing questions without being asked for answers or proof at the moment. Even something as mild as chickenpox might be an unexpected troublemaker under such a gloomy outlook.

In any event, we can expect to have the common virus infections for some time to come—*even, perhaps, in increased incidence*. The automobile and the general mobility of our population have speeded up transmission of viruses that spread by person-to-person contact, with the result that we become exposed to more different types of viruses than our more stable grandparents did. We also build resistance to them, but this constant mixing of viruses and of hosts enables the more versatile viruses to change and render obsolete the antibodies produced by their ancestors. This is particularly true of the unstable viruses, such as those causing influenza and the common cold. Small children apparently furnish a great microbiological mixing-bowl, since grandparents often acquire colds soon after visiting them. Thus we can see hazards of predicting that within two years we will have a vaccine that will prevent from sixty to seventy per cent of common colds, as Dr. Thomas G. Ward, professor of virology at Notre Dame University, *did* predict in 1959. "I realize that I have stuck my neck out," added Ward. He also hastened to predict: "People are not going to take the vaccine, just as they are not taking polio vaccine."

We see that the job of the virus hunter is not simply to discover new viruses—hu eds presumably remain to be discovered. It is also one of keeping up, as far as immunization goes, with the new models, some of them apparently changing in their molecular details almost as rapidly as our motorcars.

Second: What about cures?

The "miracle drugs" work only against a few of the larger viruses, such as those of parrot fever, lymphogranuloma venereum, and trachoma. These are not likely to present a problem —only 278 cases of parrot fever and 461 of lymphogranuloma were reported in 1957.

Someday we may have a cure for common respiratory infections; we are beginning to see signs of what it might be like. Only last year Dr. Alick Isaacs of the London Laboratories of the British Medical Research Council reported that he found something in a killed influenza virus grown in hatching hen's eggs which interferes with multiplication of live flu viruses. Isaacs suspected a protein, and called it interferon; whatever it is, the viruses can't "eat" it. The general idea is that this "chemical carrion" might be developed for local treatment of respiratory infections. Other scientists are beginning to see signs of similar or different bodily products that block virus action.

The closest thing to a cure for a human virus infection yet claimed comes from Dr. Don J. Weeks of the Peter Bent Brigham Hospital, hard by Harvard Medical School, in Boston. He reported that lactobacilli, a kind of bacteria forming in fermented milk and sold as a standard drugstore item, quickly heal canker sores, cold sores, or fever blisters in the mouth. These are caused by the famous "living-in" virus of herpes simplex; it dwells in the body continually, showing up only during passing breakdowns of bodily resistance. Weeks made his discovery in an interesting way. He was treating patients who had these chronic mouth ulcers with antibiotics. Some developed diarrrhea as a side-effect. He gave them lactobacillus tablets to control the diarrhea and noted that the tablets worked quickly against the mouth ulcers! This seems a long way around Robin's research barn, but important leads often develop in this way.

Many other clues have come out of animal or tissue-culture experiments. They are most numerous in cancer chemotherapy research, where an all-out effort is being made to screen and test "everything in the books" for possible curative effects against cancers—chemical poisons, South American head-shrinking potions, enzymes, amino acids, amino-acid "analogue" compounds that are antagonistic to cell growth, nucleic acids, various nucleic components, and antibiotics. Some new antibiotics, such as mitomycin-C, have been seen to curb some cancers in some people.

People take botany lightly, but one of the most intensive searches for cancer antibiotics is being conducted by Dr. Paul Burkholder of the Brooklyn Botanic Garden, who is the discoverer of chloromycetin. His laboratory has screened hundreds of thousands of drugs and sent the most promising on to the Sloan Kettering Institute in New York for further study. The problem is to find something that will destroy cancer but not its host.

When we add up all of these efforts in the light of past experience, we have the uneasy suspicion that science as yet may not quite have its finger on the pivotal point in cancer causation and hence, perhaps, in cancer control. The Good Lord knows that scientists are trying, but as yet He has not revealed His chosen instrument to us.

One well-intentioned effort that availed nothing was that of Huebner, in Bethesda, and also of Dr. Alice E. Moore at Sloan Kettering, to "train"—at any rate, sort out—viruses that attack human cancer. The Bethesda work began with the observation that certain viruses—polio, adeno-, and Coxsackie—grow swiftly in, and hence destroy, test-tube cultures of human-cancer cells from the uterine cervix (this is the second most common cancer in women). In twenty-three of thirty-two women patients with cervical cancer at the Clinical Center in Bethesda, adenovirus definitely caused partial destruction of the cancer. In no instance, however, was there complete destruction, and commonly the cancer began growing again as early as ten days later. The explanation of this disappointment was plain enough from the fact that the treatment did not work at all in patients who had adenovirus antibodies in the first place. Those who benefited temporarily soon developed antibodies; these apparently halted the beneficient virus!

Yet somehow we move away from these experiments with a sense of unexpended anticipation, as if there might still be something here. The *British Medical Journal* brings us back to earth with the statement that the scientific literature of antiviral chemotherapy is "a voluminous catalogue of hopes, uncritical optimism and eventual disappointment."

Third:

The whole subject of virus-disease prevention—via vaccination particularly, but also including the immune serums, or bottled antibodies—is a great deal more promising.

What is the outlook?

Fundamentally, the research problem is to learn a great deal more regarding the various ways the body goes about defending itself against invasion. Antibodies are not the whole story by any means, as the discovery of properdin has shown. We know that some people have a general resistance to most infections, and it also appears that there may be a more or less specific cell resistance. Eventually, science may give us something besides specific vaccines as resistance builders.

We can spot several trends in vaccine research.

One piece of news in 1959 takes us, by analogy, right back to Jenner and cowpox. The Jenner in this case is a Dr. John M. Adams (plus three associates, all at the University of California in Los Angeles). In place of cowpox we have an attenuated variety of virus causing canine distemper, a feverish sort of malaise common to dogs. Just as cowpox protects against smallpox, it would appear that the virus of another animal disease protects against another human disease—in this case, measles! At any rate, other scientists also have found a relationship between the anti- bodies against measles and distemper, so much so that some have wondered if distemper was not dog measles. Preliminary tests by the Adams group on two hundred mental-hospital patients indi- cated that a single shot of canine-distemper vaccine reduced human susceptibility to measles about sixty-seven per cent. As Adams pointed out, large-scale field tests need to be made to determine whether the vaccine is wholly effective and a competi- tor of the experimental measles vaccine developed by the Enders group at Harvard.

One improvement that now appears near at hand, after some years of experimentation and elimination of many hitches, would do away with the hypodermic needle. It is a so-called hypospray, or jet injector, that can shoot a "bullet" of vaccine un- der the skin so rapidly that it is possible to give up to seven hun- dred fully sterile shots an hour—these *are* shots literally. This could prove to be one of the greatest boons to vaccination since cowpox, thanks to a mere mechanical gadget. The jet injector eliminates "fear of the needle," long recognized as a great deter- rent in mass vaccination programs such as the one against polio. But the greatest deterrents, Huebner notes, are parents who are too busy or too lazy to have their children vaccinated.

Another perhaps longer-range and more basic trend may be away from the impure "viral soups"—containing proteins or other substances that can produce allergic or other toxic reactions— and toward purified antigens. Thanks to the work of Stanley and his successors, chemists can reduce some viruses to hundred-per- cent-pure crystalline form. It is possible but not as yet considered practical or feasible for mass production because of the time and expense involved. But obstacles may be overcome.

Salk has put killed-virus vaccines on the map as an effective way of producing, according to all polio evidence, a fairly durable protection against disease damage in the vast majority of per- sons vaccinated according to schedule. Yet triple vaccination against polio has failed to protect against paralysis in something like one out of ten persons vaccinated. Virologists such as

Enders have had more confidence in vaccines that will produce "live" infection with a virus that will multiply in the body and yet not produce ill effects. It is now an open question whether such vaccines are necessarily superior against all types of virus infection.

With live-virus vaccines that are made from attenuated, or mutated, viruses, there is the potential danger that they can mutate back toward virulence and, as someone has said, "go in like a lamb and come out like a lion." This is apparently not so with the more stable virus mutants, such as in yellow fever, but is a danger in the less stable ones.

Theoretically there may be a way around this problem however, as we can see from the remarks of Heinz Fraenkel-Conrat: "When an animal receives an injection of a foreign protein, it generally produces specific antibodies against that substance. Thus injections of tobacco mosaic virus into a rabbit will cause the rabbit to generate antibodies which specifically neutralize the virus's protein."

See the possibility here? Fraenkel-Conrat did not say: "neutralize the virus's nucleic acid." If most viruses are constructed as TMV is—and there is reason to believe this is so—then the infectious part of them, the nucleic acid, is wrapped inside a protein coat. If it were possible to purify the protein coat and discard the nucleic acid, the scientist might then make a vaccine that would produce antibodies against the live, protein-coated virus but would be completely safe because the virus "stinger" would have been pulled.

This would be more akin to a killed-virus vaccine than a live one, but it might be possible to make up for lack of multiplication following injection by giving a larger dose of the antigen. As a matter of fact, a vaccine like this has been made against a bacterial disease, pneumonia, using the pneumoccus's singular carbohydrate coat as the purified antigen. This vaccine was introduced as a preventive just at the time when the antibiotics arrived on the scene as a specific cure for pneumoccal pneumonia, so there has been little need for it.

Out of the research on purified antigens has come much thought about how many antigens would be needed to protect us against *all* virus infections, or against all virus infections of a given class, such as all possible types of flu, colds, or polio. Vaccines protecting against four or five viruses are already available. This gives us another glimpse of what the future may promise. Some epidemiologists, contemplating the multiple shots pediatricians now give children with apparent good effect, dolefully ask: "How many antibodies can a body be expected to make?"

"We do not know how many kinds of antibodies there are," observed Joshua Lederberg in an esoteric Harvard lecture relating antigens, genes, and antibodies to one another. However, he speculated that it would be quite possible to account for all specific immunity with not more than ten thousand kinds of antibodies. The problem, then, if this were the case, would be to find antigens that produced ten thousand different antibodies in sufficient quantities to produce immunization. This is a fascinating subject, because serologists are already aware of a number of cross-immunities, meaning different (or similar) viruses with much the same antibodies. We have just noted one new example—the cross-immunity between measles and canine distemper.

Lederberg is a scientist who is not afraid to think out loud—one does not have to be, after receiving a Nobel Prize—and is sufficiently relaxed to disarm his bombshell speculations with disclaimers like this: "For God's sake, don't think I really believe all the propositions I am setting forth." The practical scientist tiptoes from one hard brick of fact to the next, when he gets down to earth. One set of facts now sufficiently well established to be regarded as a biological principle gives us still another sense of direction. We refer to Thomas Francis's Doctrine of Original Antigenic Sin.

What it boils down to is that the golden time for vaccination is in early childhood, the most formative years for lifelong immunities just as they are for good or bad habits and psychological reactions to one's environment. In fact, the ideal time would be six months after birth, when a baby still carries its mother's antibodies in its blood. In a few more months the mother's antibodies disappear and the infant becomes susceptible to any infection that comes along.

It survives these infections at some cost in sickness, as well as incalculable costs of permanent damage, or it succumbs to them. If, through exposure to the proper combination of pure, safe antigens under the shelter of maternal immunity, the child could acquire some immunity of its own to most of the diseases it will be exposed to at some time in life, we could visualize a new race of disease-resistant men and women. Then the viruses within us could be locked out, or stalemated, as far as damaging disease is concerned.

Letting our imaginations run still further, we hence might contemplate the possibility of raising our children in a germ-free world—the cell world within them. Virus research is moving in that direction, a few microns of millimicrons at a time. Such an eventuality might, in the end, reduce the complaints of later life, even ward off that tragic second childhood of growth, cancer. But it should have the immediate effect of further reducing the infant-mortality rate. As matters now stand, the first year of life is the most dangerous of all until we pass the age of sixty-five.

In between, we have ample time to contemplate the summation of Dr. Vannevar Bush:

> The world is still full of mystery, and it will be long before we understand much, even when we limit ourselves to the mere mechanism of life and do not approach that greatest mystery of all: that we, as conscious beings, are capable of pondering it all. . . .

SELECTED READING LIST ON VIROLOGY
AND RELATED BIOLOGICAL AND MEDICAL SCIENCES

The list of books and articles which follows has been selected for the benefit of high-school or college students or general readers who wish to learn more of the scientific background of *Virus Hunters*. Many technical books and standard reference works have been omitted, as well as the hundreds of original scientific articles, monographs, and reports that one must read in the process of writing such a book.

I should guess that anyone wishing to keep abreast of new facts and current thought in the biological as well as other sciences would, as a minimum, subscribe to *Science*, the stimulating and fruitful weekly scientific journal of the American Association for the Advancement of Science, and *Scientific American*, a monthly magazine that regularly does a superb job of combining intellectually honest science-reporting and readability.

The selected reading list follows:

BACTERIA

Dubos, René J. (ed.): *Bacterial and Mycotic Infections of Man.* Third edition. Philadelphia: J. B. Lippincott; 1959.

Definitive companion to the Rivers-Horsfall *Viral and Rickettsial Diseases of Man.* Chapter ii, "The Evolution and Ecology of Microbial Diseases," by Dubos, places the host-parasite relationship in historical perspective in a fascinating way.

BEIJERINCK

Van Iterson, G., Jr., and others: *Martinus Willem Beijerinck: His Life and His Work.* The Hague: Martinus Nijhoff; 1940.

An amazingly good biography of Beijerinck by three of his colleagues, this book overlooks little but his disappointment in love. To omit that, of course, is barely forgivable.

BIOCHEMISTRY AND BIOPHYSICS

Crick, F. H. C.: "Nucleic Acids." *Scientific American*, September 1957.

The theory of DNA structure in easily readable form.

Doty, Paul: "Proteins." *Scientific American*, September 1957.

The protein picture through the eyes of an outstanding physical chemist.

Fraenkel-Conrat, Heinz: "Rebuilding a Virus." *Scientific American*, June 1956.

Fruton, Joseph S., and Simmonds, Sofia: *General Biochemistry*. Second edition. New York: John Wiley and Sons; 1958.

Recommended to the serious student as an introduction to biochemistry. At the price ($16), one has to be serious.

Hoffman, Joseph G.: *The Life and Death of Cells*. New York: Hanover House; 1957.

Good book on the living cell for laymen.

Ingram, Vernon M.: "How Do Genes Act?" *Scientific American*, January 1958.

An article answering its own title.

The Physics and Chemistry of Life. A *Scientific American* Book. New York: Simon and Schuster; 1955.

A collection of articles from *Scientific American*. Any layman interested in protein or nuclear chemistry or genetics might well start here.

Thompson, E. O. P.: "The Insulin Molecule." *Scientific American*, May 1955.

Good article on how a protein molecule was broken down and completely analyzed for first time.

Zinder, Norton D.: " 'Transduction' in Bacteria." *Scientific American*, November 1958.

"Naked genes" on the loose.

HEPATITIS

Hepatitis Frontiers. Henry Ford Hospital International Symposium. Boston: Little, Brown, and Company; 1957.

The uphill fight against the hepatitis virus step by step.

Spencer, Steven M.: "The Jaundice Plague." *The Saturday Evening Post*, March 25, 1950.

IMMUNITY

Furnas, J. C.: "So You Think You're Immune!" *The Saturday Evening Post*, September 11, 1954.

INFLUENZA

Burnet, Sir Macfarlane: "The Influenza Virus." *Scientific American*, April 1953.

——: "The Structure of the Influenza Virus." *Scientific American*, February 1957.

——: "Structure of Influenza Virus." *Science*, June 22, 1956.

Fascinating reviews of evidence and theory of why flu virus is such a vagrant.

JENNER

Baron, John: *The Life of Edward Jenner*. 2 vols. London; 1827, 1838.

A gold mine of raw, undigested fact about Jenner, including his poetry and letters from the astonishing John Hunter. Baron furnishes a classic example of why a close friend should not write a man's biography. His uncritical fawning over his hero helped provoke a century of debunking, including that of the malicious Creighton.

British Medical Journal: Jenner Centenary Number, May 23, 1896.

The symposium in this issue provides one of the richest sources of facts about Jenner and the first hundred years of smallpox vaccination.

Creighton, Charles: *Jenner and Vaccination: A Strange Chapter of Medical History.* London; 1889.

It is a pity that we must exhume Creighton from oblivion, but this misanthropic scholar is the most toxic example of Jenner's many nineteenth-century detractors. Creighton, offended by Jenner's lack of scholarly tidiness and by Baron's lack of a critical faculty, called Jenner "a fool and a knave," and called cowpox not smallpox but great pox (syphilis) of the cow. It is easy to see who was the greater fool.

Fosbroke, Thomas D.: *Berkeley Manuscripts.* London; 1821.

Contains an interesting account of the smallpox inoculation of Edward Jenner when he was eight years old, and other anecdotes. Fosbroke attempted a biography of Jenner while he was still alive, and it apparently was worth reading—the Father of Vaccination suppressed it!

LeFanu, W. R.: *A Bio-Bibliography of Edward Jenner, 1749–1823.* London: J. B. Lippincott; 1951.

Scholarly, definitive. The student of Jenner should read LeFanu first for a complete review of the writings by and about the doctor who listened to a milkmaid.

MEDICAL HISTORY AND RESEARCH

De Kruif, Paul: *Microbe Hunters.* New York: Harcourt, Brace, and Company; 1926.

A benchmark of modern popularization of medical science, this book was the take-off point for De Kruif's career as a romanticizer of the Golden Promise of Cure for Millions. Unfortunately, *Microbe Hunters* manifests an anti-Pasteur, pro-Koch bias at the cost of adequate appreciation of the depth and breadth of Pasteur's intellect and its causal relationship to "Pasteur luck."

Garrison, Fielding H.: *An Introduction to the History of Medicine.* Second edition. Philadelphia: W. B. Saunders Company; 1917.

Medical librarians generally regard this as the best history of medicine. As far as it goes (1917), they are right. Yet, as perhaps all books must, it contains disconcerting factual errors, at least about John Hunter and Edward Jenner.

Lape, Ester E.: *Medical Research: A Midcentury Survey,* 2 vols. The American Foundation. Boston: Little, Brown, and Company; 1955.

Excellent review of problems and progress in American medical research. A great deal here on viruses.

Rapport, Samuel, and Wright, Helen (eds.): *Great Adventures in*

Medicine. New York: Dial Press; 1952.

Something from most of the greats in medicine here.

Schuck, H., and others: *Nobel: The Man and His Prizes.* Norman: University of Oklahoma Press; 1951.

The Nobel Foundation's own pleasingly frank, generally well-written history of the Prizes, their donor, their winners, and the scientific achievements recognized by the Nobel Prizes.

Schwartz, George, and Bishop, Philip W.: *Moments of Discovery.* 2 vols. New York: Basic Books; 1958.

A valuable encyclopedic review of the original writings and views of many great discoverers from Hippocrates to Oppenheimer. But recapture of the actual moments of discovery eludes the editors, as in retrospect it often eludes the discoverers themselves.

PASTEUR

Dubos, René J.: *Louis Pasteur, Free Lance of Science.* Boston: Little, Brown, and Company; 1950.

Probably the best biography of the Perfect Scientist. By an imaginative microbiologist who can write.

Vallery-Radot, René: *The Life of Pasteur.* First published in Paris, 1901; translated into English by Mrs. R. L. Devonshire, 1902, and subsequently published in a variety of editions.

Official biography by Pasteur's son-in-law. A rich source, but it ducks

the details of Pasteur's emotional conflict with his close collaborator Emile Roux.

POLIO

Blakeslee, Alton L.: *Polio and the Salk Vaccine: What You Should Know About It.* New York: Grosset & Dunlap; 1956.

A useful quickie on facts about the Salk vaccine.

Coughlan, Robert: "Science Moves In on Viruses." *Life,* June 20, 1955.

——: "Tracking the Killer." *Life,* February 22, 1954.

Meier, Paul: "Safety Testing of Poliomyelitis Vaccine." *Science,* May 31, 1957.

Very probably the most critical review of the National Foundation's polio-vaccine program.

Poliomyelitis Vaccine. Hearings before the Committee on Labor and Public Welfare, United States Senate, Eighty-Fourth Congress, First Session, June 14 and 15, 1955. Part One.

Congressional investigations are always good places to learn something about public figures.

Poliomyelitis Vaccine. Hearings before the Committee on Interstate and Foreign Commerce, House of Representatives, Eighty-Fourth Congress, First Session, June 22 and 23, 1955. Part Two.

The scene shifts from Senate to House. The Stanley-Salk debate.

Sills, David L.: *The Volunteers.* Glencoe, Ill.: The Free Press; 1957.

Some insights into the operations of the National Foundation (formerly "for Infantile Paralysis").

Spencer, Steven M.: "Where Are We Now on Polio?" *The Saturday Evening Post*, September 10, 1955.

Best account of events immediately following outbreak of polio in children receiving Cutter vaccine.

Root, Lin: "The Polio Gamble." *The Reporter*, July 14, 1955.

One of the best articles on the polio-vaccine issues.

Williams, Greer: "Polio Post-Mortem: What Really Happened." *Medical Economics*, August 1955.

RABIES

Roueché, Berton: "Annals of Medicine: The Incurable Wound." *The New Yorker*, April 6, 1957.

An excellent modern account of rabies by an outstanding popular medical writer.

SALK

Krieger, June: "What Price Fame—to Dr. Salk?" *The New York Times Magazine*, July 17, 1955.

Good illumination of the 1953–5 pressures on Salk the scientist.

SMALLPOX

Nothnagel's Encyclopedia of Practical Medicine.

Truly encyclopedic on smallpox and other diseases. Written with typical German compulsiveness to be thorough.

TISSUE CULTURE

Puck, Theodore T.: "Single Human Cells in Vitro." *Scientific American*, August 1957.

YELLOW FEVER

Spencer, Steven M.: "Yellow Jack Is Back." *The Saturday Evening Post*, October 19, 1957.

Strode, George K. (ed.): *Yellow Fever*. New York: McGraw-Hill Book Co.; 1951.

A good source for the story of the Rockefeller Foundation's conquest of yellow fever. However, the book seems badly organized and sketchy in spots. It is difficult to get a clear picture of the vaccine-contamination episode from this work.

VIRUSES

Burnet, Sir Macfarlane: "Viruses." *Scientific American*, May 1951.
——: *Viruses and Man*. Baltimore: Penguin Books; 1953.

Well worth reading, though now outdated. Among virologists, Burnet is perhaps the most interesting and imaginative writer. He's not so good at prophecy, however.

Cook, J. Gordon: *Virus in the Cell*. London: George G. Harrap and Company; 1956.

An informative popular book, but the mention of Iwanowski and omission of Beijerinck as the first man to recognize a filterable virus is hard to take. Burnet, in contrast, mentions Beijerinck and ignores Iwanowski.

Dalldorf, Gilbert: *Introduction to Virology*. Springfield, Ill.; 1955.

Just what the title says it is. Simply written. Good source of background on virology prior to 1955.

Furth, Jacob, and Metcalf, Donald: "An Appraisal of Tumor-Virus Problems." *Journal of Chronic Diseases,* July 1958.

An illuminating review of a fast-moving field.

Huebner, Robert J. (ed.): *Viruses in Search of Disease.* Annals of the New York Academy of Science: Monograph, April 19, 1957.

The modern virologists in a scientific discussion of all the new viruses. There are more now.

Knight, C. A., and Fraser, Dean: "The Mutation of Viruses." *Scientific American,* July 1955.

Lwoff, André: "The Life Cycle of a Virus." *Scientific American,* May 1954.

Rivers, Thomas M., and Horsfall, Frank L., Jr. (eds.): *Viral and Rickettsial Infections of Man.* Third edition. Philadelphia: J. B. Lippincott; 1959.

The definitive text, and the place every serious student of virology should start. Comparison of this edition and second edition (1952) reveals how far virology has come in the last decade. In 1959 we find the first mention of tumor viruses. Happily, too, Shope's swine-influenza virus has finally been recognized.

Smith, Kenneth M.: *Beyond the Microscope.* Revised edition. Baltimore: Penguin Books; 1957.

All about all kinds of viruses. Also overlooks Beijerinck.

Stent, Gunther S.: "The Multiplication of Bacterial Viruses." *Scientific American,* May 1953.

INDEX

A-bombs, 422–3
abscesses, from vaccination, 295
Academy of Medicine, 46, 49, 50, 61, 62, 64
acute leukemia, 434–5, 454
AD, see adenoid degeneration agent
Adams, John, 493, 494
Adams, Roger, 93, 94
adenine, 469, 484
adenine and thymine (AT), 484
adenoid degeneration agent (AT), 371
adenoidal-pharyngeal-conjunctival group (APC), 371
adenoids, 6, 368, 369
adenoviruses, 6, 364, 368–9, 370–4, 382, 489, 492, 493
    Type 1, 370
    Type 3, 370, 371–2
    Type 4, 371, 372, 373
    Type 7, 372, 373
adjuvants, 281; see also beeswax, oil, peanut oil
Aedes aegypti, 156, 157, 164
African sleeping sickness, 162
agglutinates, 129
aggregates, 129
Agricultural High School, Wageningen, 78, 79
air pollution, 406, 414
A-Japan-305–57, 229
AK mice, 436, 437
AKR mice, 441
Allegheny College, 213
Allen, J. Garrott, 186–93
allergies, 303, 357, 358
aluminum, 112, 113
American Academy of Pediatrics, 345
American Cancer Society, 115
American College of Surgeons, 186
American Journal of Hygiene, 184
American Journal of Pathology, 148
American Journal of Public Health, 311

American Medical Association, 311, 351
American National Red Cross, 245
American Philosophical Society, 460
American Society of Pediatric Research, 395
American Surgical Association, 192
amino acids, 91, 468, 475, 492
amnion tissue, 389, 391, 393
anaplasia, 410
Anderson, Katherine, 151
Anderson, Sally A., 373
Andrewes, Christopher, 213, 215, 217, 222, 226, 229, 360, 361
angina pectoris, 18, 19
angleworm, 207–8
Animal Pathology Laboratory, (Rockefeller Institute), Princeton, 96, 98, 203
Annals of Surgery, 190
anthrax, 46, 50, 59
antibiotics, 4, 152, 284, 358, 492
antibodies, 124–5, 126, 128, 129–31; see also cancer; common cold; hepatitis; influenza; measles; poliomyelitis; yellow fever
anti-carcinogens, 445
antigens, 129, 130, 216, 218–19, 222, 225, 226, 230, 234, 280–1, 443, 495–6
antihistamines, 361
antiserum, see immune serum
antitoxins, 126, 127, 473
Anti-Vaccination League, 43, 62
anti-vaccination movement, 34, 43–4, 62
Anti-Vacks, 34, 35, 42, 43; see also Benjamin Moseley
anti-vivisection, 54, 61–2
Antivivisection League, 62
APC, see adenoidal-pharyngeal-conjunctival group; adenoviruses
appendicitis, 157, 386

A NOTE ON THE TYPE

The text of this book is set in Caledonia, a Linotype face designed by W. A. Dwiggins, the distinguished American designer, typographer, illustrator, and puppeteer. Caledonia belongs to the family of printing types called "modern face" by printers—a term used to mark the change in style of typeletters that occurred about 1800. Caledonia is, in some respects, similar to Scotch Modern in design, but is more freely drawn than that letter. It was first cut in 1939, and is one of the most readable and handsome faces available.

The book was composed, printed, and bound by Kingsport Press, Inc., Kingsport, Tennessee. Paper manufactured by S. D. Warren Company, Boston. Typography by Vincent Torre.

No human achievement is more thrilling than the conquest of disease. In this milestone book, Greer Williams unfolds the dramatic lives and triumphs of the great virologists, from Jenner and Pasteur to Salk and Enders.

The virologists began where the microbe hunters left off. Microbes have more or less been conquered by germicidal techniques, climaxed by the sulfa drugs and antibiotics. But viruses are different.

Viruses are much smaller than microbes, and resist chemical attack. They are not living cells which attack our body cells. They cannot live alone, but pursue their parasitic, infectious ends in a borderland between living matter and dead, existing in themselves only as an invisible organic dust, coming to life and reproducing only when they pierce the cells of a susceptible host.

Vaccines, not drugs, are the best weapons against them—vaccines which stimulate us to produce immunity agents called antibodies. One virus after another has yielded to thrilling vaccine break-throughs. Jenner defeated the smallpox virus and Pasteur rabies without really knowing what they were; but they knew their vaccines produced life-saving antibodies.

More recently a band of gifted and determined men, including Jonas Salk,